ACTIVE AND NONLINEAR WAVE PROPAGATION IN ELECTRONICS

ACTIVE AND NONLINEAR WAVE PROPAGATION IN ELECTRONICS

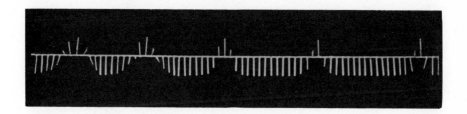

ALWYN SCOTT

Department of Electrical Engineering
The University of Wisconsin
Madison, Wisconsin

WILEY-INTERSCIENCE

A DIVISION OF JOHN WILEY & SONS

NEW YORK · LONDON · SYDNEY · TORONTO

Library of Congress Catalogue Card Number: 72-96956

SRN 471   76790   5

Printed in the United States of America

10 9 8 7 6 5 4 3 2 1

To Emmon and Allie and to Pauline

I have walked all day in an easterly way
    to quiet an urge in me,
Now I'm back again with the waves and the wind
    and the cool sweet stink of the sea.

The gulls offshore gravely glide and soar
    with the wild white caps to the lee,
As the salt white foam comes sounding home
    from the deep of the dark blue sea.

Now here I stand at the end of the land
    and the tide stands still with me,
And we pause to think before we sink
    back down in the mindless sea.

PREFACE

Over the last two decades electrical engineers have become increasingly concerned with the analysis and design of devices that involve active and/or nonlinear wave propagation. Pulse propagation on the nerve axon, the traveling wave tube and backward wave oscillator, the traveling wave maser, plasma waves, magnetohydrodynamics, parametric amplification and harmonic generation on transmission lines with nonlinear reactance, wave propagation on semiconductor and superconductor tunnel junctions, the neuristor, the laser, nonlinear optics, propagation of pressure waves in the circulatory system, traveling domains in the Gunn diode—the list is already long. It will continue to grow in future years as useful wavelengths become shorter and as interest in biological systems and in integrated circuits increases. And yet, it appears to me, there are far too few research people working and students being trained in the area of active, nonlinear wave propagation. This book has grown out of lecture notes prepared for a senior and graduate level course in this area. The objective has been to develop an appreciation for some of the generally useful theoretical tools that are currently available and to "draw the area together" or to define it as a legitimate subject of graduate study for electrical engineers. Examples of applications, although necessary to focus the student's interest and to sharpen his command of the theoretical tools, are considered to be of secondary importance.

For simplicity, consideration is limited almost entirely to waves that propagate in one spatial dimension, and the corresponding transmission systems are often represented by "transmission line equivalent circuits." This is a natural representation for electrical engineering students with their background in circuits and linear transmission line theory, and it has the advantage of putting partial differential equations into pictorial form. Pictures are easier to remember and often easier to classify than formulas.

Chapter I is merely introductory. The second chapter discusses theoretical tools for determining stability for systems which are linear but active.

Chapter III introduces the basic concepts of quasiharmonic analysis and the equivalent linearization technique developed by van der Pol and by Kryloff and Bogoliuboff. Chapter IV focuses on wave systems with strong nonlinearities in the elements which produce or absorb energy. The technique of seeking out "waves of permanent profile" through a phase space analysis is emphasized. Chapter V is concerned with systems for which the nonlinearities occur mainly in the energy storage elements. An extensive bibliography of the literature on applications of nonlinear wave theory to specific physical systems is included. I hope that this bibliography will be helpful to the "theoretical" student in defining problems of general interest as well as to the "applied" student in becoming more familiar with the physical background of a specific area. With minor exceptions each of the chapters is independent of the others. This feature should make the book useful for students with particular orientations. For example Chapters IV and V should be emphasized for bioengineering students, and Chapters II and III should be emphasized for students interested in masers, lasers and plasma waves. Since experience indicates that there is considerably more material than can be taught in a single semester, such a flexible approach will be necessary. Also there is a listing of some of the educational films on various aspects of active and nonlinear wave propagation which have been produced recently. These are, without exception, of excellent quality and they greatly facilitate the intuitive understanding of various nonlinear effects. I would venture to say that this subject should not be taught in the classroom without the aid of such films.

This book falls far short of being a definitive introduction to active, non-linear wave theory. It is, in a sense, premature. Much remains to be done before the field itself approaches maturity. Nonlinear stability problems of all sorts present an exciting and potentially rewarding challenge. The development of computer techniques which facilitate exploration of ranges of operation that are unknown and difficult to analyze will certainly continue. The catalog of problems with analytic solutions is still rather small. Study of the fascinating problem of nonlinear wave (or pulse) interaction (or collision) has only begun. Problems with additional spatial dimensions are everywhere waiting to be considered. Many of the *statements* discussed in this book need to be treated rigorously and formulated as *theorems*. Certainly many new general statements or theorems will be developed or translated from the mathematical literature.

Thus it is just because the field is immature that it presents such an exciting challenge to the young researcher. My primary aim is to encourage more graduate activity and to induce more young electrical engineers to enter the field. I sincerely hope a much better book will be written within the next few years.

I express my appreciation to all who have encouraged and assisted me in this effort and especially to the many students who have struggled with early versions of the manuscript. Particularly important have been the contributions of B. N. Prasanna, H. T. Yuan, R. D. Parmentier and W. J. Johnson. I am also indebted to R. D. Parmentier, Y. Sun and C. D. Geisler (and to several unidentified reviewers) for careful and critical readings, and to P. Luypaert and the Belgian-American Educational Foundation for the opportunity of presenting a synopsis of this work in a series of lectures at the University of Leuven (Louvain) in the spring of 1966. Without the generous financial support of the National Science Foundation and the Wisconsin Alumni Research Foundation progress would have been much slower if not altogether impossible. Finally I would like to thank E. R. Caianiello for providing, at the *Laboratorio di Cibernetica*, a stimulating haven during the horrors of proofreading and H. A. Peterson for creating, in the Department of Electrical Engineering at the University of Wisconsin, an environment where educational adventures of this sort can flourish.

Arco Felice, Italy   Alwyn Scott
September, 1969

CONTENTS

ACTIVE AND NONLINEAR WAVE PROPAGATION IN ELECTRONICS

I

LINEAR ACTIVE TRANSMISSION LINES

There are many subjects calling for the attention of a graduate student in applied science. Why, he might well wonder, should he be invited to study nonlinear active transmission line theory? A brief examination of the bibliography at the rear of this volume will show that in the past decade or two electronics research has turned increasingly toward the investigation of devices which involve active and nonlinear wave propagation. These include the traveling wave tube; the backward wave oscillator (and several other microwave amplifying and oscillating devices which use the active properties of the electron beam); the vast area of plasma research; the traveling wave maser amplifier; the traveling wave parametric amplifier; the laser amplifier and oscillator; the nonlinear interaction of high power laser light through optical media to obtain detection, mixing and harmonic generation; large area semiconductor and superconductor tunnel diodes; Gunn diodes (or solid state microwave generators); and neuristors or artificial nerve axons.

Nonlinear active wave propagation is, therefore, a manifestly practical area of study and research. In addition, however, the unusual effects which arise when superposition is discarded shed light upon a wide range of phenomena in physical and biological science. The "waves of permanent profile" (pulses which travel with fixed shape and velocity) which are studied in connection with the neuristor are closely related to pulse propagation in biological nerve and muscle, detonation waves in explosives, grass fires, and the burning of candles. Harmonic generation from laser light in nonlinear optics is connected with harmonic generation in the arteries of the blood transport system. There is a distinguished group of physicists who feel that the fundamental explanation of the "elementary" particles must be a nonlinear wave theory. The growth of "shock waves" on a nonlinear lossless transmission line is a direct analog for the "sonic boom" of jet aircraft, the collision which develops at the rear of a group of automobiles in moderately heavy traffic, and the breaking of water waves. The instability which develops in a backward wave oscillator is quite similar to those which cause a flag to flutter, clear air turbulence at high altitudes, and the formation of "white caps" on the ocean.

In this introductory chapter we shall briefly consider a few basic properties of linear wave systems which will be helpful as we proceed.

1.1. EQUIVALENT CIRCUITS FOR TRANSMISSION SYSTEMS

In many cases it is convenient to designate a particular propagating system pictorially by an "equivalent circuit." For example the various uniform, lossless, two conductor transmission lines (sometimes called *telegraph lines* or *lecher wires*) shown in Fig. 1-1a–c are all able to support TEM (*T*ransverse *E*lectro-*M*agnetic) modes of propagation [Ad 1]. The characteristic feature of TEM propagation is that the electric and magnetic fields are both perpendicular to the direction of propagation as well as to each other. Thus a unique shunt voltage can be defined as the line integral of electric field in a transverse plane from one conductor to the other.

$$v = \int_1^2 \mathbf{\mathcal{E}} \cdot \mathbf{ds} \tag{1.1-1}$$

Also a unique series current in one conductor can be defined as the closed line integral of magnetic field in a transverse plane about the conductor.

$$i = \oint \mathbf{\mathcal{H}} \cdot \mathbf{ds} \tag{1.1-2}$$

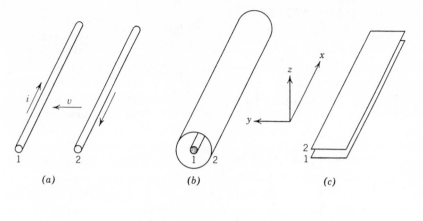

(a)   (b)   (c)

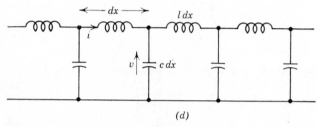

(d)

Fig. 1-1 Lossless transmission lines. (*a*) Twin lead, (*b*) coax, (*c*) strip line, (*d*) circuit equivalent.

The total power carried by the wave in the x direction is obtained by integrating the Poynting vector

$$\boldsymbol{\pi} = \boldsymbol{\mathcal{E}} \times \boldsymbol{\mathcal{H}} \ \text{W/m}^2 \tag{1.1-3}$$

over the entire transverse plane. Since both $\boldsymbol{\mathcal{E}}$ and $\boldsymbol{\mathcal{H}}$ are in the y-z plane, $\boldsymbol{\pi}$ is in the x direction and the total power

$$P = \int_{\text{entire cross section}} \boldsymbol{\pi} \cdot \mathbf{dA}$$

$$= v \cdot i. \tag{1.1-4}$$

The charge per unit area in the conductors is proportional (by Gauss' law) to the electric field at the surface. Thus the total charge per unit length q is proportional to the shunt voltage as defined in (1.1-1). The fixed ratio of charge per unit length to shunt voltage is defined as the capacitance per unit length.

$$c = \frac{q}{v} : \tag{1.1-5}$$

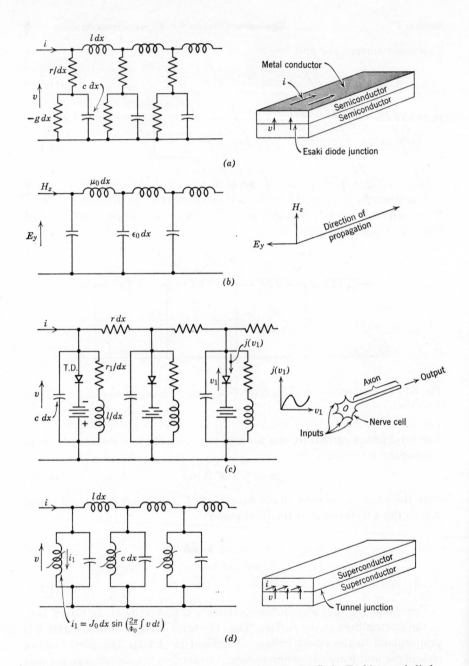

Fig. 1-2 Equivalent circuits for transmission systems. (a) Strip Esaki tunnel diode; (b) electromagnetic wave in free space; (c) model for propagation on a nerve axon; (d) strip Josephson tunnel diode.

The shunt current per unit length is

$$\frac{dq}{dt} = \frac{d(cv)}{dt} = c\frac{dv}{dt} ,\tag{1.1-6}$$

therefore the difference between the series current at x and $x + dx$ is

$$i(x) - i(x + dx) = c\,dx\frac{dv}{dt} .\tag{1.1-7}$$

In a similar way the total magnetic flux per unit length Φ between the two conductors is proportional to the series current as defined in (1.1-2). The fixed ratio of flux per unit length to series current is defined as the inductance per unit length,

$$l = \frac{\Phi}{i} .\tag{1.1-8}$$

The series voltage per unit length is

$$\frac{d\Phi}{dt} = \frac{d(li)}{dt} = l\frac{di}{dt} ,\tag{1.1-9}$$

therefore the difference between the shunt voltage at x and $x + dx$ is

$$v(x) - v(x + dx) = l\,dx\frac{di}{dt} .\tag{1.1-10}$$

Taking the limit as $dx \to 0$ and observing that v and i are functions of both x and t, (1.1-7) and (1.1-10) can be written

$$\frac{\partial v}{\partial x} = -l\frac{\partial i}{\partial t} ,$$

$$\frac{\partial i}{\partial x} = -c\frac{\partial v}{\partial t} .\tag{1.1-11a,b}$$

The circuit in Fig. 1-1d is considered "equivalent" to the two conductor transmission lines in Fig. 1-1a–c in the sense that the power flow relation (1.1-4) and the pertinent partial differential equations (1.1-11) can immediately be derived therefrom. One can look upon an equivalent circuit as an aid to the memory and a stimulant to the imagination. Several of the equivalent circuits to be considered in this book are shown in Fig. 1-2 and described briefly below.

a. Strip Esaki Tunnel Diode. The transmission line equivalent circuit is derived in detail in reference [Sc 10]. The junction contributes capacitance per unit length (c) and a negative conductance per unit length ($-g$) to the shunt admittance. In addition the shunt admittance has a series resistance element of r ohm-meters. This resistance accounts for the transverse voltage in the semiconductor caused by current flow across the junction.

b. Electromagnetic Wave Propagation in Free Space. The transmission line equivalent circuit is derived in many introductory texts on wave theory, for example, [Ad 1, Ch 7, 8]. In this case H_z and E_y have the units of amps/meter and volts/meter respectively rather than amps and volts. The product $H_z E_y$ is, therefore, the wave intensity with units of watts/meter squared.

c. Pulse Propagation on a Nerve Axon. The *axon* or outgoing fiber of a nerve cell is covered by a voltage sensitive membrane with a nonlinear characteristic somewhat similar to that of an Esaki diode. Detailed partial differential equations have been determined experimentally by Hodgkin and Huxley [Ho 5]. A simplified form of these equations has been developed by Fitzhugh [Fi 5] and modeled by Nagumo et al. [Na 1] as indicated in Fig. 1-2c. The nerve axon is discussed in greater detail in Section 4.14.

d. Strip Superconducting (Josephson) Junction. The partial differential equations for this structure were first derived by Eck et al. [Ec 1]. The shunt Josephson current can be represented by the current through a nonlinear inductor which is proportional to the sine of the shunt flux. This system is discussed in detail in Section 5.6.

1.2. WAVE SOLUTIONS ON PROPAGATION SYSTEMS

Consider the general linear distributed ladder transmission line shown in Fig. 1-3. The state of the line is described by a shunt voltage, v, and a series current, i, both of which are functions of the distance, x, and time, t. The current sees a series impedance per unit length z_{se}, and the voltage sees a

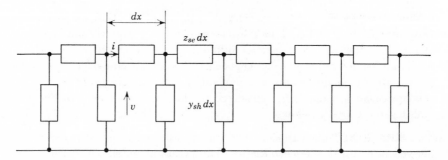

Fig. 1-3 Distributed ladder transmission line.

shunt admittance per unit length, y_{sh}. The immittances z_{se} and y_{sh} depend upon the angular frequency of excitation of the line, ω. For sinusoidal excitation at angular frequency ω the voltage and current may be written in the form

$$v(x, t) = Re[V(x)e^{j\omega t}],$$
$$i(x, t) = Re[I(x)e^{j\omega t}],$$

(1.2-1a,b)

where $V(x)$ and $I(x)$ are complex amplitudes which are functions of x on the line. These amplitudes are related by the requirements that

$$\frac{dV}{dx} = -z_{se}I,$$
$$\frac{dI}{dx} = -y_{sh}V,$$

(1.2-2a,b)

which can be written in the matrix form

$$\frac{d}{dx}\begin{bmatrix} V \\ I \end{bmatrix} = \begin{bmatrix} 0 & -z_{se} \\ -y_{sh} & 0 \end{bmatrix} \times \begin{bmatrix} V \\ I \end{bmatrix}.$$

(1.2-3)

If we seek solutions for which V and I vary as $e^{\gamma x}$, γ must be one of the eigenvalues of the matrix in (1.2-3). That is to say the determinant

$$\det\begin{bmatrix} \gamma & z_{se} \\ y_{sh} & \gamma \end{bmatrix} = 0,$$

(1.2-4)

or

$$\gamma = \pm\sqrt{z_{se}(j\omega)y_{sh}(j\omega)}$$
$$= \pm\gamma_0.$$

(1.2-5)

Equation (1.2-4) or (1.2-5) is called the *dispersion equation*. It gives the permitted values of the propagation constant γ as a function of the frequency of excitation. If V and I are proportional to $e^{\pm\gamma_0 x}$, we have from (1.2-2).

$$\frac{V}{I} = \mp\left(\frac{z_{se}}{y_{sh}}\right)^{1/2} = \mp Z_0,$$

(1.2-6)

the *characteristic impedance* of the line.

Thus a general solution for complex voltage and current amplitude on the line can be written

$$V = Ae^{-\gamma_0 x} + Be^{+\gamma_0 x},$$
$$Z_0 I = Ae^{-\gamma_0 x} - Be^{+\gamma_0 x}.$$

(1.2-7)

1.3. A SIMPLE ACTIVE TRANSMISSION LINE

A particularly simple active transmission line which serves to exemplify the ideas of the previous section is shown in Fig. 1-4. This line may be considered as a low frequency approximation to the more complex active line shown in Fig. 1-2a which describes a distributed tunnel diode line. For the line of Fig. 1-4a the series impedance and shunt admittance per unit length at frequency ω are

$$z_{se} = j\omega l,$$
$$y_{sh} = -g + j\omega c, \tag{1.3-1a,b}$$

so

$$\gamma = \pm\sqrt{j\omega l(j\omega c - g)}. \tag{1.3-2}$$

If we make the approximation that

$$\omega c \gg g, \tag{1.3-3}$$

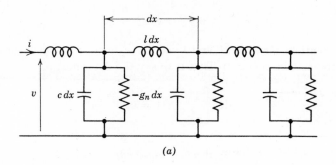

(a)

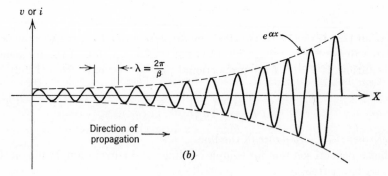

(b)

Fig. 1-4   A simple active transmission line. (a) Prototype active transmission line; (b) propagation of an active wave.

then

$$\gamma = \pm\left(-\frac{g}{2}\sqrt{\frac{l}{c}} + j\omega\sqrt{lc}\right),\qquad(1.3\text{-}4)$$

$$\equiv \pm\gamma_0.$$

Thus solutions of the form

$$v \text{ or } i \sim Re(e^{-\gamma_0 x + j\omega t})\qquad(1.3\text{-}5)$$

represent a growing wave which is propagating in the $+x$ direction as indicated in Fig. 1-4b. On the other hand, for

$$v \text{ or } i \sim Re(e^{+\gamma_0 x + j\omega t})\qquad(1.3\text{-}6)$$

the wave is still growing but propagating in the $-x$ direction.

Evidently in this simple case it is the *difference in sign* between the real and imaginary parts of γ which indicates that waves grow in the direction of propagation. If we write the propagation constant in terms of an attenuation constant, α, and a phase constant, β as

$$\gamma_0 \equiv \alpha + j\beta,\qquad(1.3\text{-}7)$$

then

$$\frac{\alpha(\omega)}{\beta(\omega)} < 0 \quad \text{for} \quad \omega > 0\qquad(1.3\text{-}8)$$

is the requirement for gain in the direction of propagation. The wavelength of the propagation is

$$\lambda = \frac{2\pi}{\beta}\qquad(1.3\text{-}9)$$

and the gain per wavelength is $|2\pi\alpha/\beta|$.

1.4. WAVE VELOCITIES [Br8, Hall, Li3]

Waves move; thus it is interesting to attempt to define and calculate their velocities. Let us consider a linear, lossless, distributed ladder line. For sinusoidal time variation z_{se} and y_{sh} will be imaginary. Over certain ranges of frequency, the real part of the propagation constant ($\gamma_0 = \alpha + j\beta$) will be zero and (1.2-5) can be considered a relation between frequency, ω, and the imaginary part of the propagation, β. Thus we can write

$$\beta = B(\omega),\qquad(1.4\text{-}1)$$

where $B(\omega)$ is a real function of a real variable. Wave solutions will then be of the form $\exp j(\beta x + \omega t)$ which are sinusoids propagating without growth or decay. There are several "wave velocities" defined according to the particular aspect of the wave being considered.

a. Phase Velocity.   The real part of the exponential solution is of the form

$$v(x, t) = V_0 \cos(\beta x + \omega t). \tag{1.4-2}$$

A point of constant phase, for example the point of zero phase, will be the point for which

$$\beta x + \omega t = 0 \tag{1.4-3}$$

or

$$x = -\frac{\omega}{\beta} t. \tag{1.4-4}$$

Thus we can define a *phase velocity*

$$u_{ph} = -\frac{\omega}{B(\omega)}. \tag{1.4-5}$$

b. Group Velocity.   One might suppose that a pulse or wave packet composed of propagating sinusoids would move at the phase velocity of those sinusoids. That this is not the case can easily be seen by supposing two sinusoids which differ slightly in frequency. Thus

$$v(x, t) = V_0 \cos(\beta_1 x + \omega_1 t) + V_0 \cos(\beta_2 x + \omega_2 t), \tag{1.4-6}$$

where

$$\omega_1 - \omega_2 = \Delta\omega. \tag{1.4-7}$$

Equation 1.4-6 is transformed with the aid of an elementary trigonometric identity to

$$v(x, t) = 2V_0 \cos\left(\frac{\Delta\beta}{2} x + \frac{\Delta\omega}{2} t\right) \cos\left(\frac{\beta_1 + \beta_2}{2} x + \frac{\omega_1 + \omega_2}{2} t\right). \tag{1.4-8}$$

Equation 1.4-8 indicates that (1.4-6) can be considered as the product of a *carrier wave,*

$$\cos\left(\frac{\beta_1 + \beta_2}{2} x + \frac{\omega_1 + \omega_2}{2} t\right),$$

moving at the average phase velocity $-(\omega_1 + \omega_2)/(\beta_1 + \beta_2)$ and an *envelope,*

$$2V_0 \cos\left(\frac{\Delta\beta}{2} x + \frac{\Delta\omega}{2} t\right),$$

moving at the velocity $-\Delta\omega/\Delta\beta$ where

$$\Delta\beta = B(\omega_1) - B(\omega_2). \tag{1.4-9}$$

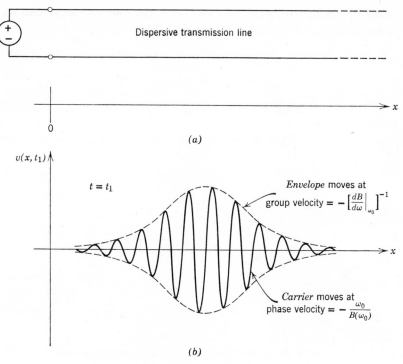

Fig. 1-5 Group velocity and phase velocity.

Since $\Delta\omega$ is assumed to be small compared with ω_1 and ω_2, the envelope velocity or *group velocity* is approximately

$$u_g = -\frac{d\omega}{d\beta} = -\left(\frac{dB}{d\omega}\right)^{-1}. \qquad (1.4\text{-}10)$$

If $B(\omega)$ is proportional to ω, the phase velocity and the group velocity are equal. Otherwise they are not equal and the transmission system is said to be *dispersive*.

A "physical" explanation for the difference between group and phase velocity can be seen by considering the situation in Fig. 1-5. A semi-infinite line is excited at one end ($x = 0$) by a voltage source $V(t)$. Thus

$$v(0, t) = V(t),$$

$$= \int_{-\infty}^{\infty} F(\omega)e^{j\omega t}\, d\omega, \qquad (1.4\text{-}11)$$

where $F(\omega)$ is the Fourier transform of $V(t)$. Each elementary solution of the form $\exp[j(\beta x + \omega t)]$ is then excited with amplitude $F(\omega)$. Therefore

$$v(x, t) = \int_{-\infty}^{\infty} F(\omega) e^{j(\beta x + \omega t)} \, d\omega. \qquad (1.4\text{-}12)$$

A peak in the wave envelope will occur at values of x and t where a relatively large number of components add in phase. Such a peak will move so that these components remain in phase. Thus the phase $(\beta x + \omega t)$ in the integrand of (1.4-12) must remain constant. For constructive interference by frequencies in the neighborhood of ω_0 this implies

$$\frac{d}{d\omega}(\beta x + \omega t)\bigg|_{\omega_0} = \frac{dB}{d\omega}\bigg|_{\omega_0} x + t = 0,$$

or

$$u_g = \frac{x}{t} = \left(\frac{dB}{d\omega}\bigg|_{\omega_0}\right)^{-1}, \qquad (1.4\text{-}13)$$

just as in (1.4-10).

c. Energy Velocity. For a system with small loss and positive energy storage, the energy moves at the group velocity. This is evident because the energy in a pulse must move at the velocity of that pulse. If the system has much loss or gain, however, a pulse will become distorted as it propagates. The group velocity then ceases to be of interest because it is difficult to define. In this situation we can still define an *energy velocity* (u_e) as the ratio of time average power flow (P) to time average stored energy per unit length (U). For the distributed ladder transmission line

$$\begin{aligned} P &= \tfrac{1}{2}\text{Re}[VI^*], \\ &= \tfrac{1}{2}II^*\text{Re}[Z_0]. \end{aligned} \qquad (1.4\text{-}14)$$

The stored energy per unit length will be proportional to the magnitude of the amplitude squared. Thus

$$U = KII^*, \qquad (1.4\text{-}15)$$

so

$$u_e = \frac{\text{Re}[Z_0]}{2K}. \qquad (1.4\text{-}16)$$

Evidently for a system with positive energy storage (positive K) the sign of the real part of the characteristic impedance will determine the direction of the energy velocity.

d. Signal Velocity. If we ask for the velocity at which a signal can be transmitted from a generator to a receiver, the answer will certainly depend upon the distortion of the pulse and upon the sensitivity of the receiver.

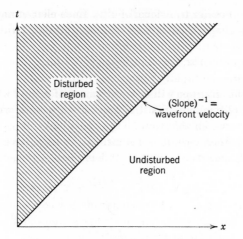

Fig. 1-6   A wavefront in the x-t plane.

For a wave in a low loss (distortionless) medium and a detector set at (say) one half of the maximum pulse amplitude, the signal velocity is approximately equal to the group velocity. For a detector of arbitrarily high sensitivity the signal velocity would be approximately equal to the *wavefront velocity* of a wave into an undisturbed medium. This velocity is illustrated in the space-time (x-t) plane of Fig. 1-6. If a signal is applied at $x = 0$ which is zero for $t < 0$, it is possible to divide the (x-t) plane into a *disturbed region* and an *undisturbed region*. The slope of the line dividing these two regions is the wavefront velocity. Techniques for determining the wavefront velocity are discussed in detail in Chapter V.

1.5. THE COMPLEX DISPERSION EQUATION

Perhaps the item of information most useful in characterizing a wave propagation system is the dispersion equation which gives the allowed values of propagation constant for an assumed excitation frequency. For the simple distributed ladder line of Fig. 1-3 we have seen that the dispersion equation becomes

$$\gamma^2 = y_{sh} z_{se}, \tag{1.5-1}$$

where y_{sh} and z_{se} are, respectively, the shunt admittance and series impedance per unit length of line.

So far we have been supposing the time variation in the problems under consideration to be a constant amplitude sinusoid. In oscillator circuits however one often designs a system so the time variation is as $e^{\sigma t} \cdot e^{j\omega t}$ just after the unit is turned on. A small initial sinusoidal variation (started by thermal noise, perhaps) then grows in amplitude at a rate $e^{\sigma t}$ until it is limited by some (hopefully nondestructive) nonlinear effect. In certain pulse circuits, (e.g., flip-flops) the system is triggered into an active region after which it should proceed rapidly toward some other stable state. In the linear approximation this transient time variation will be as $e^{\sigma t}$. Furthermore in the design of amplifying circuits it is necessary to avoid oscillations, so the theoretical tools must be able to take that possibility into account.

In many cases, therefore, it is convenient to consider not simply a real frequency ω and temporal variation $e^{j\omega t}$ but *complex frequency*

$$s = \sigma + j\omega \qquad (1.5\text{-}2)$$

and temporal variation $e^{(\sigma + j\omega)t}$. This point of view complements our previous observation that the spatial variation $e^{\gamma x}$ has a sinusoidal factor $e^{j\beta x}$ and an exponential amplitude factor $e^{\alpha x}$ where

$$\gamma = \alpha + j\beta. \qquad (1.5\text{-}3)$$

Our objective is to determine and investigate the properties of elementary solutions of the form

$$e^{(\gamma x + st)}.$$

In its most general form we can think of the dispersion equation as a *complex function* which gives the allowed complex propagation γ as a function of complex frequency s, or as a *complex transformation* which maps points from the s-plane to the γ-plane and vice-versa.

There appears to be an ambiguity in this transformation since from (1.5-1)

$$\gamma = \pm\sqrt{z_{se}(s)y_{sh}(s)}, \qquad (1.5\text{-}4)$$

and it is not evident whether we should take the $+$ sign or the $-$ sign. The propagation constant γ is not a single valued function on the complex s-plane. Consider the simple expression

$$\gamma = \pm\sqrt{s}. \qquad (1.5\text{-}5)$$

If we arbitrarily choose the $+$ sign at $s = 1$, we can proceed around the origin by *analytic continuation* [Kn 2] and we find that $\gamma = -1$ when we return to $s = 1$. Another trip around the origin via analytic continuation brings us back to $\gamma = +1$. Thus

$$\gamma = \sqrt{s} \qquad (1.5\text{-}6)$$

can be considered a single valued function if s is defined as a point on the two layer *Riemann surface* illustrated in Fig. 1-7. This surface features a *branch cut* which is chosen for convenience along the $-\sigma$ axis from $-\infty$ to the *branch point* at the origin. If we cross this line, we make a transition from

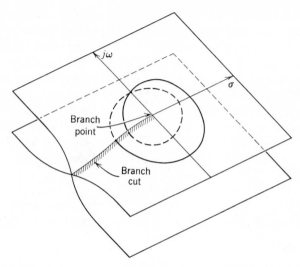

Fig 1-7   A two layer Riemann surface suitable for a single valued definition of $\sqrt{s}$.

one surface (or *branch*) to the other. Thus it is necessary to change branches as we go around the origin.

As a slightly more interesting example consider the simple active transmission line shown in Fig. 1-4. The dispersion equation for complex frequency is

$$\gamma = \sqrt{ls(cs - g)}. \qquad (1.5\text{-}7)$$

This function has branch points at $s = 0$ and at $s = -g/c$ so it is convenient to choose a branch cut for $s = \sigma$ where $0 \leq \sigma \leq g/c$ as is indicated in Fig. 1-8*a*.

If ω and β have the same sign, waves propagate in the $-x$ direction; thus a wave which grows spatially in the direction of propagation must have α negative or have a complex propagation constant which lies in the left half of the γ-plane. If ω and β have opposite signs, on the other hand, a wave which grows spatially in the direction of propagation must have a complex propagation constant which lies in the right half of the γ-plane.

In Fig. 1-8 we have arbitrarily chosen the branch of (1.5-7) for which α is large and positive for σ large and positive. The $j\omega$ axis then maps onto the γ-plane as

$$\gamma = +\sqrt{j\omega l(j\omega c - g)}, \qquad (1.5\text{-}8)$$

and we can easily indicate the mapping of the right half of this branch onto the γ-plane as in Fig. 1-8*b*. Since ω and β have the same sign, the region of spatial growth in the direction of propagation lies in the left half of the

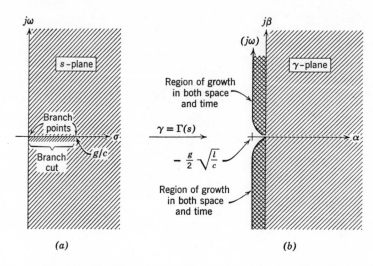

Fig. 1-8 The dispersion equation as a complex transformation.

γ-plane. Thus the doubly shaded region of Fig. 1-8b corresponds to both spatial and temporal growth.

If we had chosen the other branch, the mapping onto the γ-plane would simply have been rotated by 180° and we would have been considering waves which propagate in the $+x$ direction.

PROBLEMS

1. Show for the general semi-infinite two conductor transmission line with uniformity in the x direction, infinite conductivity in the wires and no losses in the air space that a TEM mode of propagation does exist. Demonstrate that the electric and magnetic field configurations between the conductors are the same at any frequency as if the line were excited by direct current.

2. If the voltage and current of an equivalent transmission line are defined as in (1.1-1) and (1.1-2), show in detail by integration of Poynting's vector that the power carried by the actual line $v \cdot i$.

3. Calculate the inductance per unit length l and capacitance per unit length c for the strip line in Fig. 1-1c.

4. Repeat Problem 3 for Fig. 1-1b.

5. Show in general that $lc = \mu_0 \varepsilon_0$ for a two conductor transmission line with air dielectric.

6. Write the differential equations corresponding to the equivalent circuits in Fig. 1-2.

7. In the equivalent circuits of Fig. 1-2 the series impedance and the shunt admittance elements have units respectively of ohms and mhos *per unit length*. Explain why this is so.

8. Consider the distributed matrix transmission line shown in Fig. P1-1 for which the complex amplitudes of voltage and current obey

$$\frac{d}{dx}\begin{bmatrix} V \\ I \end{bmatrix} = [A]\begin{bmatrix} V \\ I \end{bmatrix},$$

where

$$[A] = \begin{bmatrix} a & b \\ c & d \end{bmatrix}.$$

Determine the dispersion relation and the characteristic impedance for this system.

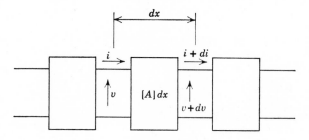

Fig. P1-1

9. Small amplitude waves in water which is deep compared with a wavelength obey the dispersion relation [La 2]

$$\omega^2 = g\beta + \frac{T\beta^3}{\rho},$$

where the acceleration of gravity

$$g = 981 \text{ cm/sec}^2,$$

the surface tension of water

$$T = 74 \text{ dynes/cm},$$

and the density of water

$$\rho = 1 \text{ g/cm}^3.$$

Evidently for short wavelength (large β) surface tension forces dominate and for long wavelength (small β) gravity forces dominate.

(a) What is the approximate wavelength in centimeters which divides surface tension and gravity waves?

(b) Determine whether $u_g > u_{ph}$ or $u_{ph} < u_g$ for both surface tension and gravity waves.

(c) Suggest some simple experiments to demonstrate the results of (b).

10. Since β is the number of wave crests per unit length and ω is the number of wave crests per unit time, the "conservation of wave crests" implies the continuity equation

$$\frac{\partial \beta}{\partial t} + \frac{\partial \omega}{\partial x} = 0.$$

Assuming $\beta = B(\omega)$ use this continuity equation to derive the group velocity formula.

11. Sketch the equivalent circuit for a lossless transmission line for which the group and phase velocities are in opposite directions.

12. Calculate $\gamma(s)$ for the active transmission line of Fig. 1-2a.

13. For the line of Fig. 1-2a shade the region which maps on the γ-plane from the right half of the s-plane. Indicate the region which corresponds to waves which grow in the direction of propagation and also with time.

II

STABILITY OF LINEAR ACTIVE WAVE SYSTEMS

In dealing with active transmission systems we are necessarily concerned with questions of stability. These questions are almost as varied as the possible useful applications. Initially when a new active propagating system is proposed we ask "Is it *really* active? Can it show gain?" If this question is answered affirmatively (very likely by experimental evidence) one might be interested in an amplifier application. He would then ask, "In this particular environment of generator and load impedance will the line remain stable or will it oscillate? If it oscillates, what (if anything) can one do to stabilize it and still achieve useful gain?" Or one might be interested in oscillator applications. He would then ask, "At what frequencies can the line be made to oscillate? Will it oscillate at a single sinusoidal frequency? or several? or undergo relaxation oscillations?" Evidently in dealing with questions of this sort there is not one necessary and sufficient "stability criterion" which will serve all purposes. There are many individual criteria, some only necessary, some only sufficient. It pays to be acquainted with them all. Certain of the stability criteria which pertain to linear systems are discussed in this chapter. Stability criteria which arise in the consideration of nonlinear phenomena will be discussed in following chapters.

2.1. STABILITY OF A DISTRIBUTED AMPLIFIER
[Ma4, Ma5]

In this section we consider the design of an amplifying circuit from an active line for which we know the propagation constant γ and the characteristic impedance Z_0 as functions of complex frequency s. Such a line might be either the distributed ladder of Fig. 1-3 or the distributed matrix line of Problem 8 (Chapter I). If the line is to be useful as an amplifier, we must be able to terminate it with passive impedances in such a way that the gain function has no poles in the right half of the s-plane.

Consider the system of Fig. 2-1 and assume that the line is reciprocal so both the characteristic impedance and the propagation constant are equal in the two directions of propagation. The source voltage and current are related to the input voltage and current of the line by

$$\begin{bmatrix} V_s \\ I_1 \end{bmatrix} = \begin{bmatrix} 1 & Z_s \\ 0 & 1 \end{bmatrix} \times \begin{bmatrix} V_1 \\ I_1 \end{bmatrix}, \tag{2.1-1}$$

and from standard transmission line theory [Ra 2, p. 41] the input and output line voltages and currents are related by

$$\begin{bmatrix} V_1 \\ I_1 \end{bmatrix} = \begin{bmatrix} \cosh \gamma_0 a & Z_0 \sinh \gamma_0 a \\ \dfrac{1}{Z_0} \sinh \gamma_0 a & \cosh \gamma_0 a \end{bmatrix} \times \begin{bmatrix} V_L \\ I_L \end{bmatrix}. \tag{2.1-2}$$

Thus the voltage gain is

$$\frac{V_L}{V_s} = \frac{2 Z_L Z_0 e^{-\gamma_0 a}}{(Z_L + Z_0)(Z_s + Z_0)(1 - \rho_s \rho_L e^{-2\gamma_0 a})}, \tag{2.1-3}$$

where ρ_S and ρ_L are respectively the voltage reflection coefficients at the

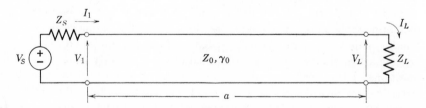

Fig. 2-1   An active transmission line amplifier.

source and load ends of the line.

$$\rho_s = \frac{Z_s - Z_0}{Z_s + Z_0}, \qquad \rho_L = \frac{Z_L - Z_0}{Z_L + Z_0}. \qquad (2.1\text{-}4a,b)$$

To ensure stable amplification the voltage gain must have no poles in the RHP. One source of such poles would be zeros of the factor $1 - \rho_s\rho_L e^{-2\gamma_0 a}$. Instabilities generated by this factor have the following simple physical interpretation. The loop gain of a voltage wave which is initiated at the source end, travels to the load end with phasor gain $e^{-\gamma_0 a}$, is reflected from the load with phasor reflection coefficient ρ_L, travels back to the source end with phasor gain $e^{-\gamma_0 a}$, and finally is reflected from the source end with phasor reflection coefficient ρ_s is

$$\text{voltage loop gain} = \rho_s\rho_L e^{-2\gamma_0 a} \qquad (2.1\text{-}5)$$

In general we must impose the standard requirement that the loop gain plotted as a function of $j\omega$ should not enclose the point $+1$ as ω varies from $-\infty$ to ∞. It is evident that this aim can always be achieved (at the expense of gain) by making the line short enough so the magnitude of (2.1-5) is less than unity.

Let us now assume that we can eliminate instabilities associated with the loop gain by matching the load to the line. Thus $Z_L = Z_0$ and $\rho_L = 0$. The voltage gain then becomes

$$\frac{V_L}{V_s} = \frac{Z_0 e^{-\gamma_0 a}}{(Z_s + Z_0)}. \qquad (2.1\text{-}6)$$

Suppose the source impedance is a *positive real* (pr) function [Gu 2] for which

$$\measuredangle Z_s(s) < \measuredangle s \qquad \text{for Re } (s) > 0. \qquad (2.1\text{-}7)$$

The denominator of (2.1-6) can have no RHP zeros if we require that the characteristic impedance be a *positive* function [Gu 2, p. 6] for which

$$\text{Re } [Z_0(s)] > 0 \qquad \text{for Re } (s) > 0. \qquad (2.1\text{-}8)$$

This is evident for then Re $(Z_s + Z_0) > 0$ in the entire right half of the s-plane. If Z_0 is not positive, on the other hand, we can always find a source impedance such that $(Z_s + Z_0)$ is equal to zero in the RHP. Thus we can make the

Statement. *If the distributed amplifier of Fig. 2-1 is matched at the load end, a necessary and sufficient condition for stability of the voltage gain (2.1-3) with*

any pr source impedance is that the characteristic impedance be a positive function.

From a physical point of view we can say that it is difficult to build an amplifier if Z_0 is not positive for then the energy velocity will change sign for some RHP frequency.

It is important to notice that the requirements for a pr function (2.1-7) are considerably more severe than the requirements for a positive function (2.1-8). If Z_0 were a pr function it could be synthesized by standard techniques from passive components and could not contribute power gain.

The requirement that $Z_0(s)$ be positive, on the other hand, does not even mean that it cannot have singularities in the right half of the s-plane; for example, the simple active line of Fig. 1-4 has a characteristic impedance

$$Z_0 = \left(\frac{ls}{cs-g}\right)^{1/2}.\tag{2.1-9}$$

In this case Z_0 is double valued and must be plotted on a Riemann surface of two layers or branches. On the upper branch Re $[Z_0(s)]$ becomes positive and real as $|s| \to \infty$. This is what we expect for the mode propagating in the $+x$ direction (or an elementary solution of the form exp $[st - \gamma_0 x]$) for Z_0 will certainly appear passive at high enough frequency. The lower branch corresponds to the mode propagating in the $-x$ direction.

The branch cuts must be taken along the σ-axis where z_{se}/y_{sh} is negative. To see this consider, as has been pointed out by Gross and Braga [Gr 4], that Z_0 should be considered as the limit of the input impedance of a finite length of line as the length approaches infinity. Since the input impedance

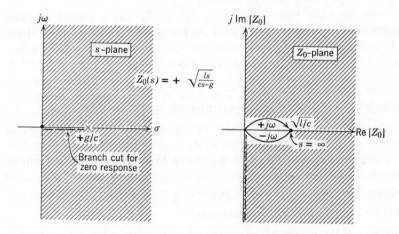

Fig. 2-2   Characteristic impedance for the simple active line.

of a length a of the general ladder line which is shorted at the far end is

$$Z_i = \left(\frac{z_{se}(s)}{y_{sh}(s)}\right)^{1/2} \tanh\,[a\sqrt{z_{se}(s)y_{sh}(s)}], \qquad (2.1\text{-}10)$$

then we can define Z_0 as

$$Z_0 = \lim_{a \to \infty} \left(\frac{z_{se}(s)}{y_{sh}(s)}\right)^{1/2} \tanh\,[a\sqrt{z_{se}(s)y_{sh}(s)}]. \qquad (2.1\text{-}11)$$

There are poles of Z_i distributed along the σ axis where $z_{se}(s)y_{sh}(s)$ is negative, for there the argument of the hyberbolic tangent function is purely imaginary. In the limit as $a \to \infty$ these become *branch lines* which are the locus of a dense distribution of poles and across which one cannot proceed by analytic continuation. But the lines where $z_{se}y_{sh}$ is negative are also the lines where z_{se}/y_{sh} is negative. As Bode has mentioned [Bo 1, p. 301], such branch cuts are acceptable because the physical response to a current excitation, say, at the cut is zero. For a current source $I_0 e^{\sigma t}$ applied to a semi-infinite line, the corresponding voltage response will be

$$v(t) = \mathrm{Re}\left[\left(\frac{z_{se}(\sigma)}{y_{sh}(\sigma)}\right)^{1/2} I_0 e^{\sigma t}\right], \qquad (2.1\text{-}12)$$
$$= 0.$$

since the bracket is purely imaginary at the cuts. The physical response can *only* be zero along a real axis branch cut; because if s has a nonzero imaginary part on the cut, the angle of $\exp(st)$ changes with time. The only allowed branch cuts must therefore lie on the $s = \sigma$ axis. Thus an examination of the positive character of Z_0 might proceed as follows.

1. Check for RHP poles or zeros in Z_0^2. If Z_0^2 has a pair of complex conjugate poles or zeros in the RHP, Z_0 is not positive for one cannot introduce branch cuts which connect these poles or zeros without having a discontinuity in the physical response (Fig. 2-3a).

2. Check whether $-\pi < (\angle Z_0^2) < \pi$ along the $s = \sigma$ axis from $\sigma = 0$ to $\sigma = \infty$ and along the $s = j\omega$ axis from $\omega = 0$ to $\omega = \infty$. Along the $s = \sigma$ axis we can count poles. Start with the pole or zero furthest to the right and count toward the left π for each zero and $-\pi$ for each pole. If the magnitude of this count exceeds π, Z_0 is not positive (Fig. 2-3b,c). The $\angle Z_0^2$ along the $j\omega$ axis depends in part upon the pole-zero constellation of Z_0^2 in the LHP.

Instabilities connected with the voltage loop gain (2.1-5) can be eliminated in practice by two alternative approaches:

1. The range of complex frequency over which the line appears active (i.e., has both spatial and temporal growth) could be restricted to small

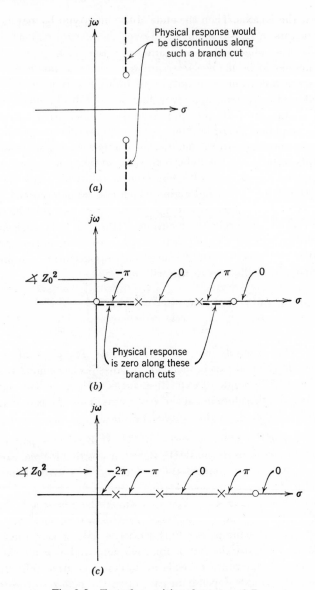

Fig. 2-3   Tests for positive character of Z_0.

regions near the $j\omega$ axis. Then the ends of the line could be matched and the reflection factors in (2.1-5) made small over these small regions. This is the case with laser amplifiers.

2. The line could be made *nonreciprocal* so the gain factor $e^{\alpha a}$ associated with the wave reflection from output to input would be greatly reduced. This is automatically true in a traveling wave tube because of the non-reciprocal character of the electron beam, and also in a traveling wave parametric amplifier. Ferrite materials have been used in conjunction with tunnel diode amplifiers to attenuate the reverse wave and achieve stable amplification [Hi 2].

2.2. MODES OF A DISTRIBUTED OSCILLATOR

Consider now a reciprocal active transmission line which is loaded with impedances Z_1 and Z_2 as in Fig. 2-4a, and suppose that our intent is to construct an oscillator rather than an amplifier. If we assume that Z_0 is a positive function and both Z_1 and Z_2 are pr, (2.1-3) indicates oscillations will occur for RHP roots of the *characteristic equation*

$$e^{-2\gamma_0 a}\left(\frac{Z_1 - Z_0}{Z_1 + Z_0}\right)\left(\frac{Z_2 - Z_0}{Z_2 + Z_0}\right) = 1 \qquad (2.2\text{-}1)$$

As we noted previously, (2.2-1) can be interpreted as the requirement that the complex voltage gain of a wave which starts at one end of the line, travels to the other end, is reflected, travels back, and is reflected again to its starting point must be unity for a natural mode of oscillation. Equation

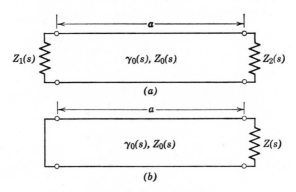

Fig. 2-4   Oscillator structures.

2.2-1 can be rewritten as a *gain condition*

$$e^{-2\alpha a}\,|\rho_1|\,|\rho_2| = 1, \tag{2.2-2}$$

and a *phase condition*

$$\theta_1 + \theta_2 - 2\beta a = 2\pi n \qquad (n = \pm 1, 2, 3, \ldots), \tag{2.2-3}$$

where $|\rho_1|$, $|\rho_2|$ and θ_1, θ_2 are respectively the magnitudes and angles of the reflection coefficients at the ends. That is to say

$$\frac{Z_1 - Z_0}{Z_1 + Z_0} = |\rho_1|\,e^{j\theta_1},$$

$$\frac{Z_2 - Z_0}{Z_2 + Z_0} = |\rho_2|\,e^{j\theta_2}. \tag{2.2-4a,b}$$

We shall see in Chapter 3 that an interesting oscillator structure is obtained when one end is shorted as indicated in Fig. 2-4b. The shorted end is a convenient point to introduce voltage bias and a single load is often more practical than two. For a given load impedance we can determine the roots of (2.2-1) as

$$s_i = \sigma_i + j\omega_i. \tag{2.2-5}$$

It is necessary for at least one of these to lie in the RHP (i.e., have σ_i positive) if we are to have an oscillator. Let us suppose that we wish to design a *sinusoidal* oscillator. Then we must not permit RHP roots for which $\sigma_i > 0$ and $\omega_i = 0$. Such a root would indicate a normal mode with temporal variation of the form $\exp(\sigma_i t)$ which in turn would imply a *blocking* oscillation rather than a sinusoidal oscillation.

We can determine conditions for avoiding blocking oscillations if we *assume* $s = +\sigma$ and then ask that (2.2-1) have no root. Suppose for example the line under consideration is the simple active system of Fig. 1-4. Then

$$Z_0(s) = \left(\frac{ls}{cs - g}\right)^{1/2} \quad \text{and} \quad \gamma_0(s) = \sqrt{ls(cs - g)},$$

and for $s = \sigma$

$$Z_0(\sigma) = \left(\frac{l\sigma}{c\sigma - g}\right)^{1/2}, \tag{2.2-6}$$

$$\gamma_0(\sigma) = \sqrt{l\sigma(c\sigma - g)}. \tag{2.2-7}$$

Equation 2.2-1 becomes

$$-e^{-2\gamma_0 a}\left(\frac{Z - Z_0}{Z + Z_0}\right) = 1,$$

which can be written in the form

$$Z_0(\sigma) \tanh [a\gamma_0(\sigma)] + Z(\sigma) = 0. \qquad (2.2\text{-}8)$$

If the load impedance $Z(s)$ is pr, $Z(\sigma)$ will be real and positive and (2.2-8) can have a solution only if $Z_0(\sigma) \tanh (a\gamma_0(\sigma))$ is real. But with $Z_0(\sigma)$ and $\gamma_0(\sigma)$ as in (2.2-6) and (2.2-7) and for

$$0 < \sigma < \frac{g}{c},$$

(2.2-8) can be written

$$\left(\frac{l\sigma}{g - c\sigma}\right)^{1/2} \tan (a\sqrt{l\sigma(g - c\sigma)}) = Z(\sigma). \qquad (2.2\text{-}9)$$

For $\sigma = 0$ the left-hand side of (2.2-9) is equal to zero. If the line length, a, is long enough so the argument of the tangent can reach $\pi/2$, the left hand side will range over all the positive numbers. Both sides of (2.2-9) will then be equal for some positive value of σ no matter what pr load impedance is chosen. It is easily demonstrated that the maximum value of $a\sqrt{l\sigma(g - c\sigma)}$ occurs for $\sigma = g/2c$ and is equal to $(a/2)g\sqrt{l/c}$. Thus a *necessary* condition to avoid blocking oscillation is that this maximum argument be less than $\pi/2$ or that

$$a < \frac{\pi}{g} \left(\frac{c}{l}\right)^{1/2}. \qquad (2.2\text{-}10)$$

2.3. CONVECTIVE AND ABSOLUTE INSTABILITIES ON INFINITE LINES

The rather considerable difficulties which one encounters in the stability analysis of terminated active systems [e.g., determining the roots of (2.2-1)] suggest that it might be of interest to consider, as a simplification, the stability of a system of infinite length. Sturrock [St 2] has shown that two distinct forms of instability can be distinguished which are illustrated in Fig. 2-5. To see this suppose that the infinite line is excited at zero time by a voltage $v(x, 0)$ which is limited in space. If the system is unstable this disturbance will grow with time but in two distinct ways.

1. The disturbance may propagate away from the region of excitation so the voltage at any point on the line eventually returns to zero. This is called a *convective instability*.

2. The disturbance may remain localized in space so the voltage in the vicinity of the region of excitation grows without bound. This is called an *absolute instability*.

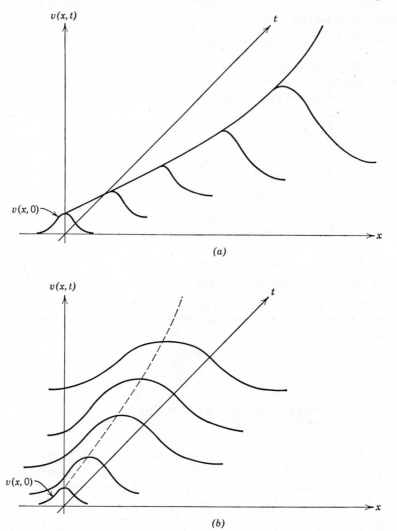

Fig. 2-5 Modes of linear wave instability. (*a*) Convective instability; (*b*) nonconvective or absolute instability.

The initial disturbance may be represented by a spatial Fourier integral of the form

$$v(x, 0) = \int_{\text{along } j\beta \text{ axis}} V(\gamma)e^{\gamma x} \, d\gamma, \qquad (2.3\text{-}1)$$

where $\gamma = \alpha + j\beta$ and $V(j\beta)$ is the Fourier transform of $v(x, 0)$. Elementary solutions of the wave equation are of the form $\exp(\gamma x + st)$ and from the dispersion equation

$$s = S(\gamma). \tag{2.3-2}$$

In general s will be a multiple valued function of γ or, equivalently, a single valued function of γ defined on a multilayer Reimann surface. The degree of this multiplicity will be equal to the algebraic order of (2.3-2) which for a ladder line will be equal to the number of independent energy storage elements in z_{se} and y_{sh}. Thus the multiplicity is equal to the number of initial conditions which must be specified on the system at zero time. If we restrict our attention to those values of s which correspond to only one branch of the Riemann surface for γ, then we are considering only one set of the several modes which can be excited on the system. Only one initial condition [say $v(x, 0)$] is then necessary to determine the mode amplitude. The disturbance as a function of space and time is

$$v(x, t) = \int_{\text{along } j\beta \text{ axis}} V(\gamma) e^{[\gamma x + S(\gamma)t]} \, d\gamma. \tag{2.3-3}$$

If the initial disturbance is a spatial impulse function (or Dirac delta function), the character of the Fourier integral transform $V(\gamma)$ is fixed; it is a constant. In this case the question of convective or absolute instability depends only upon the character of the dispersion relation. But *any* initial perturbation can be constructed as a sum of properly chosen impulse functions and the response of each will be either a convective or an absolute instability depending upon the nature of the dispersion relation. Thus we should be able to classify a transmission *system* as convectively unstable or absolutely unstable from a sufficiently detailed investigation of the dispersion relation.

Although these concepts have been developed for the rather unrealistic case of an infinitely long system, they are still of some value and interest when one is concerned with the stability of finite systems. A convectively unstable line should be more useful in an amplifier application, although it can serve as an oscillator. The requirements for stabilization were discussed above in relation to the finite line in Fig. 2-1 and the corresponding characteristic equation (2.2-1). An absolutely unstable system should be more useful as an oscillator; however, as we shall see in Section 2.7, it can be stabilized if a short enough length is properly terminated.

Generally before we attempt to decide whether a wave system is absolutely or only convectively unstable, we should determine whether it is unstable at all. From the considerations in the last section of Chapter I it is evident that this question can also be answered from an investigation of the dispersion relation. If the transformation from the γ-plane to the s-plane which is implied by (2.3-2) does not map the $j\beta$ axis into the right half of the s-plane, then there is no region which corresponds to both spatial and temporal growth.

2.4. INVESTIGATION OF THE DISPERSION EQUATION FOR CONVECTIVE INSTABILITY

If we have a system with a convective instability (as illustrated in Fig. 2-5a), it should be possible to apply a sinusoidal excitation at some point and observe growing waves which propagate away from the point of excitation. The condition for convective instability might appear to be simply that the dispersion relation should indicate a complex propagation constant $\gamma = \alpha + j\beta$ for an imaginary frequency variable $s = j\omega$ and for which α is *positive* when ω and β have opposite sign (propagation with growth in the $+x$ direction) or *negative* when ω and β have the same sign (propagation with growth in the $-x$ direction). (Note that we are considering elementary solutions to be of the form exp $[\gamma x + st]$). That the question is not so simple can be seen from an examination of the obviously passive system of Fig. 2-6. The series impedance and shunt admittance per unit length are

$$z_{se} = ls \tag{2.4-1}$$

$$y_{sh} = \frac{cs(s^2 + (c_1 + c)/l_1 c_1 c)}{s^2 + 1/l_1 c} . \tag{2.4-2}$$

For $s = j\omega$, z_{se} is a positive imaginary while y_{sh} is a negative imaginary for

$$\frac{1}{\sqrt{l_1 c}} < |\omega| < \left(\frac{c_1 + c}{l_1 c_1 c}\right)^{1/2} . \tag{2.4-3}$$

Thus if the frequency lies within the range indicated by (2.4-3) then

$$\gamma = \pm\sqrt{z_{se} y_{sh}} \tag{2.4-4}$$

is a real number and *formally* indicates solutions which grow exponentially for large x. We know, however, from our physical intuition that the growing solution cannot be used for gain because the system is entirely passive.

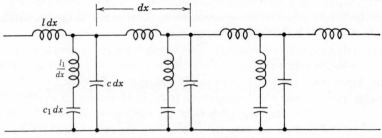

Fig. 2-6   A lossless transmission line.

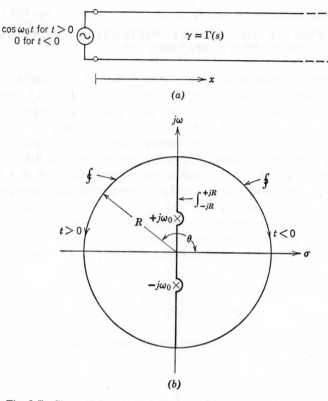

Fig. 2-7   Sinusoidal excitation of a semi-infinite transmission line.

Solutions of this sort are called *evanescent* and are physically necessary to match boundary conditions at the ends of a finite length line. For an infinite line they would require the application of an infinite amplitude at $x = \pm \infty$ and are of no physical interest. Our problem in this section is to formulate a criterion which is sufficiently sharp to discriminate between evanescence and convective instability.

Let us suppose that we have a semi-infinite transmission line as shown in Fig. 2-7a for which the dispersion equation

$$\gamma = \Gamma(s) \tag{2.4-5}$$

is known. At the left-hand end ($x = 0$) a voltage of the following form is applied.

$$v(0, t) = \cos \omega_0 t \quad \text{for} \quad t > 0,$$
$$v(0, t) = 0 \qquad \text{for} \quad t < 0. \tag{2.4-6}$$

We can represent such an excitation by its Laplace transform [Ga 2]

$$V(0, s) = \frac{s}{s^2 + \omega_0^2} = \frac{1}{2}\left(\frac{1}{s - j\omega_0} + \frac{1}{s + j\omega_0}\right), \tag{2.4-7}$$

where it is supposed that (2.4-6) can be determined from (2.4-7) by an evaluation of the integral

$$v(0, t) = \frac{1}{2\pi j} \int V(0, s)e^{st}\, ds. \tag{2.4-8}$$

$$\text{along } j\omega\text{-axis}$$

The evaluation of this integral is greatly facilitated by *Cauchy's residue theorem* [Gu 1, pp. 302–307] which states that the integral of a complex function around a *closed* path in a positive (counter-clockwise) sense is

$$\oint f(s)\, ds = 2\pi j \sum \text{residues}. \tag{2.4-9}$$

The "residues" in (2.4-9) are simply the coefficients of the terms of the form

$$\frac{1}{s - s_0}$$

which appear in the Laurent expansions about the singular points.

For the evaluation of the inverse transform of (2.4-8) we wish to integrate only along the $j\omega$ axis from $-j\infty$ to $+j\infty$. This integral can be considered as part of the integrals around either of the two closed paths indicated in Fig. 2-7b.

$$\oint_L = \oint + \int_{-jR}^{+jR} \tag{2.4-10}$$

$$\oint_R = \oint + \int_{-jR}^{+jR}, \tag{2.4-11}$$

where it is assumed that R can be made arbitrarily large. It is important to notice that in defining the path for $\int_{-jR}^{+jR}$ in Fig. 2-7b we have supposed that it passes the poles of (2.4-7) slightly to the *right*. This is equivalent to the assumption that the poles lie slightly in the left half of the frequency plane or that the sinusoidal time function given in (2.4-6) is damped by an arbitrarily small amount [Gu 1, pp. 547–553].

Along the large semicircles the integrand of (2.4-8) is approximately

$$\frac{e^{st}\, ds}{s},$$

where $s = R\,(\cos\theta + j\sin\theta)$. Thus the integrals along the semi-circles are always less than

$$e^{Rt\cos\theta}\, d\theta,$$

where θ is defined in Fig. 2-7*b*. For $t > 0$

$$\lim_{R \to \infty} \left[\oint \right] = 0, \tag{2.4-12}$$

while for $t < 0$

$$\lim_{R \to \infty} \left[\oint \right] = 0. \tag{2.4-13}$$

Equations 2.4-12 and 2.4-13 together with (2.4-10) and (2.4-11) imply that for $t > 0$

$$\int_{-j\infty}^{+j\infty} = \oint_L, \tag{2.4-14}$$

which *includes* the poles of the integrand and from (2.4-9) gives

$$v(0, t) = \tfrac{1}{2}(e^{j\omega_0 t} + e^{-j\omega_0 t}) = \cos \omega_0 t,$$

while for $t < 0$

$$\int_{-j\infty}^{+j\infty} = \oint_R, \tag{2.4-15}$$

which *excludes* the poles of the integrand and gives

$$v(0, t) = 0.$$

We see that a considerable amount of thought is required to recover our original time function, (2.4-6) from its Laplace transform, (2.4-7) if we decide to do it without the assistance of a transform table. This labor has not been wasted, however, because we can now construct an expression for the transform of $v(x, t)$ at some arbitrary point on the line and think with some clarity about its evaluation. From (2.4-5) elementary solutions are of the form $\exp [\Gamma(s)x + st]$ and from (2.4-7) and (2.4-8) these are excited with complex amplitudes $s/(s^2 + \omega_0^2)$. Thus

$$v(x, t) = \frac{1}{2\pi j} \int_{-j\infty}^{+j\infty} \frac{s e^{[\Gamma(s)x + st]}}{s^2 + \omega_0^2} \, ds. \tag{2.4-16}$$

Let us now suppose that the wave system has a high frequency limiting velocity (or *characteristic* velocity) given by

$$u_c = -\lim_{s \to \infty} \left[\frac{s}{\Gamma(s)} \right]. \tag{2.4-17}$$

For any sort of electromagnetic wave system u_c would of course be equal to the velocity of light. The minus sign in (2.4-17) appears because for the particular form of the elementary solutions (i.e., $\exp [\gamma x + st]$) propagation is in the $+x$ direction when ω and β have the opposite sign. We can state the requirement of causality as

$$v(x, t) = 0 \quad \text{for} \quad x > u_c t. \tag{2.4-18}$$

Along the large semicircles the integrand of (2.4-16) becomes approximately

$$\frac{e^{(1-x/u_c t)st}}{s}.$$

If $1/u_c > 0$ and $x < u_c t$, the integral along $\oint$ is zero and the integral along $\int_{-j\infty}^{+j\infty}$ (the desired time response) is evaluated just as before. If $1/u_c > 0$ but $x > u_c t$, it is the integral along $\oint$ which is zero. The integral along $\int_{-j\infty}^{+j\infty}$ must now be evaluated by completing the path to the right with the result that the response is zero as is expected.

If $1/u_c < 0$ and if $t > 0$, $(1 - x/u_c t)$ is positive for all positive x; it does not change sign at some large value of x. The integral along $\oint$ is then zero for all values of x. Therefore the time response (the integral along $\int_{-j\infty}^{+j\infty}$) must be evaluated by completing the path to the left for all values of x. This means that we have a finite value of the voltage for all values at $t = 0$ which violates the causality condition of (2.4-18).

We are therefore led to the conclusion that the only solutions of the dispersion equation which satisfy causality are those for which [Fe 1]

$$\frac{1}{u_c} = -\lim_{s \to \infty}\left[\frac{\Gamma(s)}{s}\right] > 0. \tag{2.4-19}$$

The condition of (2.4-19) assures that the wave is *convective*; that it does in fact propagate away from the point of excitation.

If the wave is to be *convectively unstable* it must grow in the direction of propagation. This means that α must be *positive* for a wave which is propagating in the $+x$ direction. But if the characteristic velocity, u_c, is positive then for $s = \sigma$ this implies that

$$\lim_{\sigma \to \infty}\left(\frac{\Gamma(\sigma)}{\sigma}\right) < 0, \tag{2.4-20}$$

or that α must become *negative* as σ approaches $+\infty$. Our condition for convective instability can therefore be summarized by the following

Statement. *A transmission system which is not absolutely unstable will be convectively unstable at some frequency $s_0 = j\omega_0$ if the sign of α changes along the path $s = \sigma + j\omega_0$ with σ approaching $+\infty$.*

It is evidently a necessary condition for convective instability that there be some RHP frequency for which the corresponding value of γ is a pure imaginary; that is, the $j\beta$-axis must map into the right half of the s-plane under $s = S(\gamma)$.

Returning now to our example of Fig. 2-6 it is immediately evident that the sign of the real part of γ as given by (2.4-4) does not change sign as $\sigma \to \infty$. Thus the system is not convectively unstable; it is evanescent, and our physical intuition is confirmed by the analysis.

2.5. INVESTIGATION OF THE DISPERSION EQUATION FOR ABSOLUTE INSTABILITY

In this section we discuss the question of determining absolute instability from a point of view which was developed by Bers and Briggs [Br 3]. It is supposed that an infinite transmission system is excited at the center point $(x = 0)$ as indicated in Fig. 2-8. The resulting response on the line is given by the evaluation of a Laplace integral.

$$v(x, t) = \frac{1}{2\pi j} \int_{\sigma-j\infty}^{\sigma+j\infty} V(x, s) f(s) e^{st} \, ds \qquad (2.5\text{-}1)$$

for which the integrand is determined by a Fourier integral

$$V(x, s) = \frac{1}{2\pi j} \int_{-j\infty}^{+j\infty} G(\gamma, s) g(\gamma) e^{\gamma x} \, d\gamma. \qquad (2.5\text{-}2)$$

In (2.5-1) and (2.5-2) the functions $f(s)$ and $g(\gamma)$ are respectively the transforms of the temporal and spatial aspects of the source function. For the arrangement of Fig. 2-8 the source is an impulse function of x so

$$g(\gamma) = \text{const.} \qquad (2.5\text{-}3)$$

For the indicated time function

$$v(0, t) = \cos \omega_0 t \quad \text{for} \quad t > 0,$$

$$= 0 \qquad \text{for} \quad t < 0,$$

the corresponding transform is

$$f(s) = \frac{s}{s^2 + \omega_0{}^2}, \qquad (2.5\text{-}4)$$

as was previously discussed in connection with (2.4-7).

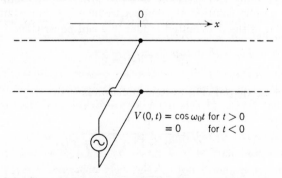

Fig. 2-8   Sinusoidal excitation of an infinite transmission line.

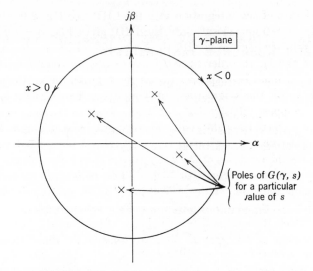

Fig. 2-9   Poles of $G(\gamma, s)$ in the γ-plane.

The complex function $G(\gamma, s)$ which appears in (2.5-2) contains information related to the natural spatial response of the system. In most physical situations we would expect to find poles (as indicated in Fig. 2-9) which, upon integration in (2.5-2), would determine the exact nature of the response as a function of x. In order to evaluate (2.5-2) it is again convenient to use Cauchy's residue theorem and suppose that the integration path is closed to the right for $x < 0$ and to the left for $x > 0$. Thus for a particular value of complex frequency the RHP poles of $G(\gamma, s)$ (in the γ-plane) determine the response for $x < 0$ while the LHP poles determine the response for $x > 0$. It is important to note that the position of these poles depend upon the complex frequency, s. Evidently the poles of $G(\gamma, s)$ correspond to roots of the dispersion relation in the γ-plane since they determine the spatial character of an elementary solution at complex frequency s. For example, the dispersion relation of the distributed ladder line can be written

$$\gamma^2 - \Gamma^2(s) = 0, \tag{2.5-5}$$

where $\Gamma^2(s) = z_{se}(s)y_{sh}(s)$. The system function is then

$$G(\gamma, s) = \frac{1}{\gamma - \Gamma(s)} + \frac{1}{\gamma + \Gamma(s)},$$

$$= \frac{2\gamma}{\gamma^2 - \Gamma^2(s)}, \tag{2.5-6}$$

since closure of the integration into the LHP (see Fig. 2-9) gives $V(x, s) = e^{\Gamma(s)x}$ for $x > 0$ and closure into the RHP gives $V(x, s) = e^{-\Gamma(s)x}$ for $x < 0$.

Our primary concern is with the evaluation of the inverse Laplace transform of (2.5-1). In order to satisfy the *causality* requirement the path of integration must be displaced to the right by an amount σ which is large enough so *all* the singularities of $V(x, s)$ can be excluded from an RHP closure. Suppose initially that σ is large enough so the path of integration in (2.5-1) does lie to the right of all s-plane singularities of $V(x, s)$. We can locate the singularities by supposing that σ decreases for a fixed value of ω. As we do this the positions of the poles of $G(\gamma, s)$ will move in the γ-plane. This effect is indicated in Fig. 2-10. When a pole of $G(\gamma, s)$ crosses the $j\beta$-axis in the γ-plane the value of $V(x, s)$ will jump by an amount which is related to the residue of the pole in question. Thus the function $V(x, s)$ has *branch lines* across which it changes discontinuously. These branch lines coincide with the mapping of the $j\beta$-axis into the s-plane by the dispersion relation. (Mappings of this sort were studied in connection with Fig. 1-7.) These branch lines are an unfortunate factor in the evaluation of (2.5-1) because they greatly complicate the contour integration. This difficulty can be avoided by defining a new function which is *equal* to $V(x, s)$ when s lies to the right of the branch lines but which does not have the branch lines. The desired function is

$$\tilde{V}(x, s) \equiv \frac{1}{2\pi j} \int_C G(\gamma, s)e^{\gamma x}\, d\gamma, \tag{2.5-7}$$

where the integration is *not* along the $j\beta$-axis [as in (2.5-2)] but rather along the contour C indicated in Fig. 2-10b. This contour is specifically chosen to pass to the left all the poles which originally lay to the right of the $j\beta$-axis, and to pass to the right all poles which originally lay to the left. The branch lines have simply been *defined out* of the function $\tilde{V}(x, s)$. The function $\tilde{V}(x, s)$ is perfectly satisfactory for the evaluation of the Laplace integral in (2.5-1) because over the required path of integration it is equal to $V(x, s)$. It is in fact *more* appropriate than $V(x, s)$ because it is simpler.

In order to answer questions concerning stability it is necessary only to determine the asymptotic character of (2.5-1) as $t \to +\infty$. This asymptote is determined by the pole or poles of $\tilde{V}(x, s)f(s)$ which lie farthest to the right. If $\tilde{V}(x, s)$ has no RHP poles then the asymptotic character is determined by the poles of $f(s)$ which from (2.5-4) occur at $s = \pm j\omega_0$. At large values of time then

$$v(x, t) \approx \tfrac{1}{2}[\tilde{V}(x, j\omega_0)e^{j\omega_0 t} + \tilde{V}(x, -j\omega_0)e^{-j\omega_0 t}]. \tag{2.5-8}$$

Referring to the poles of $G(\gamma, s)$ indicated in the γ-plane of Fig. 2-10b it is evident that A is a wave which contributes to spatial growth in the $+x$ direction (since α is $+$) and which enters into the response for $x > 0$ (since

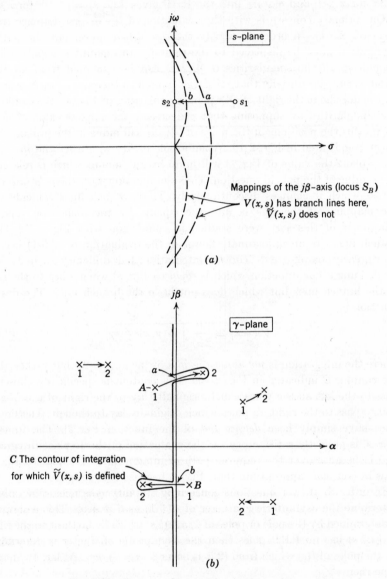

Fig. 2-10 Contour of integration in the γ-plane.

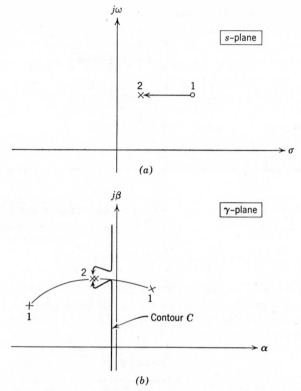

Fig. 2-11 A situation which implies absolute instability.

it lies to the left of the contour C). The pole A therefore represents an active wave. Likewise the pole B represents an active wave which is propagating in the $-x$ direction. The other poles represent passive waves. Thus the conclusion of the last section is confirmed; the location of a zero of the dispersion relation must cross the $j\beta$-axis as σ becomes large for active wave propagation.

We now wish to ask how RHP poles of $\tilde{V}(x, s)$ can occur since these imply *growing* asymptotic behavior of $v(x, t)$ at all values of x and therefore absolute instability. Such a situation is indicated in Fig. 2-11. As the complex frequency moves from 1 to 2 in the s-plane, two poles of $G(\gamma, s)$ in the γ-plane which originate from *opposite sides* of the $j\beta$-axis *merge together*. It is then impossible to choose a contour C which passes to the right of one and to the left of the other. The integral along a segment of the contour C, which is near where the two poles are separated by a small amount 2ε is of the form

$$K \int \frac{d(j\beta)}{(j\beta - \varepsilon)(j\beta + \varepsilon)} = \frac{K}{2j\varepsilon} \int \left[\frac{1}{(\beta - j\varepsilon)} - \frac{1}{(\beta + j\varepsilon)} \right] d\beta. \quad (2.5\text{-}9)$$

This evidently approaches infinity as $\varepsilon \to 0$ both for closure to the left $(x > 0)$ and for closure to the right $(x < 0)$.

At a double pole of $G(\gamma, s)$ in the γ-plane the inverse function $G^{-1}(\gamma, s)$ will have a double zero in the γ-plane and therefore its series expansion is

$$G^{-1}(\gamma, s) \approx \left(\frac{\partial G^{-1}}{\partial s}\right)\bigg|_{\gamma_2, s_2} (s - s_2) + \frac{1}{2}\left(\frac{\partial^2 G^{-1}}{\partial \gamma^2}\right)\bigg|_{\gamma_2, s_2} (\gamma - \gamma_2)^2. \quad (2.5\text{-}10)$$

Substitution into (2.5-7) gives

$$\tilde{V}(x, s) = \left(\frac{1}{2\pi j}\right)\left(\frac{1}{2jB\sqrt{s - s_2}}\right)$$
$$\times \int_C \left[\left(\frac{e^{\gamma x}}{A(\gamma - \gamma_2) - jB\sqrt{s - s_2}}\right) - \left(\frac{e^{\gamma x}}{A(\gamma - \gamma_2) + jB\sqrt{s - s_2}}\right)\right] d\gamma, \quad (2.5\text{-}11)$$

where

$$B = \left(\frac{\partial G^{-1}}{\partial s}\right)^{1/2}, \qquad A = \frac{1}{\sqrt{2}}\left(\frac{\partial^2 G^{-1}}{\partial \gamma^2}\right)^{1/2}. \quad (2.5\text{-}12)$$

The pole of one of the terms in the integrand of (2.5-11) will lie on one side of the contour C and the pole of other term will lie on the other side. One of these terms will contribute to the response for $x > 0$ and the other will contribute for $x < 0$. Thus for $x > 0$

$$\tilde{V}(x, s) = \frac{j \exp\left(\gamma_2 - j\dfrac{B}{A}\sqrt{s - s_2}\right)x}{2AB\sqrt{s - s_2}}. \quad (2.5\text{-}13)$$

Substituting into (2.5-1) we can determine the asymptotic response as $t \to \infty$ by integrating along the contour F (indicated in Fig. 2-12) which has been displaced to the $j\omega$-axis. At large values of time the major contribution to the integral comes from the portion of F which extends into the RHP of the s-plane. The contributions along the outward and inward paths do not cancel; they add because the $\sqrt{s - s_2}$ factors which are in (2.5-13) require a change in sign as one moves completely around the pole s_2. A branch cut is sketched in Fig. 2-12 to emphasize this point. Thus, as $t \to \infty$,

$$\lim_{t \to \infty} v(x, t) = \frac{e^{\gamma_2 x}}{2\pi AB} \int_0^{\sigma_2} \frac{e^{(\sigma + j\omega_2)t} \cos\left(\dfrac{B}{A}\sqrt{s - s_2}\, x\right) d\sigma}{\sqrt{\sigma - \sigma_2}}, \quad (2.5\text{-}14)$$

or if we write $\sigma = \sigma_2 - \varepsilon$

$$\lim_{t \to \infty} v(x, t) = \frac{je^{(\gamma_2 x + s_2 t)}}{2\pi AB} \int_0^{\sigma_2} \frac{e^{-\varepsilon t} \cosh\left(\dfrac{B}{A}\sqrt{\varepsilon}\, x\right) d\varepsilon}{\sqrt{\varepsilon}}.$$

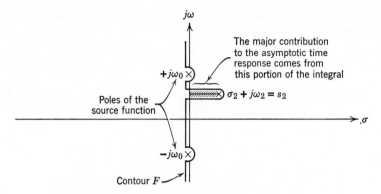

Fig. 2-12 Integration around a branch line in the s-plane.

This integral can be approximated by taking the upper limit to be ∞ and noting that

$$\int_0^\infty \frac{e^{-\varepsilon t}\, d\varepsilon}{\sqrt{\varepsilon}} = \left(\frac{\pi}{t}\right)^{\frac{1}{2}}.$$

Thus our final result is

$$\lim_{t \to \infty} v(x, t) \approx \frac{je^{(\gamma_2 x + s_2 t)}}{2\sqrt{\pi}\, AB\sqrt{t}}. \tag{2.5-15}$$

Equation 2.5-15 definitely indicates absolute instability since the factor $e^{s_2 t}$ implies exponential growth with time at all values of x. After resting a moment from our labor we can summarize our results with the following

Statement. *A transmission system is absolutely unstable when two zeros (in the γ-plane) of the dispersion relation merge together at some RHP frequency from opposite sides of the $j\beta$-axis as the real part of the complex frequency is reduced from plus infinity.*

This condition has been given the following satisfying physical explanation by Briggs [Br 3]. In general we expect the spatial variation in the $+x$ direction ($\exp \gamma_+ x$) to differ from the variation in the $-x$ direction ($\exp (\gamma_- x)$). This implies a discontinuity in the slope at $x = 0$ which must be supplied by the source. However, if for some growing natural frequency we have a double root in the γ-plane so $\gamma_+ = \gamma_-$, then the spatial response for $x > 0$ can be joined smoothly to that for $x < 0$ with no source at $x = 0$. The system then has a growing natural frequency.

Let us now consider as a specific example the simple active line of Fig. 1-5. The dispersion relation is given in (2.5-5) and $G(\gamma, s)$ in (2.5-6) where

$$\gamma^2 = \Gamma^2(s) = ls(cs - g), \tag{2.5-16}$$

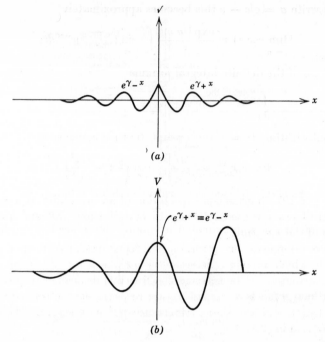

Fig. 2-13 Responses which are (a) unmatched and (b) matched at the source.

and for $x > 0$

$$\tilde{V}(x, s) = e^{\Gamma(s)x}.$$

As s approaches $+g/c$ by moving to the left along the σ-axis, the γ-plane zeros of (2.5-16) converge from the RHP and the LHP to the origin. Thus we expect an unstable mode with infinite wavelength at the open circuit natural frequency of the shunt admittance. To determine the time response in detail we must evaluate

$$v(x, t) = \frac{1}{2\pi j} \int_F \exp{(\Gamma(s)x + st)} f(s) \, ds \qquad (2.5\text{-}17)$$

along the contour F indicated in Fig. 2-12. For simplicity we can take the excitation to be a unit impulse function in time (as well as in space) so $f(s) = 1$. It is not possible to directly apply (2.5-15) in this case because the expansion constants (A and B) are not defined, but the asymptotic time response is determined as before by evaluating the integral along the branch cut. Thus

$$\lim_{t \to \infty} v(x, t) = \frac{1}{2\pi j} \int_0^{g/c} [\exp{(+jx\sqrt{l\sigma(g - c\sigma)})} - \exp{(-jx\sqrt{l\sigma(g - c\sigma)})}] e^{\sigma t} \, d\sigma,$$

and if we write $\sigma = g/c - \varepsilon$ this becomes approximately

$$\lim_{t \to \infty} v(x, t) \approx \frac{\exp\left[(g/c)t\right]}{\pi} \int_0^\infty \sin\left(\sqrt{lg\varepsilon}\, x\right)e^{-\varepsilon t}\, d\varepsilon. \qquad (2.5\text{-}18)$$

With the use of the definite integral formula

$$\int_0^\infty \phi e^{-a^2\phi^2} \sin m\phi\, d\phi = \frac{m\sqrt{\pi}}{4a^3}\, e^{-m^2/4a^2},$$

and the substitution $\phi^2 = \varepsilon$, the asymptotic time response is

$$\lim_{t \to \infty} v(x, t) \approx \frac{(lg)^{\frac{1}{2}}x}{2\sqrt{\pi}\, t^{\frac{3}{2}}} \exp\left(\frac{g}{c}\, t - \frac{lgx^2}{4t}\right). \qquad (2.5\text{-}19)$$

Equation (2.5-19) confirms our expectation of an instability at $s = g/c$ and in addition shows how the initial impulse of excitation "diffuses" away from the origin of the x-t plane.

In this development our attention has been concentrated upon absolute instabilities which arise in connection with zeros of the dispersion relation. For the distributed ladder transmission line this dispersion relation can be written $\gamma^2 = z_{se}y_{sh}$, where z_{se} and y_{sh} are respectively the series impedance per unit length and the shunt admittance per unit length. The response function $G(\gamma, s)$ in (2.5-2) is

$$G(\gamma, s) = \frac{2\gamma}{\gamma^2 - z_{se}(s)y_{sh}(s)}, \qquad (2.5\text{-}20)$$

as was noted in (2.5-6). Absolute instabilities occur therefore at zeros of either $y_{sh}(s)$ or $z_{se}(s)$; that is to say they occur either at RHP open circuit natural frequencies of the shunt admittance per unit length or at RHP short circuit natural frequencies of the series impedance per unit length. Writing the dispersion relation in the form

$$\Gamma(s) = [z_{se}(s)y_{sh}(s)]^{\frac{1}{2}}, \qquad (2.5\text{-}21)$$

it is evident that an RHP pole of the series impedance or shunt admittance leads to an *essential singularity* in the s-plane of the integrand of (2.5-17). A function with an essential singularity such as

$$F(s) = \exp\left(\frac{1}{s - s_0}\right)$$

has the uncomfortable property that $F(s)$ can be equal to *any* value in the vicinity of the singularity, s_0 [Gu 1, p. 296]. Such a singularity probably implies absolute instability, but it would appear to be a rather "unphysical" characteristic of the fundamental impulse response of a real system. Also since such a singularity would imply an infinite value of γ, the corresponding wavelength would be zero. In most cases one would expect that the assumptions made in deriving the transmission line equivalent circuit for a real physical system would no longer be valid at zero wavelength.

2.6. PROPAGATION AND STABILITY ON DISCRETE LINES [Br7, Lll]

We now turn our attention to a transmission system which is no longer completely distributed but constructed from discrete components. We shall be primarily concerned with the "lumped ladder line" of Fig. 2-14a where Y and Z are respectively the shunt admittance and series impedance *per section* rather than per unit length. Propagation is now governed not by

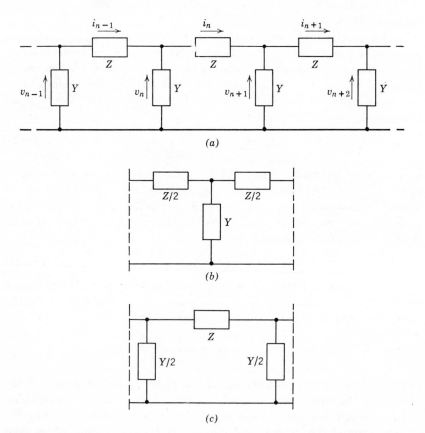

Fig. 2-14   (*a*) Lumped ladder transmission line; (*b*) symmetrical T-section; (*c*) symmetrical π section.

partial differential equations but by the *difference equations*

$$i_n - i_{n+1} = v_{n+1}Y,$$
$$v_n - v_{n+1} = i_n Z. \tag{2.6-1a,b}$$

According to Floquet's theorem these equations have solutions for which voltage and current changes by a constant factor as the section index n changes by one. Writing this factor as $\exp(\Gamma)$ we have

$$v_{n+1} = e^\Gamma v_n \quad \text{and} \quad i_{n+1} = e^\Gamma i_n. \tag{2.6-2}$$

The constant Γ is in general a complex number

$$\Gamma = A + jB, \tag{2.6-3}$$

where A is the gain per section (in nepers) and B is the phase shift per section (in radians). It is not difficult to show from (2.6-1) and (2.6-2) that Γ is determined as the root of the transcendental equation

$$\sqrt{YZ} = 2 \sinh \frac{\Gamma}{2}. \tag{2.6-4}$$

If we write

$$\sqrt{YZ} = a + jb, \tag{2.6-5}$$

then a and b are respectively the gain and phase shift per section which the line would have if it were fully distributed. Thus to determine the effect of discrete sections in a system for which we already have determined the distributed solution, we would like to have A and B as functions of a and b. From (2.6-4) and (2.6-5)

$$a = 2 \sinh\left(\frac{A}{2}\right) \cos\left(\frac{B}{2}\right),$$
$$b = 2 \cosh\left(\frac{A}{2}\right) \sin\left(\frac{B}{2}\right). \tag{2.6-6a,b}$$

These relations are plotted in Fig. 2-15. It is possible to find approximate solutions to (2.6-6) which are valid over certain ranges of the variables a and b. These ranges are indicated in Fig. 2-16 and listed below together with the pertinent approximation.

   Region I. $a < 1$ and $b < 1$

               $A \approx a$ and $B \approx b$.

   These approximations are good to about 10%. Over Region I the line may be considered fully distributed.

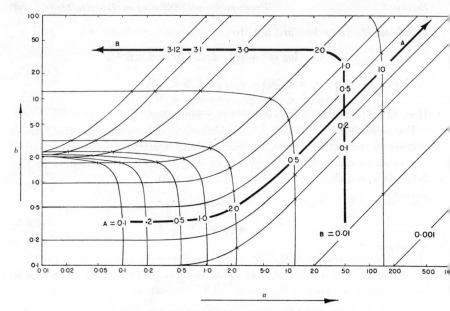

Fig. 2-15 The transformation of (2.6-6).

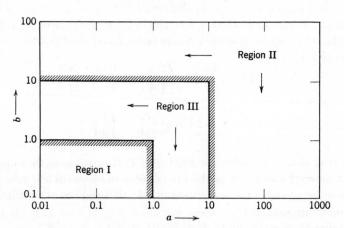

Fig. 2-16 Regions of approximation for the curves of Fig. 2-15.

Region II. $a > 10$ *or* $b > 10$

$$A \approx \log (a^2 + b^2) \quad \text{and} \quad B \approx 2 \tan^{-1} \frac{b}{a}$$

Region III. $\begin{pmatrix} 1 < a < 10 \\ \text{and } b < 10 \end{pmatrix}$ *or* $\begin{pmatrix} 1 < b < 10 \\ \text{and } a < 10 \end{pmatrix}$.

Here (2.6-6) must be used without approximations.

For a lumped line we define the characteristic impedance as the ratio of voltage to current of a traveling wave at the input to either a symmetrical *T*-section as indicated in Fig. 2-14*b* or a symmetrical π-section as in Fig. 2-14*c*. It is not difficult to show from (2.6-1) that

T-section

$$Z_{0T} = \sqrt{\frac{Z}{Y} \left(1 + \frac{YZ}{4} \right)}, \tag{2.6-7}$$

π-section

$$Z_{0\pi} = \sqrt{\left(\frac{Z/Y}{(1 + YZ/4)} \right)}. \tag{2.6-8}$$

If Z/Y is a positive function, the zeros of the factor $(1 + YZ/4)$ will determine whether or not Z_{0T} and $Z_{0\pi}$ are positive.

Consider for example the simple active line shown in Fig. 1-4 but assume that the elements are not distributed but lumped. Then

$$Z = Ls,$$
$$Y = Cs - G, \tag{2.6-9a,b}$$

where L, C and $-G$ are lumped elements with units of henrys per section, farads per section and mhos per section, respectively. The factor

$$\left(1 + \frac{YZ}{4} \right) = \frac{LC}{4} \left(s^2 - \frac{G}{C} s + \frac{16}{LC} \right), \tag{2.6-10}$$

with zeros at

$$s = \frac{1}{2} \left[\frac{G}{C} \pm \left(\frac{G^2}{C^2} - \frac{16}{LC} \right)^{\frac{1}{2}} \right]. \tag{2.6-11}$$

For $0 < G < 4\sqrt{C/L}$ the factor $(1 + YZ/4)$ introduces an additional pole onto the real axis of the RHP for $(Z_{0\pi})^2$ and an additional zero for $(Z_{0T})^2$. From the considerations of Section 2.1, this implies that Z_{0T} remains a positive function but $Z_{0\pi}$ does not. For $G > 4\sqrt{C/L}$, (2.6-11) indicates a complex conjugate pair of roots in the RHP so both Z_{0T} and $Z_{0\pi}$ are no longer positive functions.

Thus, if one were planning to construct an amplifier by using lumped elements to fabricate the simple active line, it would be advisable to use

T-sections (i.e., inductors equal to $L/2$ at the input and output) and also to limit the negative conductance so that

$$G < 4 \left(\frac{C}{L}\right)^{1/2}. \tag{2.6-12}$$

The amplifier application of a lumped line with a resistive series element has recently been studied by Kabaservice [Ka 1]

2.7. A MECHANICAL TRANSMISSION LINE

Let us now consider the mechanical transmission line shown in Figs. 2-17 and 2-18. This consists of a series of pendula (nails) connected by a steel spring and supported horizontally on a taut length of piano wire. If we take ϕ to be the angle of rotation of the pendula, then for the ith pendulum we can write the nonlinear differential difference equation

$$M \frac{d^2\phi_i}{dt^2} = K[\phi_{i+1} - 2\phi_i + \phi_{i-1}] - T \sin \phi, \tag{2.7-1}$$

where M is the moment of inertia of a single pendulum (kgm-meter²), K is the torque constant of a section of spring between two pendula (newton-meters/radian), and $T \sin \phi$ is the gravitational restoring torque (newton-meters). Taking the distance between two pendula to be Δx, (2.7-1) can be

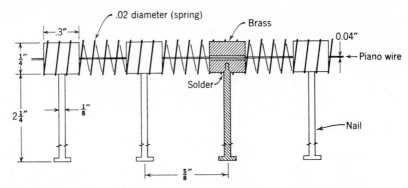

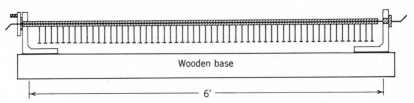

Fig. 2-17   Design for the mechanical transmission line.

Fig. 2-18 Wave propagation on the mechanical transmission line.

written in the form

$$\frac{(\phi_{i+1} - \phi_i)/\Delta x - (\phi_i - \phi_{i-1})/\Delta x}{\Delta x} - \frac{(M/\Delta x)}{(K\,\Delta x)} \frac{d^2\phi_i}{dt^2} = \frac{(T/\Delta x)}{(K\,\Delta x)} \sin \phi. \quad (2.7\text{-}2)$$

For wave processes that change only slightly over a distance Δx (2.7-2) can be written as a partial differential equation in the normalized form

$$\frac{\partial^2\phi}{\partial x^2} - \frac{\partial^2\phi}{\partial t^2} = \sin \phi, \quad (2.7\text{-}3)$$

where distance is measured in units of

$$\lambda_0 = \left[\frac{K}{T}\right]^{1/2} \Delta x, \quad (2.7\text{-}4)$$

and time in units of

$$\tau_0 = \left[\frac{M}{T}\right]^{1/2}. \quad (2.7\text{-}5)$$

For the dimensions indicated in Fig. 2-17, λ_0 is about 5 cm and τ_0 is about 0.1 sec.

Equation 2.7-3 is a *nonlinear* equation which will be investigated in detail in Chapter V. If the angles of the pendula make only small excursions about $\phi = 0$ (the down position) then $\sin \phi \approx \phi$ and we can approximate (2.7-3) with the linear equation

$$\frac{\partial^2 \phi}{\partial x^2} - \frac{\partial^2 \phi}{\partial t^2} = \phi. \tag{2.7-6}$$

Assuming an elementary solution of the form

$$\phi \sim e^{(\gamma x + st)}, \tag{2.7-7}$$

the dispersion equation is found to be

$$\gamma^2 - s^2 = 1. \tag{2.7-8}$$

Suppose now the line is excited by a sinusoidal source of frequency ω. Then $s = j\omega$ and (2.7-8) becomes

$$\gamma^2 = 1 - \omega^2. \tag{2.7-9}$$

If $|\omega| > 1$, γ is purely imaginary and

$$\beta = \pm\sqrt{\omega^2 - 1}, \tag{2.7-10}$$

while if $|\omega| < 1$, γ is real and

$$\alpha = \pm\sqrt{1 - \omega^2}. \tag{2.7-11}$$

Equations 2.7-10 and 2.7-11 are sketched in Fig. 2-19a. It is evident from inspection of (2.7-6) that the critical frequency, $\omega = 1$, (for which $\gamma = 0$) is the normalized frequency at which all the pendula oscillate in unison. This frequency is easily observed on the mechanical transmission line. It is then a simple matter to manually excite (as indicated in Fig. 2-18) at a higher frequency and observe sinusoidal propagation or to excite at a lower frequency and observe a damped exponential or evanescent wave.

Let us suppose now that the pendula are all balanced in their unstable (upright) position. This is evidently a very unstable situation, but we can investigate the nature of the instability by considering only small displacements in ϕ from its (unstable) equilibrium value of π. Since $\sin (\pi + \phi') = -\sin \phi' \approx -\phi'$, we can approximate (2.7-3) by the linear equation

$$\frac{\partial^2 \phi'}{\partial x^2} - \frac{\partial^2 \phi'}{\partial t^2} = -\phi', \tag{2.7-12}$$

with the dispersion equation

$$\gamma^2 - s^2 = -1. \tag{2.7-13}$$

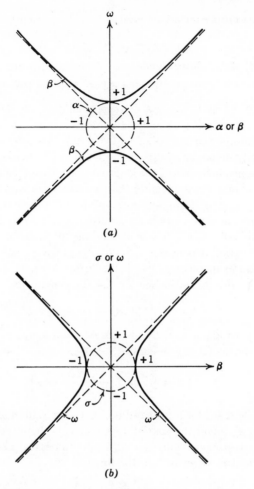

Fig. 2-19 (*a*) Evanescence; (*b*) absolute instability.

In this case we can suppose that both ends of a length a of the line are fixed in the upright position. Then ϕ' must equal zero at the two ends, and the propagation constant can be a pure imaginary, $j\beta$, such that $\sin \beta a = 0$ or

$$\beta = \frac{n\pi}{a} \ (n = 1, 2, \ldots). \tag{2.7-14}$$

The corresponding complex frequency is obtained from (2.7-13) as

$$s^2 = 1 - \beta^2. \tag{2.7-15}$$

If $|\beta| > 1$, s is purely imaginary and

$$\omega = \pm\sqrt{\beta^2 - 1}, \qquad (2.7\text{-}16)$$

whereas, if $|\beta| < 1$, s is real and

$$\sigma = \pm\sqrt{1 - \beta^2}. \qquad (2.7\text{-}17)$$

Equations 2.7-16 and 2.7-17 are sketched in Fig. 2-19*b*. If the length of the line a is made less than a normalized value of π (or an actual value of about 15 cm), all the allowed values of β [from (2.7-14)] are greater than unity. It is then easily demonstrated that the temporal response is sinusoidal with a frequency which increases as the length a is decreased (i.e., as β is increased). If the length of line is made greater than a normalized value of π (or an actual value of about 15 cm), β can be less than unity and the natural time response includes a growing exponential, $e^{\sigma t}$, where σ is given by (2.7-17). This effect is also easily observed; the center of the line "flops down."

That the spatial dependence of (2.7-8) which is indicated in (2.7-11) implies only an evanescent or damped solution is easily seen by application of the criterion developed in Section 2.4. In general (2.7-8) can be written

$$\gamma = \pm\sqrt{1 + \sigma^2 - \omega^2 + 2j\sigma\omega}, \qquad (2.7\text{-}18)$$

where for $\sigma = 0$ and $|\omega| < 1$, the $+$ sign *formally* indicates growth in the $+x$ direction. However for the $+$ sign

$$\measuredangle \gamma = \tfrac{1}{2}\tan^{-1}\left(\frac{2\sigma\omega}{1 + \sigma^2 - \omega^2}\right), \qquad (2.7\text{-}19)$$

which is less than 45° for $\sigma > 0$ and $|\omega| < 1$. The sign of α cannot change as σ approaches $+\infty$ and the spatial dependence is therefore evanescent.

That the dispersion equation (2.7-13) indicates absolute instability becomes evident if we write it in the form

$$\gamma = \pm\sqrt{s^2 - 1}, \qquad (2.7\text{-}20)$$

and apply the criterion developed in Section 5. There is a double zero for γ at $s = +1$. As $\sigma \rightarrow +\infty$, one value of γ approaches $+\infty$ and the other approaches $-\infty$. Thus the two zeros merge together from opposite sides of the $j\beta$ axis as is required for absolute instability.

2.8. THE MOVING MECHANICAL TRANSMISSION LINE

In the previous section we observe that if the pendula on the mechanical line of Fig. 2-18 were all balanced in the upward position, the system would be absolutely unstable. In this section we suppose the line to be moving with velocity u in the x-direction, and show that if u is high enough the instability becomes convective rather than absolute.

We will continue to use the independent variables x and t to represent space and time in the laboratory coordinate system, but we shall introduce the new independent variables ξ and τ to represent space and time in the moving coordinate system. If the translational velocity is small compared with the velocity of light, we can ignore relativistic effects and write

$$t = \tau \quad \text{and} \quad \xi = x - ut \quad \text{or} \quad x = \xi + u\tau. \tag{2.8-1}$$

From (2.7-12) the pde in the moving (ξ, τ) coordinate system can be written

$$\frac{\partial^2 \phi'}{\partial \xi^2} - \frac{\partial^2 \phi'}{\partial \tau^2} = -\phi'. \tag{2.8-2}$$

We are interested in finding the corresponding pde in the laboratory (x, t) system. To effect this note that

$$\frac{\partial \phi(\xi, \tau)}{\partial \xi} = \frac{\partial \phi(x, t)}{\partial x} \frac{\partial x}{\partial \xi} + \frac{\partial \phi(x, t)}{\partial t} \frac{\partial t}{\partial \xi},$$

$$= \frac{\partial \phi(x, t)}{\partial x}, \tag{2.8-3}$$

and

$$\frac{\partial \phi(\xi, \tau)}{\partial \tau} = \frac{\partial \phi(x, t)}{\partial x} \frac{\partial x}{\partial \tau} + \frac{\partial \phi(x, t)}{\partial t} \frac{\partial t}{\partial \tau},$$

$$= u \frac{\partial \phi(x, t)}{\partial x} + \frac{\partial \phi(x, t)}{\partial t}. \tag{2.8-4}$$

Thus we can say that the transformation (2.8-1) from the independent variables (ξ, τ) to the independent variables (x, t) require that the partial derivatives transform as

$$\frac{\partial}{\partial \xi} \rightarrow \frac{\partial}{\partial x},$$

$$\frac{\partial}{\partial \tau} \rightarrow \frac{\partial}{\partial t} + u \frac{\partial}{\partial x}. \tag{2.8-5a,b}$$

In the laboratory system (2.8-2) becomes

$$\frac{\partial^2 \phi'}{\partial x^2} - \left(\frac{\partial}{\partial t} + u \frac{\partial}{\partial x} \right)^2 \phi' = -\phi', \tag{2.8-6}$$

with the dispersion equation

$$(s + \gamma u)^2 = \gamma^2 + 1. \tag{2.8-7}$$

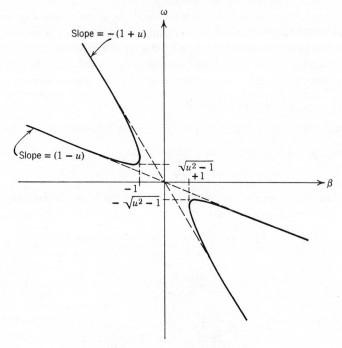

Fig. 2-20 Convective instability.

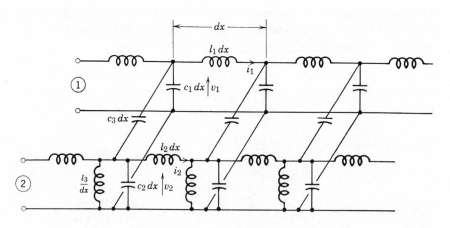

Fig. 2-21 Coupled transmission lines.

We can solve (2.8-7) for s to obtain

$$s = -\gamma u \pm \sqrt{\gamma^2 + 1}, \tag{2.8-8}$$

and for γ to obtain

$$\gamma = \frac{us \pm \sqrt{u^2 + s^2 - 1}}{1 - u^2}. \tag{2.8-9}$$

From (2.8-9) it is evident that the term $(u^2 + s^2 - 1)$ has no zeros in the right half of the s-plane if

$$u > 1. \tag{2.8-10}$$

Thus, if (2.8-10) is satisfied, γ has no double root for s in the RHP and according to the results of Section 2.5 the system is no longer absolutely unstable. It is seen from (2.8-8) that the system is still active for with $\gamma = j\beta$

$$s = \pm\sqrt{1 - \beta^2} - j\beta u, \tag{2.8-11}$$

which indicates temporal growth when $|\beta| < 1$. From (2.8-9) with $s = j\omega$

$$\gamma = \frac{\pm\sqrt{u^2 - 1 - \omega^2} + j\omega u}{1 - u^2}, \tag{2.8-12}$$

which indicates spatial growth when $\omega < (u^2 - 1)^{1/2}$. For large magnitudes of γ and s, (2.8-8) indicates

$$s \approx (-u \pm 1)\gamma. \tag{2.8-13}$$

Thus the plot of ω versus β can be sketched as in Fig. 2-20.

The result of this section is that if the line is moved at a normalized velocity greater than unity, or an actual velocity greater than $\lambda_0/\tau_0 \approx 50$ cm/sec, the nature of the propagation changes from absolute to convective. The physical explanation for this effect is that growing perturbations are being carried away from their point of excitation faster than they can propagate backward. This is vividly demonstrated in the film "Instability, convection and amplification" by Melcher which is listed in the Bibliography.

2.9. COUPLED MODE THEORY [Lo4]

Let us suppose that we are interested in analyzing the transmission system sketched in Fig. 2-21. We can assume temporal variation of the form $\exp(j\omega t)$ and take V_1, V_2, I_1 and I_2 to be the spatially dependent phasor amplitudes of v_1, v_2, i_1 and i_2 respectively. Using the techniques outlined in Chapter I we can then write ordinary differential equations for the phasor amplitudes as

$$\frac{dV_1}{dx} = -j\omega l_1 I_1,$$

$$\frac{dI_1}{dx} = -j\omega(c_1 + c_3)V_1 + j\omega c_3 V_2,$$

$$\frac{dV_2}{dx} = -j\omega l_2 I_2,$$

(2.9-1a,b,c,d)

$$\frac{dI_2}{dx} = -\left[j\omega(c_2 + c_3) + \frac{1}{j\omega l_3}\right]V_2 + j\omega c_3 V_1.$$

In matrix form (2.9-1) becomes

$$\frac{d}{dx}\begin{bmatrix} V_1 \\ I_1 \\ V_2 \\ I_2 \end{bmatrix} = \begin{bmatrix} 0 & -j\omega l_1 & 0 & 0 \\ -j\omega(c_1 + c_3) & 0 & j\omega c_3 & 0 \\ 0 & 0 & 0 & -j\omega l_2 \\ j\omega c_3 & 0 & -\left[j\omega(c_2 + c_3) + \frac{1}{j\omega l_3}\right] & 0 \end{bmatrix} \times \begin{bmatrix} V_1 \\ I_1 \\ V_2 \\ I_2 \end{bmatrix}$$

$$= [A]\begin{bmatrix} V_1 \\ I_1 \\ V_2 \\ I_2 \end{bmatrix}.$$

(2.9-2)

For spatial variation of the form $\exp(\gamma x)$ the dispersion equation is

$$\det[[A] - \gamma[I]]$$

(2.9-3)

where $[I]$ is the identity matrix. To proceed further we must solve (2.9-3) which is 4th order in γ and 5th order in ω.

The problem is somewhat simpler if

$$c_3 \ll c_1 \text{ or } c_2,$$

(2.9-4)

for then we have essentially a small lossless coupling between two less complex systems. An analytic technique which takes advantage of this simplification is called *coupled mode theory*. The concept of mode coupling is extremely helpful in understanding various propagation systems which involve the interaction of electron beams with waveguides and the interaction of simple modes on time varying (parametric) systems.

In order to put this into more general terms suppose we have two lossless, independent propagating systems each of which can carry a well understood mode of propagation. Since the modes are assumed lossless, the dispersion relations give the phase constants as functions of frequency. That is for mode 1

$$\beta = B_1(\omega), \tag{2.9-5}$$

and for mode 2

$$\beta = B_2(\omega). \tag{2.9-6}$$

These modes will propagate sinusoidal waves

$$v_1(x, t) = V_{01} \cos (B_1(\omega)x + \omega t),$$
$$v_2(x, t) = V_{02} \cos (B_2(\omega)x + \omega t), \tag{2.9-7a,b}$$

which can be conveniently written as the real parts of rotating phasors.

$$v_1(x, t) = \mathrm{Re}\, [(V_{01}e^{jB_1x})e^{j\omega t},$$
$$v_2(x, t) = \mathrm{Re}\, [(V_{02}e^{jB_2x})e^{j\omega t}. \tag{2.9-8a,b}$$

The modes can therefore be imagined as having the complex amplitudes

$$V_1 = V_{01}e^{jB_1x},$$
$$V_2 = V_{02}e^{jB_2x}, \tag{2.9-9a,b}$$

which evidently obey the differential equations

$$\frac{dV_1}{dx} = jB_1V_1,$$

$$\frac{dV_2}{dx} = jB_2V_2. \tag{2.9-10a,b}$$

Equation 2.9-10 can be written in the matrix form

$$\frac{d}{dx}\begin{bmatrix} V_1 \\ V_2 \end{bmatrix} = \begin{bmatrix} jB_1 & 0 \\ 0 & jB_2 \end{bmatrix}\begin{bmatrix} V_1 \\ V_2 \end{bmatrix}, \tag{2.9-11}$$

where the zeroes in the off diagonal positions indicate that we have so far assumed no coupling between the modes.

The total energy carried by the system will be conserved since the individual modes are assumed lossless. Thus we can write

$$a_1 |V_1|^2 \pm a_2 |V_2|^2 = \mathrm{const}, \tag{2.9-12}$$

where a_1 and a_2 are positive constants which relate the stored energies in the modes to the complex mode amplitudes. The plus $(+)$ sign in (2.9-12) holds when both modes carry positive power in the same direction or when one carries positive power in the positive direction and the other carries negative power in the negative direction. The $(-)$ sign holds for positive power in opposite directions or positive and negative powers in the same direction.

We now suppose that we introduce (or decide to consider) a small *lossless coupling* between the modes by writing (2.9-11) in the form

$$\frac{d}{dx}\begin{bmatrix} V_1 \\ V_2 \end{bmatrix} = \begin{bmatrix} jB_1 & K_{12} \\ K_{21} & jB_2 \end{bmatrix} \times \begin{bmatrix} V_1 \\ V_2 \end{bmatrix}. \tag{2.9-13}$$

By supposing the coupling to be *small* we are able to represent it by off diagonal entries in the matrix *without changing* the diagonal entries (or phase constants) B_1 and B_2.

By supposing the coupling to be *lossless* we can assert that energy is still conserved or that (2.9-12) remains valid. From (2.9-12) and (2.9-13) one can show that

$$a_1 K_{12} = \mp a_2 K_{21}^*, \tag{2.9-14}$$

where the asterisk (*) indicates complex conjugate and the ($\mp$) signs in (2.9-14) correspond to the ($\pm$) signs in (2.9-12). That is to say for lossless coupling between two modes which carry positive power in the same direction or between a mode which carries positive power in one direction and a mode which carries negative power in the other direction we must have $a_1 K_{12} = -a_2 K_{21}^*$.

Weak coupling will be most important at frequencies for which the two modes have approximately the same phase constants [i.e., for $B_1(\omega) \approx B_2(\omega)$] for then the effect of mode 1 upon mode 2 (and vice-versa) will remain in phase over an extended length of the transmission system for an appreciable time. From (2.9-13) the dispersion relation with coupling is

$$(jB_1 - \gamma)(jB_2 - \gamma) - K_{12}K_{21} = 0, \tag{2.9-15}$$

or

$$\gamma = j\left(\frac{B_1 + B_2}{2}\right) \pm j\left(\frac{B_1 - B_2}{2}\right)\left(1 - \frac{4K_{12}K_{21}}{|B_1 - B_2|^2}\right)^{1/2}, \tag{2.9-16}$$

which for small coupling evidently differs from the uncoupled values of jB_1 and jB_2 only at frequencies for which

$$B_1(\omega) \approx B_2(\omega). \tag{2.9-17}$$

From (2.9-14) we can assert that for the coupling of two modes which carry positive power in the same direction (or positive power in one direction and negative power in the other) $K_{12}K_{21}$ in (2.9-16) is a *negative real* number. Also for the coupling of two modes which carry positive power in opposite directions (or positive and negative powers in the same directions) $K_{12}K_{21}$ is a *positive real* number.

Let us now return to the system sketched in Fig. 2-21 assuming the small coupling approximation of (2.9-4). We can write

$$I_1 = \frac{V_1}{Z_{01}},$$

$$I_2 = \frac{V_2}{Z_{02}},$$

(2.9-18a,b)

where

$$Z_{01} = \left(\frac{l_1}{c_1}\right)^{1/2},$$

$$Z_{02} = \left(\frac{l_2/c_2}{1 - (1/\omega^2 l_3 c_2)}\right)^{1/2}.$$

(2.9-19a,b)

Substituting (2.9-18a) and (2.9-19a) into (2.9-1b) and assuming $c_3 \ll c_1$ yields

$$\frac{dV_1}{dx} = -j\omega\sqrt{l_1 c_1}\, V_1 + j\omega c_3 \left(\frac{l_1}{c_1}\right)^{1/2} V_2.$$

(2.9-20a)

Substituting (2.9-18b) and (2.9-19b) into (2.9-1d) and assuming $c_3 \ll c_2$ yields

$$\frac{dV_2}{dx} = -j\omega\left[l_2 c_2 \left(1 - \frac{1}{\omega^2 l_2 c_3}\right)\right]^{1/2} V_2 + j\omega c_3 \left(\frac{l_2/c_2}{1 - (1/\omega^2 l_3 c_2)}\right)^{1/2} V_1$$

(2.9-20b)

The net power flow on the system is

$$P = \tfrac{1}{2} \operatorname{Re}\,[V_1 I_1^* + V_2 I_2^*],$$

$$= \frac{|V_1|^2}{Z_{01}} + \frac{|V_2|^2}{Z_{02}}.$$

(2.9-21)

Thus in the notation of (2.9-13)

$$K_{12} = j\omega c_3 \left(\frac{l_1}{c_1}\right)^{1/2},$$

$$K_{21} = j\omega c_3 \left(\frac{l_2/c_2}{1 - (1/\omega^2 l_3 c_2)}\right)^{1/2};$$

(2.9-22a,b)

while in the notation of (2.9-12)

$$a_1 = \left(\frac{c_1}{l_1}\right)^{1/2},$$

$$a_2 = \left[\frac{c_2}{l_2}\left(1 - \frac{1}{\omega^2 l_3 c_2}\right)\right]^{1/2}.$$

(2.9-23a,b)

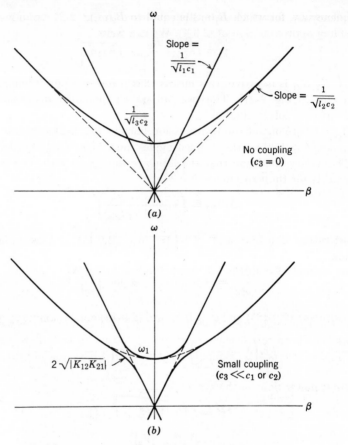

Fig. 2-22   (*a*) Uncoupled modes; (*b*) coupled modes.

Evidently $a_1 K_{12}$ does equal $-a_2 K_{21}^*$ as we have expected for two modes which carry positive power in the same direction. The product $K_{12} K_{21}$ must therefore be negative as is seen from (2.9-22).

We now turn our attention back to (2.9-16). For $c_3 = 0$, $K_{12} K_{21} = 0$ and $\gamma = B_1(\omega)$ or $B_2(\omega)$. This is the *uncoupled* situation which is illustrated in Fig. 2-22a. If c_3 is not equal to zero but is still small compared with c_1 and c_2, as indicated in (2.9-4), we still have

$$\gamma \approx B_1(\omega) \quad \text{or} \quad B_2(\omega),$$

except at frequencies which satisfy (2.9-17). From a physical point of view (2.9-17) is the condition for both spatial and temporal resonance. At the frequency ω_1, for which $B_1(\omega_1)$ is equal to $B_2(\omega_1)$,

$$\gamma = j\frac{B_1 + B_2}{2} \pm \sqrt{K_{12}K_{21}}. \tag{2.9-24}$$

Since $K_{12}K_{21}$ is negative, this means that γ remains purely imaginary as is indicated in Fig. 2-21b. Thus we can sketch the entire dispersion equation without ever solving (2.9-3).

If we excite one of the transmission lines in Fig. 2-21 (say line ①) at the frequency ω_1, both of the coupled modes must be excited in order to satisfy the boundary condition that the input to line ② be zero. The propagation constants for the two modes differ by

$$\Delta\beta = 2\sqrt{|K_{12}K_{21}|},$$
$$= 2\omega c_3\left(\frac{l_1l_2/c_1c_2}{1 - (1/\omega^2 l_3 c_2)}\right)^{\!1/2}.$$

Thus we find at a distance x_1 down the line such that

$$\Delta\beta x_1 = \pi$$

that the two modes cancel on line ① and add on line ②. Thus the input power has been transferred from line ① to line ② as is illustrated in Fig. 2-23. At a distance $2x_1$ the power is transferred back to line ①.

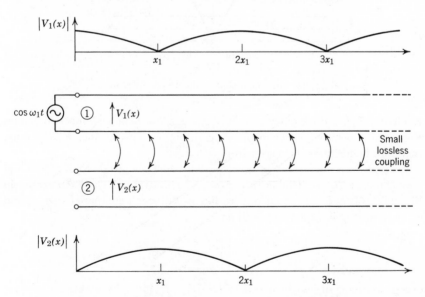

Fig. 2-23 Amplitude variation on coupled transmission lines.

2.10. THE ELECTRON BEAM [Pi3]

An interesting active transmission line is the electron beam shown in Fig. 2-24a. We assume that all the electrons at a given point on the beam are moving in the x-direction with a well defined velocity $u(x, t)$. The charge per unit length of the beam is $\rho(x, t)$ and the current in the beam is $I(x, t)$. The electric potential will actually vary in the transverse direction, but we will assume this to be qualitatively unimportant and define an effective beam potential $V(x, t)$. Such a model appears to be highly idealized, but it does serve as an adequate representation for a real electron beam in a constraining longitudinal magnetic field.

The nature of possible beam propagation is determined from the following requirements.

1. *Poisson's equation,*

$$\frac{d^2V}{dx^2} = -\frac{\rho}{A\varepsilon}.$$ (2.10-1a)

where A is the cross-sectional area of the beam.

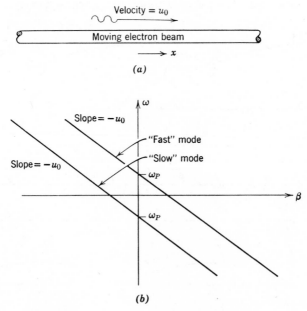

Fig. 2-24   (a) An electron beam; (b) dispersion curves for fast and slow modes.

2. *Conservation of charge,*

$$\frac{dI}{dx} = -\frac{d\rho}{dt}.$$ (2.10-2a)

3. *Newton's second law,*

$$m\frac{du}{dt} = e\frac{dV}{dx}.$$ (2.10-3a)

4. *Definition of current,*

$$I = \rho u.$$ (2.10-4a)

These four equations allow us to solve for the four beam variables V, I, ρ and u. Equation 2.10-4a, however, is nonlinear. We can obtain the small signal ac solution by writing the variables as the sum of a steady (dc) component plus the real parts of small alternating component. Thus

$$V = V_0 + V_1 e^{j\omega t}, \qquad V_1 \ll V_0,$$

$$I = I_0 + I_1 e^{j\omega t}, \qquad I_1 \ll I_0,$$

$$\rho = \rho_0 + \rho_1 e^{j\omega t}, \qquad \rho_1 \ll \rho_0,$$

$$u = u_0 + u_1 e^{j\omega t}, \qquad u \ll u_0.$$

Then (2.10-1a)–(2.10-4a) imply for the small alternating components

$$\frac{d^2 V_1}{dx^2} = -\frac{\rho_1}{A\varepsilon},$$ (2.10-1a)

$$\frac{dI_1}{dx} = -j\omega\rho_1,$$ (2.10-2a)

$$j\omega u_1 + u_0\frac{du_1}{dx} = \frac{e}{m}\frac{dV_1}{dx},$$ (2.10-3a)

$$I_0 = \rho_0 u_0,$$ (2.10-4a)

$$I_1 = \rho_0 u_1 + u_0 \rho_1.$$ (2.10-4b)

In deriving these equations we have neglected all product terms of ac amplitudes. In obtaining (2.10-3a) we must be careful to note that du/dt is the net acceleraton of a particular electron. Thus since the velocity is a function of both distance and time, we must write

$$\frac{du}{dt} = \frac{\partial u}{\partial t} + u\frac{\partial u}{\partial x}.$$

We can reduce these equations to the following set:

$$\frac{du_1}{dx} = -\frac{j\omega}{u_0}u_1 - \frac{\omega_p^2}{j\omega I_0}I_1,$$

$$\frac{dI_1}{dx} = \frac{j\omega\rho_0}{u_0}u_1 - \frac{j\omega}{u_0}I_1.$$ (2.10-5a,b)

In (2.10-5) we have defined

$$\omega_p{}^2 \equiv -\frac{\rho_0 e}{A\,m\varepsilon}. \tag{2.10-6}$$

The frequency ω_p is called the *plasma frequency* of the electron beam. It is the frequency at which inertia of the electrons resonates with the dielectric constant of vacuum. Note that ρ_0 will be negative for an electron beam.

Equation (2.10-5a,b) will have eigenfunctions of the form $\exp(\gamma x)$ for

$$\gamma^2 + \frac{2j\omega}{u_0}\gamma - \left(\frac{\omega^2 - \omega_p{}^2}{u_0{}^2}\right) = 0 \tag{2.10-7}$$

or

$$\gamma = -\frac{j\omega}{u_0}\left(1 \pm \frac{\omega_p}{\omega}\right). \tag{2.10-8}$$

Thus the propagation constant is purely imaginary and the *phase velocity*

$$u_{ph} = -\frac{\omega}{\beta},$$

$$= \frac{u_0}{1 \pm \omega_p/\omega}. \tag{2.10-9}$$

There are two modes of propagation: a "slow" mode for which $\beta = -\omega(1 + \omega_p/\omega)/u_0$ and the phase velocity is less than the beam velocity, and a "fast" mode for which $\beta = -\omega(1 - \omega_p/\omega)/u_0$ and the phase velocity is greater than the beam velocity. The two dispersion equations are sketched in Fig. 2-24b. Notice that the group velocity

$$u_g = -\frac{d\omega}{d\beta},$$

$$= u_0, \tag{2.10-10}$$

the dc beam velocity for both modes.

If we define the beam potential to be zero when the beam velocity is zero, the equation for conservation of energy becomes

$$-eV + \frac{m}{2}u^2 = 0, \tag{2.10-11}$$

which implies for the ac amplitudes

$$V_1 = \frac{mu_0}{e}u_1. \tag{2.10-12}$$

The average ac power carried by the beam is

$$P = \tfrac{1}{2}\,\mathrm{Re}\,[V_1 I_1^*]$$

$$= \tfrac{1}{2}\,\mathrm{Re}\,[Z_{0B}]I_1 I_1^*, \tag{2.10-13}$$

where

$$Z_{0B} = \frac{V_1}{I_1} \tag{2.10-14}$$

is the characteristic impedance for small signal propagation on the beam From (2.10-12) this characteristic impedance is determined as

$$Z_{0B} = \frac{mu_0}{e} \frac{u_1}{I_1}, \tag{2.10-15}$$

where u_1/I_1 is the ratio for the eigenvectors of (2.10-5) which correspond to the eigenvalue or propagation constant of interest. For $d/dx \to \gamma$, (2.10-5) becomes

$$\begin{bmatrix} \pm \dfrac{j\omega_p}{u_0} & -\dfrac{\omega_p^2}{j\omega I_0} \\[2ex] \dfrac{ju\rho_0}{u_0} & \pm \dfrac{j\omega_p}{u_0} \end{bmatrix} \times \begin{bmatrix} u_1 \\[2ex] I_1 \end{bmatrix} = 0, \tag{2.10-16}$$

which implies

$$\frac{u_1}{I_1} = \mp \left(\frac{\omega_p u_0}{\omega I_0} \right) \tag{2.10-17}$$

or

$$Z_{0B} = \mp \frac{2V_0}{I_0} \frac{\omega_p}{\omega}. \tag{2.10-18}$$

In (2.10-17) and (2.10-18) the $-$ sign corresponds to the slow mode and the $+$ sign to the fast mode.

The group velocity for the slow mode is positive (equal to u_0) but its characteristic impedance is negative. Thus the ac stored energy for the slow mode appears to be negative. The concept of negative ac stored energy on the slow mode might seem somewhat strange at first, but the physical explanation is quite simple. From (2.10-17) it is evident that ac current and ac velocity are 180° out of phase for the slow mode. Where the velocity is greater than u_0, the current is less than I_0 and vice-versa, so an increase in slow wave amplitude *slows down* the average beam velocity. Thus we must *remove* energy from the slow wave in order to excite it.

2.11. THE TRAVELING WAVE TUBE [Pi2, Pi5]

We now consider the analysis of a device which takes advantage of coupling between an electron beam and a wave on a passive transmission line. Such a device is the helix type traveling wave tube (TWT) which is sketched in

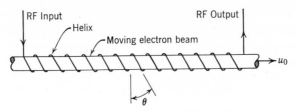

Fig. 2-25   A traveling wave amplifier.

Fig. 2-25. In this arrangement an electron beam is forced to flow through the center of a helical coil of wire. An RF signal is fed into the downstream end of the helix and amplified by interaction with the beam as it passes toward the other end. The function of the helix is twofold; first, to slow the signal velocity down to a convenient beam velocity and second, to provide a longitudinal component of electric field so the circuit can interact with the beam.

To a fairly good approximation the RF signal follows the helical wire at the velocity of light, c, so the phase velocity on the helix $v_{ph} = c \sin \theta$ where θ is the pitch angle of the helix. Thus the propagation constant on the helix

$$\beta_c = \frac{\omega}{c \sin \theta}. \tag{2.11-1}$$

We are interested in examining the interaction between the helix and the longitudinal plasma waves on the electron beam. We therefore express the RF power flow in the helix in terms of the longitudinal electric field on the axis E_x which can be expressed as a voltage by writing

$$V_c = \frac{E_x}{\beta_c}. \tag{2.11-2}$$

A characteristic impedance Z_{0c} can then be defined for the helix such that the RF power flow on the helix is

$$P_c = \frac{1}{2} \frac{V_c V_c^*}{Z_{0c}} = \frac{1}{2} \frac{E_x E_x^*}{\beta_c^2 Z_{0c}}. \tag{2.11-3}$$

The power flow on the beam is given by

$$P_B = \tfrac{1}{2} Z_{0B} I_1 I_1^*, \tag{2.11-4}$$

where from (2.10-18)

$$Z_{0B} = \mp \frac{2V_0}{I_0} \frac{\omega_p}{\omega} \tag{2.11-5}$$

and I_1 is the ac component of beam current. The negative sign in (2.11-5) is for the slow (negative energy) mode and the positive sign is for the fast (positive energy) mode.

We shall now use the *coupled mode theory* introduced in Section 9 to determine the nature of the propagation when the helix and the beam interact. Assuming *zero* coupling between axial electric field and beam mode currents we can write

$$\frac{d}{dx}\begin{bmatrix} E_x \\ I_{1F} \\ I_{1S} \end{bmatrix} = \begin{bmatrix} -j\beta_c & 0 & 0 \\ 0 & -j\dfrac{\omega-\omega_p}{u_0} & 0 \\ 0 & 0 & -j\dfrac{\omega+\omega_p}{u_0} \end{bmatrix} \times \begin{bmatrix} E_x \\ I_{1F} \\ I_{1S} \end{bmatrix}, \quad (2.11\text{-}6)$$

where I_{1F} is the longitudinal beam current in the fast mode and I_{1S} the longitudinal current in the slow mode.

We will neglect the interaction between the fast and slow beam modes [their dispersion curves do not intersect (see Fig. 2-24b)] but we will assume *small, lossless* coupling between both beam modes and the helix. Since the coupling is small, the diagonal terms are left unchanged.

$$\frac{d}{dx}\begin{bmatrix} E_x \\ I_{1F} \\ I_{1S} \end{bmatrix} = \begin{bmatrix} -j\beta_c & K_{CF} & K_{CS} \\ K_{FC}-j\left(\dfrac{\omega-\omega_p}{u_0}\right) & 0 & 0 \\ K_{SC} & 0 & -j\left(\dfrac{\omega+\omega_p}{u_0}\right) \end{bmatrix} \times \begin{bmatrix} E_x \\ I_{1F} \\ I_{1S} \end{bmatrix}. \quad (2.11\text{-}7)$$

Since the coupling is lossless, the net power flow of the three modes must remain constant or

$$\frac{1}{2}\frac{E_xE_x^*}{\beta_c^2 Z_c} + \frac{V_0\omega_p}{I_0\omega}I_{1F}I_{1F}^* - \frac{V_0\omega_p}{I_0\omega}I_{1S}I_{1S}^* = \text{constant}. \quad (2.11\text{-}8)$$

Thus from (2.9-14)

$$K_{CF} = -\left(\frac{2\beta_c^2 Z_c V_0\omega_p}{I_0\omega}\right)K_{FC}^*, \quad (2.11\text{-}9)$$

and

$$K_{CS} = +\left(\frac{2\beta_c^2 Z_c V_0\omega_p}{I_0\omega}\right)K_{SC}^*. \quad (2.11\text{-}10)$$

We can evaluate these coefficients as follows [Ya 1]. Suppose the amplitude of the slow mode is zero. Then

$$\frac{d}{dx}[E_xE_x^*] = E_x\frac{dE_x^*}{dx} + E_x^*\frac{dE_x}{dx}$$

$$= E_x(j\beta_c E_x^* + K_{CF}^* I_{1F}^*) + E_x^*(-j\beta_c E_x + K_{CF}I_{1F})$$

$$= K_{CF}E_x^*I_{1F} + K_{CF}^*E_xI_{1F}^*. \quad (2.11\text{-}11)$$

Now, if K_{CF} is real,

$$K_{CF} = \frac{(d/dx)[E_x E_x^*]}{2 \operatorname{Re}[E_x I_{1F}^*]}, \tag{2.11-12}$$

whereas, if K_{CF} is imaginary,

$$K_{CF} = \frac{j(d/dx)[E_x E_x^*]}{2 \operatorname{Im}[E_x I_{1F}^*]}. \tag{2.11-13}$$

Similarly for a real coupling coefficient between the helix and the slow mode

$$K_{CS} = \frac{(d/dx)[E_x E_x^*]}{2 \operatorname{Re}[E_x I_{1S}^*]}, \tag{2.11-14}$$

and for an imaginary coupling coefficient

$$K_{CS} = j\frac{(d/dx)[E_x E_x^*]}{2 \operatorname{Im}[E_x I_{1S}^*]}. \tag{2.11-15}$$

Now

$$\frac{1}{2Z_c \beta_c^2} \frac{d}{dx}[E_x E_x^*]$$

is the space rate of increase of power in the helix mode. It must equal

$$-\tfrac{1}{2} \operatorname{Re}[E_x(I_{1F}^* + I_{1S}^*)],$$

the power absorbed per unit length by the helix mode from the beam current. Thus

$$\frac{d}{dx}[E_x E_x^*] = -Z_c \beta_c^2 \operatorname{Re}[E_x(I_{1F}^* + I_{1S}^*)]. \tag{2.11-16}$$

If $E_x I_{1F}^*$ and $E_x I_{1S}^*$ were imaginary, the helix could not absorb power from the beam. Thus we assume them to be real and evaluate K_{CF} and K_{CS} from (2.11-12) and (2.11-14) as

$$K_{CS} = K_{CF} = -\tfrac{1}{2}Z_c \beta_c^2. \tag{2.11-17}$$

From (2.11-9) and (2.11-10)

$$K_{SC} = -K_{FC} = -\frac{I_0 \omega}{4V_0 \omega_p}. \tag{2.11-18}$$

We can now return to (2.11-7) and determine the eigenvalues or propagation constants for beam circuit interaction. To simplify the notation somewhat we write

$$\beta_p = \frac{\omega_p}{u_0}, \tag{2.11-19}$$

$$\beta_e = \frac{\omega}{u_0}. \tag{2.11-20}$$

Then the determinantal equation for eigenfunctions $e^{+\gamma x}$ is

$$-[\gamma + j(\beta_e + \beta_p)][\gamma + j(\beta_e - \beta_p)][\gamma + j\beta_c] + K_{CS}K_{SC}[\gamma + j(\beta_e - \beta_p)]$$
$$+ K_{CF}K_{FC}[\gamma + j(\beta_e + \beta_p)] = 0. \quad (2.11\text{-}21)$$

From (2.11-17) and (2.11-18)

$$K_{SC}K_{SC} = -K_{FC}K_{CF} = \frac{Z_c\beta_c{}^2 I_0\omega}{8V_0\omega_p}. \quad (2.11\text{-}22)$$

We can now present the solution to (2.11-21) in the notation originally introduced by J. R. Pierce in his classical work on traveling wave tubes [Pi 2]. Pierce defined the *gain parameter, C*, by

$$C^3 = \frac{Z_c I_0}{4V_0}, \quad (2.11\text{-}23)$$

and the *space charge parameter, Q*, by

$$\frac{\omega_p}{\omega} = C\sqrt{4QC} \quad (2.11\text{-}24)$$

or

$$Q = \frac{\omega_p{}^2}{4C^3\omega^2}. \quad (2.11\text{-}25)$$

Then if we write

$$\gamma = -j\beta_e(1 + jC\delta) \quad (2.11\text{-}26)$$

and

$$\beta_c = \beta_e(1 + Cb), \quad (2.11\text{-}27)$$

Equation 2.11-21 becomes

$$(\delta^2 + 4QC)(j\delta - b) = 1. \quad (2.11\text{-}28)$$

The gain parameter C is essentially the ratio of the characteristic impedance of the helix to the ratio of dc beam voltage to dc beam current. Evidently C will be quite small, it often is of the order of 0.01. The actual propagation constant is determined by the unitless complex parameter

$$\delta = x + jy \quad (2.11\text{-}29)$$

through (2.11-26). The real part of delta gives the gain constant

$$\alpha = -C\beta_e x, \quad (2.11\text{-}30)$$

while the imaginary part give the phase constant

$$\beta = +\beta_e(1 - Cy). \quad (2.11\text{-}31)$$

Graphical solutions for the real and imaginary part of δ are given by Pierce for various values of the product QC as a function of the *phase velocity*

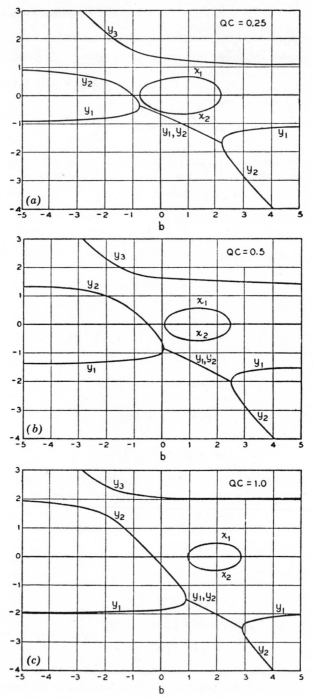

Fig. 2-26 Normalized gain and phase shift for a TWA. (*a*) The *x*'s and *y*'s for the three waves with space charge ($QC = 0.25$); (*b*) the *x*'s and *y*'s with greater space charge ($QC = 0.5$); (*c*) the *x*'s and *y*'s with still greater space charge ($QC = 1$). (reprinted from J. R. Pierce, *Traveling Wave Tubes* [Pi2].)

parameter b defined in (2.11-27) are reproduced in Fig. 2-26. The phase velocity parameter indicates the relationship between the velocity of a wave on the helix alone and the velocity of the beam. It is adjusted experimentally by changing the dc beam voltage. The product QC from (2.11-25) is

$$QC = \frac{\omega_p{}^2}{4C^2\omega^2}, \tag{2.11-32}$$

and is essentially a measure of the ratio of the plasma frequency of the beam to the operating frequency. If $QC \approx 1$, the operating frequency is well above the plasma frequency.

2.12. THE LASER OSCILLATOR

Isolated dynamical systems are often observed to vibrate in a characteristic manner at one or more frequencies. Several systems which exhibit natural modes of oscillation are shown in Fig. 2-27. Here we see a single mode mechanical system (the simple pendulum), a single mode electrical system (the parallel L-C tank circuit) and two multimode mechanical systems (the quartz crystal and the violin string). Natural modes of oscillation are analyzed by assuming a sinusoidal time variation and then finding the configuration of the dynamical variables which satisfies the boundary conditions.

Another simple but very important example is the L-C tank which is shunted with a small conductance G_L, as shown in Fig. 2-28. Without the shunting conductance the system will have one simple oscillatory mode at frequency

$$\omega_0 = \frac{1}{\sqrt{LC}}, \tag{2.12-1}$$

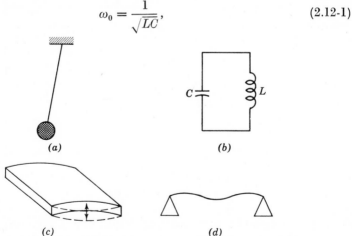

Fig. 2-27 Modes of oscillation. (*a*) Pendulum, (*b*) tank circuit, (*c*) quartz crystal, (*d*) violin string.

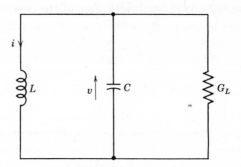

Fig. 2-28   High Q tank circuit.

as is well known. The dynamical variables are

$$v(t) = V \cos \omega_0 t,$$

$$i(t) = I \sin \omega_0 t,$$

and the energy pulsates back and forth between electrical energy stored in the capacitor and magnetic energy stored in the inductor. The total energy

$$U = \tfrac{1}{2}Cv^2 + \tfrac{1}{2}Li^2 \tag{2.12-2}$$

must be constant so

$$U = \tfrac{1}{2}CV^2$$

$$= \tfrac{1}{2}LI^2. \tag{2.12-3a,b}$$

Addition of G_L to the system means that energy will be dissipated at the rate

$$P = \tfrac{1}{2}G_L V^2. \tag{2.12-4}$$

The energy stored in the tank divided by the energy dissipated in a radian is called the "Q" of the tank. Thus

$$Q = \frac{\omega_0 V}{P}$$

$$= \frac{\omega_0 C}{G_L}. \tag{2.12-5}$$

If the Q of the tank is large (compared with unity), the energy lost to G_L per cycle is small and the dynamical variables remain approximately sinusoidal functions of time. The Q is also equal to the ratio of the resonant frequency to the half-power bandwidth, $\Delta\omega$, of the energy absorbed by G_L. Thus

$$Q = \frac{\omega_0}{\Delta\omega}, \tag{2.12-6}$$

or

$$\Delta\omega = \frac{G_L}{C}. \tag{2.12-7}$$

It is often the practice to represent each oscillatory mode of a multimode system by an equivalent L-C tank with shunt conductance, G_L, such that the resonant frequency of the mode is given by (2.12-1), the Q by (2.12-5) and the stored energy by (2.12-3a). Quartz crystals and tuning forks which are used to stabilize the frequency of electronic oscillators are often represented in this manner. These resonators are actually mechanical but they can be considered as loosely coupled electrical tank circuits.

In the study of laser oscillators we are concerned with the excitation of the natural modes of oscillation in an electromagnetic cavity. Such a cavity is shown in Fig. 2-29. The boundary conditions require that the tangential electric field be zero at the walls, which is equivalent to the conditions that each of the dimensions be an integral number of half wavelengths at a resonant frequency. Evidently there are an infinite number of modes which satisfy this condition; a cross section of one low order mode is also shown in Fig. 2-29. Each of these modes can be represented by an equivalent tank as in Fig. 2-28.

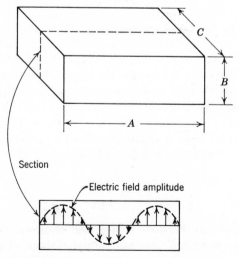

Fig. 2-29 A rectilinear electromagnetic cavity.

It would seem from ordinary experience that it should be possible to set the energy level of an oscillator to any desired value. The quantum theory tells us that this is not so. If the stored energy in a mode is a quadratic function of the dynamical variables, as in (2.12-2), then that energy can have only certain *discrete* values given by [Sl 1]

$$U = (n + \tfrac{1}{2})\frac{h\omega_0}{2\pi}, \qquad (n = 0, 1, 2, \ldots), \qquad (2.12\text{-}8)$$

where ω_0 is the resonant frequency of the mode and

$$h = 6.6 \times 10^{-34}\,\text{J-sec}$$

is Planck's constant.

Evidently for ordinary oscillators up to the microwave range (10^{11} cps or less) the allowed energy levels lie extremely close together and in a practical sense the energy can be set as closely as desired to any level. Quantum theory also tells us that the only allowed transitions of the oscillator are such that the energy changes by one level. When this occurs the oscillatory mode either absorbs or emits with a frequency of

$$\omega = \frac{2\pi\,\Delta U}{h}. \qquad (2.12\text{-}9)$$

Equations 2.12-8 and 2.12-9 together indicate that the quantum mechanical version of the simple harmonic oscillator can only emit or absorb energy at a frequency

$$\omega = \omega_0. \qquad (2.12\text{-}10)$$

Since the energy level of an oscillatory mode is given by the "staircase" function of (2.12-8), it is sufficient to give only the resonant frequency, ω_0, and the number of the step, n. It is customary to refer to the integer n as the *number of photons* in the mode. The physical motivation for this terminology is the fact that the radiation must be absorbed by or emitted from the mode in lumps of energy $h\omega_0/2\pi$. Each lump of input or output radiation is called a photon.

Not all oscillators have a quadratic potential energy function. In the hydrogen atom, for example, the potential energy of the orbital electron is

$$PE = \frac{-e^2}{4\pi\varepsilon_0 r},$$

where r is the distance between proton and electron. From the classical point of view the electron in this oscillator should travel an approximately elliptical path which spirals toward the proton. Quantum mechanics (and observation of hydrogen atoms) tells us once again that only certain energy level are allowed and only certain transitions between these levels are permitted. When an allowed transition does occur, energy is either absorbed or emitted at a frequency given by (2.12-9) (see Fig. 2-30).

Although there are several types of laser oscillators, all consist of a large number of atomic oscillators contained within an electromagnetic cavity. We can make a fairly general model of this situation by supposing we have a rectangular cavity containing a large number of atomic oscillators as is indicated in Fig. 2-31. The atomic oscillators will be excited gas atoms in a gas laser, isolated rare earth atoms held by a transparent crystal in the solid state laser and the electrons in a semiconductor laser.

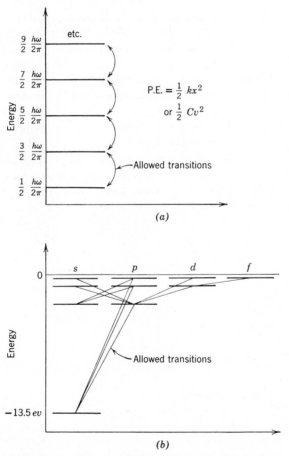

Fig. 2-30 (*a*) Allowed energy levels and allowed transitions for an harmonic oscillator. (*b*) Allowed energy levels and allowed transitions for a hydrogen atom.

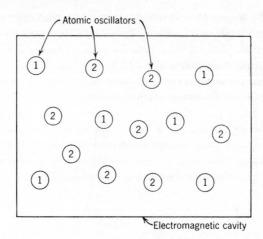

Fig. 2-31 Simplified laser model.

The laser oscillation consists of the emission of energy by the atomic (mechanical) oscillators and the absorption by one of the modes of the electromagnetic cavity. Although the energy level diagram for the atomic oscillators will in general be extremely complex, we can simplify matters by concentrating attention upon the two levels between which the radiation of interest is emitted. This situation is shown in Fig. 2-32. N_1 of the atomic oscillators are in energy state E_1 and N_2 are in the *higher* energy state E_2. In thermal equilibrium the lower energy state will be populated more fully the ratio being given by the Boltzmann factor

$$\frac{N_2}{N_1} = e^{-(E_2 - E_1)/kT}$$

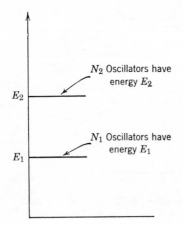

Fig. 2-32 Simple energy level picture for atomic oscillators of an arbitrary nature.

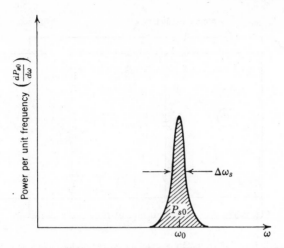

Fig. 2-33 Representative emissive lineshape for an assembly of oscillators.

If the population of level 2 is increased above this ratio, a *spontaneous emission* of radiation will be observed which will tend to bring the population ratio back into thermal equilibrium. If by some means a permanent non-equilibrium condition is established, a steady output of radiation will occur. The art of making a laser oscillator lies in establishing and maintaining this unbalanced population ratio. The spontaneous radiation from the atomic oscillators will not be perfectly sharp but will be spread over some range of frequency $\Delta\omega_s$ as indicated in Fig. 2-33.

Each mode of the electromagnetic cavity with frequency near ω_0 will receive an input of spontaneous radiation given by

$$P_s = \frac{P_{s0}}{N(\omega_0)\,\Delta\omega_s}, \tag{2.12-11}$$

where P_{s0} is the *total* spontaneous emission and $N(\omega_0)\,\Delta\omega_s$ is the number of electromagnetic modes of the cavity which have natural frequencies within a range of $\Delta\omega_s$ about ω_0. It is not difficult to show from the condition that the cavity must be an integral number of half wavelengths in each dimension that

$$N(\omega_0)\,\Delta\omega_s = \frac{\omega_0^{2}\,\Delta\omega_s}{\pi^2 c^3}\,ABC, \tag{2.12-12}$$

where c is the velocity of light in the laser medium.

Once energy has been absorbed by an electromagnetic mode the mode is excited and can influence the emission from the atomic oscillators. This influence can be described simply as follows [Sl 1 pp. 98–101]. Atomic

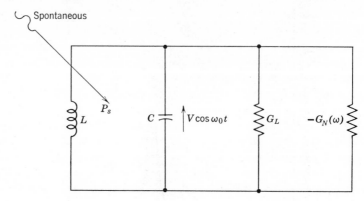

Fig. 2-34   An equivalent circuit for a laser oscillator.

transitions from level 2 to level 1 which emit energy into the mode will be induced at a rate equal to the spontaneous emission times the number of photons in the mode. Atomic transitions from level 1 to level 2 which absorb energy from the mode will also occur. These up transitions will go at a rate of N_1/N_2 times the rate of down transitions. Thus the *net* rate of energy emission into a mode will be given by

$$P_I = nP_s \left(1 - \frac{N_1}{N_2}\right),$$
(2.12-13)

where n is the number of photons in the mode. The form of (2.12-13) is quite significant for it indicates that the power induced into a mode is proportional to the energy stored in the mode. Reference to (2.12-3) and (2.12-4) indicate that the induced emission can therefore be accounted for in the simple equivalent circuit for the mode by putting a negative conductance G_N in parallel with the positive conductance G_L (as is shown in Fig. 2-34) to represent the net induced emission into the mode. The condition for oscillation in the mode is then approximately

$$G_L = G_N,$$
(2.12-14)

which indicates that energy can be absorbed from the atomic oscillators at the same rate at which it must be dissipated in the cavity losses. Another way of writing this condition is

$$\frac{\omega_0 U}{Q} = P_I$$
(2.12-15)

or

$$P_{s0} = \frac{\hbar \omega_0^4 \, \Delta\omega_s}{2\pi^3 c^3 Q(1 - N_1/N_2)} \, ABC.$$
(2.12-16)

Evidently one necessary requirement for laser oscillation is that the population of the upper state be greater than the population of the lower state. In addition it helps to have the Q of the electromagnetic mode as large as possible and the spontaneous line width, the volume of the cavity and the operating frequency as small as possible.

In general the output bandwidth or the uncertainty in oscillator frequency for an active mode will be considerably less than the natural bandwidth of the electromagnetic mode which is being excited. To see what the active bandwidth will be we note first that the power balance between net induced emission and power absorbed in the load which is assumed in (2.12-14) and (2.12-15) is not quite correct. Actually it is the sum of the net induced emission and the spontaneous emission which must equal the power absorbed in the load and in the cavity losses. This spontaneous emission has no fixed phase relation to the oscillation of the mode and can be considered as a source of random noise. If the mode amplitude is V, the spontaneous power will be

$$P_s = \tfrac{1}{2}(G_L - G_N)V^2, \tag{2.12-17}$$

and the stored energy,

$$U = \tfrac{1}{2}CV^2. \tag{2.12-18}$$

From (2.12-13) we can write

$$P_s = \frac{P_I}{n(1 - N_1/N_2)}, \tag{2.12-19}$$

where

$$P_I = \tfrac{1}{2}G_N V^2 \tag{2.12-20}$$

and

$$n \approx \frac{2\pi U}{h\omega_0}, \tag{2.12-21}$$

for more than a few photons in the mode. Equating the right hand members of (2.12-17) and (2.12-19), we can write

$$\frac{G_L - G_N}{C} = \left(\frac{G_L}{C}\right)^2 \frac{h\omega_0}{2\pi P_I}\left(\frac{N_2}{N_2 - N_1}\right). \tag{2.12-22}$$

With reference to (2.12-7) we define $\Delta\omega_p = G_L/C$ as the *passive* band width of the electromagnetic mode without the active laser medium and $\Delta\omega_a \equiv (G_L - G_N)/C$ as the *active* bandwidth of the energy emitted by the laser oscillator. Then (2.12-22) becomes

$$\Delta\omega_a = (\Delta\omega_p)^2 \frac{h\omega_0}{2\pi P_I(1 - N_1/N_2)}. \tag{2.12-23}$$

In the equivalent circuit of Fig. 2-34 the negative conductance $(-G_N)$ which represents the induced emission into the mode must be a function of

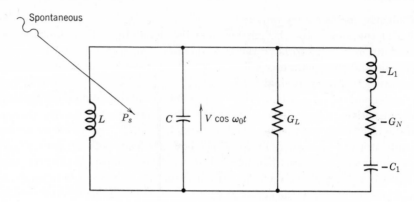

Fig. 2-35 Another equivalent circuit for a laser oscillator.

frequency since, from Fig. 2-33, the spontaneous power emitted by the atomic population is a function of frequency. It is pointed out in the Appendix that if the real part of a causal response function, such as a stable admittance, is a function of frequency the corresponding imaginary part is uniquely determined by the Hilbert transform. We suppose $-G_N(\omega)$ to be the real part of a *causal* admittance since power is induced into the electromagnetic mode by the energy which is stored in the mode. If we knew the shape of the spontaneous emission curve in Fig. 2-33 (i.e., $dP_{s0}/d\omega$ as a function of ω), we could calculate the spontaneous emission into a single mode as a function of ω as

$$P_s(\omega) = \frac{dP_{s0}/d\omega}{N(\omega_0)}, \qquad (2.12\text{-}24)$$

and then calculate $-G_N(\omega)$ from (2.12-19) and (2.12-20). The corresponding susceptance could then be obtained from (A-11).

The results of such a procedure can be approximately obtained by constructing an admittance from frequency independent elements for which the real part is approximately equal to $-G_N(\omega)$. Broadly speaking we know that $-G_N(\omega)$ has a maximum magnitude G_N, at a frequency of ω_0, and it has a bandwidth of $\Delta\omega_s$. The series combination of a frequency independent negative conductance $(-G_N)$ and a negative inductance $(-L_1)$ and a negative capacitance $(-C_1)$ has an admittance with real part

$$-G_N(\omega) = \frac{-G_N}{1 + G_N{}^2(\omega L_1 - 1/\omega C_1)^2}. \qquad (2.12\text{-}25)$$

This is often called a Lorentzian approximation to the true line shape. It is not difficult to show that $G_N(\omega)$ does reach a maximum of G_N at ω_0 with a bandwidth of $\Delta\omega_s$ if

$$L_1 = \frac{1}{\Delta\omega_s G_N},$$

$$C_1 = \frac{\Delta\omega_s G_N}{\omega_0{}^2}.$$

(2.12-26a,b)

Such an admittance is indicated in Fig. 2-35. All three elements must be negative so the admittance will have no short circuit natural frequencies in the right half of the s-plane since this is a necessary requirement for causality [Ky 1, Ky 2].

2.13. THE LASER AMPLIFIER

In this section we show how the previously developed concepts can be used to analyze plane wave propagation in a laser medium. To this end we construct the transmission line equivalent circuit shown in Fig. 2-36 [Ad 1, Ch. 7 & 8]. Propagation is in the x direction, and electric field in the y direction and magnetic field in the z direction are taken as analogous to transmission line voltage and current respectively. The shunt capacitance and series inductance are analogous to the dielectric and magnetic permittivities, respectively, and the passive losses are represented by a positive shunt conductivity σ_+.

An excited laser medium has in addition a negative shunt conductivity, σ_-, which appears at the frequency ω_0 of down transitions for the inverted

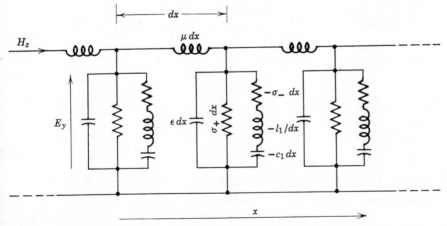

Fig. 2-36   Linear equivalent circuit for laser wave amplification.

atomic population and extends over the frequency range for population inversion $\Delta\omega$. Since σ_- is causal and frequency-dependent, it must have an associated reactance which can be calculated from the Hilbert transforms (discussed in the Appendix) for any particular population inversion spectrum. Here we shall assume a simple Lorentzian line shape so the associated reactance is given by a series capacitance and inductance. These reactive elements must be *negative* since they are derived from the Hilbert transform of a negative conductance [Ky 1, Ky 2]. Thus

$$l_1 = \frac{1}{\Delta\omega\sigma_-}, \tag{2.13-1}$$

$$c_1 = \frac{\Delta\omega\sigma_-}{{\omega_0}^2}. \tag{2.13-2}$$

A characteristic impedance for the laser medium can be calculated as

$$Z_0^2 = \frac{\mu s\left(l_1 c_1 s^2 + \dfrac{c_1}{\sigma_-}s + 1\right)}{l_1 c_1 \varepsilon s^3 + \left(\dfrac{c_1\varepsilon}{\sigma_-} + c_1 l_1 \sigma_+\right)s^2 + \left[\varepsilon + \left(\dfrac{\sigma_+}{\sigma_-} - 1\right)c_1\right]s + \sigma_+}. \tag{2.13-3}$$

Using (2.13-1) and (2.13-2) and denoting the dielectric relaxation time of the passive medium as

$$\tau_d = \frac{\varepsilon}{\sigma_+}, \tag{2.13-4}$$

Equation 2.13-3 becomes

$$Z_0^2 = \left(\frac{\mu}{\varepsilon}\right)\frac{s(s^2 + \Delta\,\omega s + \omega_0^2)}{s^3 + (\Delta\omega + 1/\tau_d)s^2 + \omega_0^2\left[1 + \dfrac{\Delta\omega}{\omega_0^2\tau_d}\left(1 - \dfrac{\sigma_-}{\sigma_+}\right)\right]s + \dfrac{\omega_0^2}{\tau_d}}. \tag{2.13-5}$$

The condition for gain is evidently,

$$\sigma_- > \sigma_+, \tag{2.13-6}$$

for at $s = j\omega_0$, the series resonance of l_1 and c_1,

$$y_{sh} = (\sigma_+ - \sigma_-) + j\omega_0\varepsilon,$$

$$z_{se} = j\omega_0\mu,$$

and $\gamma = \sqrt{y_{sh}z_{se}}$ has a negative real part if the inequality (2.13-6) is satisfied. The denominator of Z_0^2 (and the numerator of y_{sh}) is of the form $s^3 + as^2 + bs + c$ where a and c are always positive. Using Routh's method [Ga 2, pp. 197–199] it is easily demonstrated that such a polynomial has two RHP zeros if $b < c/a$; otherwise it has no RHP zeros. This inequality can be written

$$\left(\frac{\sigma_-}{\sigma_+} - 1\right) > \frac{\omega_0{}^2\tau_d{}^2}{1 + \Delta\omega\tau_d} .$$
(2.13-7)

In Section 2.1 we note that if $Z_0{}^2(s)$ has two RHP poles, $Z_0(s)$ is not positive. Furthermore in Section 2.5 we find that if y_{sh} has an RHP zero, the system is absolutely unstable. Thus if a laser medium is so active that (2.13-7) is satisfied, we should expect that medium to be relatively useless for amplification.

2.14. THE KELVIN-HELMHOLTZ INSTABILITY

Consider now the classical problem of the Kelvin-Helmholtz instability at the interface between two fluids in relative motion [La 2, p. 373; Ge 2]. Perhaps the most important practical problem of this sort is the generation of waves on the surface of water by the wind. The simplest possible model is shown in Fig. 2-37. In the absence of surface waves the water is assumed to be at rest and the air to be moving with uniform velocity u. Assuming also that the air and water motion remain vortex free in the presence of waves, velocity potentials for the air and water can be written in the linear small signal approximation as

$$\phi_a = A_a \exp\left[-\beta y + j(\omega t - \beta x)\right],$$
$$\phi_w = A_w \exp\left[+\beta y + j(\omega t - \beta x)\right],$$
(2.14-1a,b)

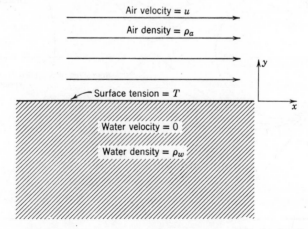

Fig. 2-37 Geometry for wind-water interaction.

where A_a and A_w are amplitudes and the frequency ω is related to the propagation constant β by the dispersion relation

$$\frac{\omega}{\omega_0} = \left(\frac{a}{1+a}\right)\left(\frac{\mu\beta}{u_0\beta_0}\right) \pm \left[\frac{1}{(1+a)}\left(\frac{\beta}{\beta_0}\right)^3 - \frac{a}{(1+a)^2}\left(\frac{u\beta}{u_0\beta_0}\right)^2 + \left(\frac{1-a}{1+a}\right)\frac{\beta}{\beta_0}\right]^{\frac{1}{2}},$$

$$(2.14\text{-}2)$$

where for air over water

$$a = \frac{\rho_a}{\rho_w} = 0.00122,$$

$$\omega_0 = \left(\frac{\rho_w g^3}{T}\right)^{\frac{1}{4}} = 60 \text{ rad/sec},$$

$$\beta_0 = \left(\frac{\rho_w g}{T}\right)^{\frac{1}{2}} = 3.65 \text{ rad/cm},$$

$$u_0 = \left(\frac{Tg}{\rho_w}\right)^{\frac{1}{4}} = 16.4 \text{ cm/sec},$$

$$T = 74 \text{ dyn/cm},$$

$$g = 981 \text{ cm/sec}^2.$$

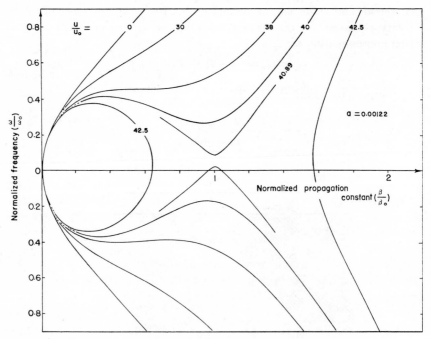

Fig. 2-38   Dispersion curves for simple wind-water interaction.

Figure 2-38 shows a plot of this dispersion relation. For $u/u_0 > 38$ we have standing waves and for

$$\frac{u}{u_0} > \left(\frac{2}{a}\right)^{1/2}(1 + a - a^2 - a^3)^{1/4} \approx 40.9, \qquad (2.14\text{-}3)$$

ω from (2.14-2) is complex and these standing waves grow with time. This is an example of an *absolute instability* which is easily observed in nature. A (u/u_0) of 41 corresponds to a wind velocity of about 650 cm/sec or about 12.8 knots (i.e., a brisk breeze), and Munk has shown that this is about the wind speed at which there is a marked change in texture of the water surface and a sharp increase in the incidence of "white-caps" [Mu 2]. This effect has also been observed for different values of the parameters (fluid density, surface tension) on an oil surface with relatively good quantitative agreement [Fr 1]. The physical explanation for this effect is simply that a local *increase* in the liquid surface level causes a local increase in surface wind speed which (by Bernoulli's effect) implies a local decrease in pressure. This process is self supporting when the inequality (2.14-3) is satisfied.

It is also easily observed that wind generates waves on water at speeds much below 12.8 knots. One might speculate that this process constitutes a *convective instability* which obtains for the simple model of Fig. 2-22 when (2.14-3) is not satisfied. Inversion of (2.14-2) yields a *cubic* equation for β.

$$\left(\frac{\beta}{\beta_0}\right)^3 - a\left(\frac{u}{u_0}\right)^2\left(\frac{\beta}{\beta_0}\right)^2 + \left[1 - a + 2a\left(\frac{\omega}{\omega_0}\right)\left(\frac{u}{u_0}\right)\right]\left(\frac{\beta}{\beta_0}\right) - (1 + a)\left(\frac{\omega}{\omega_0}\right)^2 = 0.$$

$$(2.14\text{-}4)$$

This equation will have three roots for each particular value of ω/ω_0 and u/u_0. The real roots are plotted in Fig. 2-38. It is evident that for some values of ω/ω_0 and u/u_0 there is only one real root; thus the other two must be a complex conjugate pair. There are two possible interpretations of these complex roots: the first is that they represent evanescent or damped waves which are of no physical interest, and the second is that they represent convectively unstable waves which grow in the direction of propagation. As was discussed in Section 2.4, a necessary condition for a convective instability is that the real part of γ must change sign as the real part of s approaches $+\infty$.

In (2.14-1) we have assumed an elementary solution of the form $\exp(j\omega t - j\beta x)$, but we are interested in considering situations in which both ω and β are complex. Thus we must write

$$\omega = \omega_r + j\omega_i,$$
$$(2.14\text{-}5a,b)$$
$$\beta = \beta_r + j\beta_i.$$

If we had assumed the elementary solution in our standard form as $\exp(\gamma x + st)$, where

$$\gamma = \alpha + j\beta,$$
$$s = \sigma + j\omega,$$ (2.14-6a,b)

then

$$\sigma + j\omega = j(\omega_r + j\omega_i),$$
$$\alpha + j\beta = -j(\beta_r + j\beta_i),$$ (2.14-7a,b)

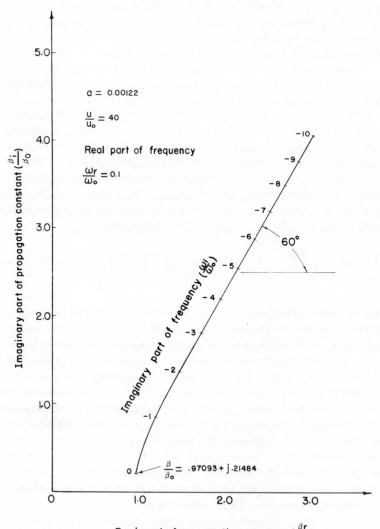

Fig. 2-39 Complex branch of dispersion curve for wind-water interaction.

and

$$\sigma = -\omega_i,$$

$$\alpha = +\beta_i.$$

We can, therefore, restate our necessary condition for convective instability as that the imaginary part of β should change sign as the imaginary part of ω approaches $-\infty$.

This condition is not satisfied for the dispersion equation (2.14-4); for example, with $\omega/\omega_0 = 0.1$ and $u/u_0 = 40$,

$$\frac{\beta}{\beta_0} = 0.971 \pm j0.215.$$

The trajectory of the positive root in the complex β-plane is plotted in Fig. 2-39 as the imaginary part of ω increases toward $-\infty$ and no crossing of the real β-axis occurs. Thus the growth of waves at wind speeds below 12.8 knots must be connected with unrealistic approximations in the simple model of Fig. 2-37; in particular one must consider both a vertical profile in wind velocity and turbulence [Ki 2, Ch. 12]. For an excellent visual introduction to some of these complexities, see the film "Flow Instabilities" by Mollo-Christensen which is listed in the Bibliography.

PROBLEMS

1. Derive the characteristic equation corresponding to (2.2-1) for a non-reciprocal system (i.e., $\gamma_+ \neq \gamma_-$ and $Z_{0+} \neq Z_{0-}$).

2. Why does a natural frequency occur when the sum of the driving point admittance and the admittance of the termination is zero as implied by (2.2-8)?

3. Suppose a small boy has an infinitely long transmission line which has a convective instability traveling with velocity u. Suppose also that the boy runs along beside the line at velocity u. Does the system then appear convectively or absolutely unstable to the boy?

4. Is it possible to stabilize an arbitrarily short piece of the transmission system shown in Fig. P2-2 (a) when $l_1 g < rc$? (b) when $l_1 g > rc$?

5. Consider the simple telegraph line shown in Fig. 1-1, but suppose that both l and c are *negative*. Is Z_0 a positive function?

6. Plot $\beta(\omega)$ in the pass bands and $\alpha(\omega)$ in the attenuation band from the dispersion equation for the line shown in Fig. 2-6.

7. Verify (2.4-12) and (2.4-13).

8. Demonstrate in detail (using integration in the complex plane) that the inverse Laplace transform of $1/(s + 1)$ is e^{-t} for $t > 0$ and 0 for $t < 0$.

9. Determine the nature of the instability of the line shown in Fig. P2-1 from an investigation of the dispersion equation.

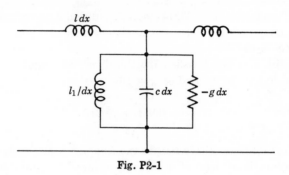

Fig. P2-1

10. Calculate the asymptotic time response for the line shown in Fig. P2-1.

11. Show for the system of Fig. P2-2 that Z_0 is a positive function if

$$\frac{l_1 g}{rc} < 1.$$

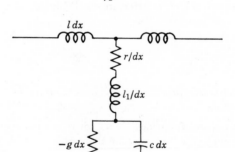

Fig. P2-2

12. For the two systems in Fig. P2-3 assume

$$\frac{r}{l} = \frac{g}{c} = \frac{1}{\sqrt{l_1 c}}.$$

(a) Show that these two systems have the same dispersion equation.

(b) Investigate this dispersion relation to determine whether or not these systems are absolutely unstable.

13. Derive (2.6-4).

14. Derive (2.6-7).

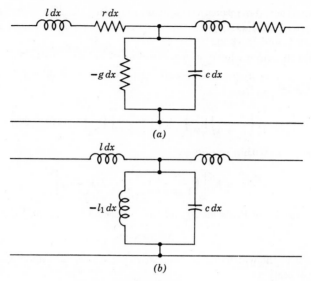

Fig. P2-3

15. (a) Use (2.5-10) to show that Briggs' criterion for absolute instability implies that the "complex group velocity" $dS(\gamma)/d\gamma$ goes to zero in the right half of the s-plane.
    (b) What is the physical explanation of this result? (See [Su 1].)
    (c) Show in detail for the simple active line of Fig. 1-4, that $ds/d\gamma = 0$ at the instability.

16. Using a diagram similar to Fig. 2-10 show that the group velocity is not necessarily positive when $d\omega/d\beta$ is negative for an active line.

17. What is the requirement on the matrix $[A]$, defined in Problem 8 of Chapter I, for reciprocity (i.e., $\gamma_+ = \gamma_-$ and $Z_{0+} = Z_{0-}$)?

18. Verify (2.9-14).

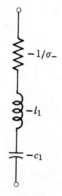

Fig. P2-4

19. (a) Show that the resonant frequency, ω_0, and the line width $\Delta\omega$ of the negative conductivity for the series resonant circuit in Fig. P2-4 satisfy (2.13-1) and (2.13-2).

    (b) Does this circuit have an o.c. instability? ... a s.c. instability?

20. Show from (2.14-2) that the imaginary part of ω ($\omega = \omega_r + j\omega_i$) is equal to zero when β equals

$$\frac{\beta}{\beta_0} = \frac{1}{2}\left\{\left(\frac{a}{1+a}\right)\left(\frac{u}{u_0}\right)^2 \pm \left[\left(\frac{a}{1+a}\right)^2\left(\frac{u}{u_0}\right)^4 - 4(1-a)\right]^{\frac{1}{2}}\right\}$$

or when β lies within the range

$$\Delta\beta = \beta_0\left[\left(\frac{a}{1+a}\right)^2\left(\frac{u}{u_0}\right)^4 - 4(1-a)\right]^{\frac{1}{2}}.$$

21. Use the results of Problem 20 and the "uncertainty relation" in the form

$$\Delta x\, \Delta\beta \approx 2\pi$$

to show that the width of a growing wave packet depends upon wind velocity approximately as

$$\Delta x \approx \frac{\pi/(1-a)\beta_0}{[(u/u_c)^4 - 1]^{\frac{1}{2}}},$$

where u_c is the critical wind velocity for the Kelvin-Helmholtz instability defined by (2.14-3).

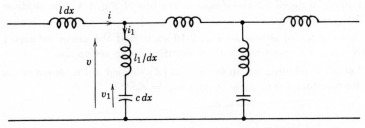

Fig. P2-5 *Note:* This system serves as a simple model for an optical medium such as glass.

22. (a) Write four first order partial differential equations which describe the system of Fig. P2-5 in terms of the dependent variables v, i, v_1 and i_1.

    (b) What is the dispersion equation for this system?

    (c) Plot ω versus β for this system and discuss the relative magnitudes of the group and phase velocities as a function of β.

23. Show, using as little algebra as is necessary, that a system with the dispersion equation

$$\gamma^2 - 4\gamma + 4 = s^2 + s - 2$$

is absolutely unstable.

24. Consider the transmission line shown in Fig. P2-6. It is of length a and is short circuited at both ends. Assume that the dispersion equation is

$$\gamma^2 = s(s - 1).$$

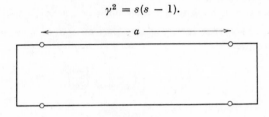

Fig. P2-6

(a) What are the allowed values of β as a function of the length a?
(b) Derive the condition on a such that an oscillation be *sinusoidal* in character (i.e., that a natural frequency be $s = \sigma + j\omega$ for $\omega \neq 0$).

III

QUASIHARMONIC ACTIVE PROPAGATION

In the previous chapters we consider briefly some aspects of *linear* active wave propagation. In order to have linear transmission systems upon which waves could propagate with gain, we postulate linear negative resistances and conductances and energy storage elements. The concept of a linear negative resistance can only be an approximation, however, since a truly linear negative resistor would be able to supply an arbitrarily large amount of power and would require the standby service of an infinite source. Thus all negative elements appear to become less negative and eventually positive as the amplitude of the excitation is increased. In this chapter we consider an approximate theory which is appropriate for small nonlinearity. The essential idea of the theory is to suppose in the first approximation that the system is linear and lossless. Nonlinear effects are included as a second order correction. Applications of this approach to the study of multimode oscillators, lasers and plasma waves are described.

3.1. NONLINEAR CONDUCTANCE AND RESISTANCE

A resistive element which has a range of terminal voltage and current for which

$$\frac{dv}{di} < 0$$

will in general fall into one of the three classifications shown in Fig. 3-1. In Fig. 3-1a the terminal current is a single valued function of the terminal voltage. We will refer to such an element as a *nonlinear conductor* (NLC) and suppose that in most cases it will be possible to express the dc terminal current by a Taylor series in the dc terminal voltage as

$$i(v) = a_0 + a_1 v + a_2 v^2 + \cdots. \tag{3.1-1}$$

In Fig. 3-1b the terminal voltage is a single valued function of the terminal current. Such an element will be called a *nonlinear resistor* (NLR) and we suppose again in most cases that it will be possible to express the dc terminal voltage by a Taylor series in the dc terminal current as

$$v(i) = b_0 + b_1 i + b_2 i^2 + \cdots. \tag{3.1-2}$$

We should expect a complete description of an NLC to include a certain amount of shunt parasitic capacitance designated by C_p in Fig. 3-1a. If C_p were not present, it would be possible to make a transition from A to B (in Fig. 3-1a) in zero time. A complete description of an NLR should likewise include some series parasitic inductance L_p to account for a finite transition time from A to B in Fig. 3-1b.

A v-i characteristic of the sort indicated in Fig. 3-1c would be a multivalued function of both current and voltage. It would have no Taylor series expansion valid beyond the negative resistance region. Furthermore it would require *both* series parasitic inductance (to account for finite transition times from A' to B') and also shunt parasitic capacitance (to account for finite transition times from A to B). In this chapter we are concerned mainly with the NLC and the NLR.

3.2. THE EQUIVALENT LINEARIZATION PROCEDURE

The *equivalent linearization* procedure of Kryloff and Bogoliuboff is an attempt to account for the presence of a nonlinear element by substituting a linear element the magnitude of which depends upon the amplitude of excitation [Kr 5]. It is assumed that the excitation is sinusoidal and the *approximate* response is taken to be the component of the actual response

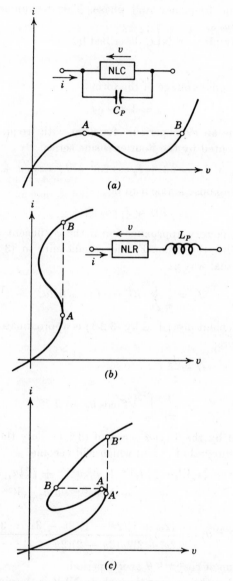

Fig. 3-1 Typical volt-ampere characteristics.

which has the same frequency and phase. This technique is also called *quasiharmonic analysis*.

Consider, for example, and NLC described by

$$i = i(v) \tag{3.2-1}$$

and assume a sinusoidal voltage of the form

$$v = V \cos \omega t. \tag{3.2-2}$$

The current will be an even periodic function with frequency ω and can therefore be represented by the Fourier cosine series

$$i(t) = I_0 + I_1 \cos \omega t + I_2 \cos 2\omega t + I_3 \cos 3\omega t + \cdots. \tag{3.2-3}$$

The approximate response is taken to be

$$i(t) \approx I_1 \cos \omega t. \tag{3.2-4}$$

This will be a satisfactory approximation if the coefficient I_1 is sufficiently large compared with the other Fourier coefficients in (3.2-3). I_1 can be evaluated in the usual way as

$$I_1 = \frac{1}{\pi} \int_0^{2\pi} i(V \cos \theta) \cos \theta \, d\theta, \tag{3.2-5}$$

so the nonlinear element described by (3.2-1) is approximated by an *effective conductance* $\tilde{G}$, where

$$\tilde{G} = \frac{I_1}{V}$$

$$= \frac{1}{\pi V} \int_0^{2\pi} i(V \cos \theta) \cos \theta \, d\theta. \tag{3.2-6}$$

If $i(v)$ is described by the Taylor series of (3.1-1), only the odd terms will contribute to the integral of (3.2-6) which will become

$$\tilde{G} = a_1 + \tfrac{3}{4}a_3 V^2 + \tfrac{5}{8}a_5 V^4 + \tfrac{35}{64}a_7 V^6 + \tfrac{63}{128}a_9 V^8 + \tfrac{231}{512}a_{11} V^{10}$$
$$+ \cdots + 2\langle \cos^{2(n+1)}\theta \rangle a_{2n+1} V^{2n} + \cdots, \tag{3.2-7}$$

where

$$\langle \cos^{2(n+1)} \theta \rangle = \frac{(2n+1)(2n-1)(2n-3)\cdots 3 \cdot 1}{(2n+2)2n(2n-2)(2n-4)\cdots 4 \cdot 2} \tag{3.2-8}$$

is the average value of $\cos^{2(n+1)} \theta$ over a period.

If we suppose that the current through an NLR is the sinusoidal function

$$i = I \cos \omega t, \tag{3.2-9}$$

then we can show in a similar way that the NLR can be approximated by an *effective resistance*

$$\tilde{R} = \frac{1}{\pi I} \int_0^{2\pi} v(I \cos \theta) \cos \theta \, d\theta, \tag{3.2-10}$$

and if the NLR is represented by the Taylor series expansion of (3.1-2) we can also write

$$\tilde{R} = \sum_{n=0}^{\infty} 2\langle\cos^{2(n+1)}\theta\rangle b_{2n+1} I^{2n}. \tag{3.2-11}$$

As a simple application of these results consider the L-C tank circuit of Fig. 3-2b to which an NLC has been attached. Let us assume that the NLC presents only a small perturbation to the operation of the tank circuit so the voltage v is approximately sinusoidal.

$$v = V \cos \omega t. \tag{3.2-2}$$

If

$$i(v) = -G\left(v - \frac{4}{3}\frac{v^3}{V_0^2}\right), \tag{3.2-12}$$

as shown in Fig. 3-2a, then from (3.2-7) the effective conductance of the NLC becomes

$$\tilde{G} = -G\left(1 - \frac{V^2}{V_0^2}\right). \tag{3.2-13}$$

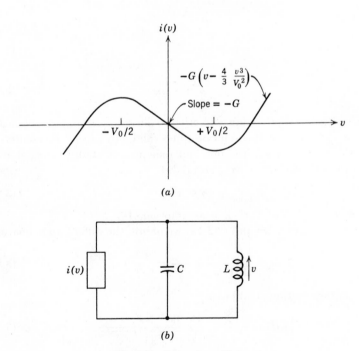

(a)

(b)

Fig. 3-2   A simple oscillator.

Thus, if we are content with accounting only for the first harmonic in the resonator we can suppose that the tank is shunted by an amplitude dependent negative conductance given by (3.2-13). The natural frequencies of the resonator will then be given by the zeroes of the total admittance or the roots of

$$Cs + \tilde{G} + \frac{1}{Ls} = 0, \qquad (3.2\text{-}14)$$

which are

$$s_{1,2} = \frac{1}{2}\left\{ \frac{-\tilde{G}}{C} \pm \left[\left(\frac{\tilde{G}}{C}\right)^2 - \frac{4}{(LC)} \right]^{1/2} \right\}. \qquad (3.2\text{-}15)$$

Since $\tilde{G}$ is a function of the sinusoidal voltage amplitude V, (3.2-15) indicates that the natural response of the system also depends upon V. If we suppose that

$$\frac{\tilde{G}}{2C} \ll \frac{1}{\sqrt{LC}}, \qquad (3.2\text{-}16)$$

then the natural response will be of the form

$$v(t) = V(t) \cos \omega t, \qquad (3.2\text{-}17)$$

where

$$\frac{dV}{dt} = \sigma V, \qquad (3.2\text{-}18)$$

$$\sigma = \frac{-\tilde{G}}{2C}, \qquad (3.2\text{-}19)$$

$$\omega = \frac{1}{\sqrt{LC}}. \qquad (3.2\text{-}20)$$

Equation 3.2-18 represents a correction to the initial assumption of constant voltage amplitude. For this solution to be valid, however, it is essential that $V(t)$ varies only slowly with time and remains essentially constant over a period of the oscillation. This is ensured if

$$\sigma \ll \omega C, \qquad (3.2\text{-}21)$$

which is identical to our previous assumption of (3.2-16)

From (3.2-13), (3.2-18) and (3.2-19) we obtain the differential equation

$$\frac{dV}{V(1 - V^2/V_0^2)} = \frac{G}{2C}\, dt, \qquad (3.2\text{-}22)$$

which has the solution [Po 2]

$$V(t) = \frac{V(0)e^{(G/2C)t}}{\sqrt{1 - [V^2(0)/V_0^2][1 - e^{(G/C)t}]}}. \qquad (3.2\text{-}23)$$

Equation 3.2-23 indicates that for $V \ll V_0$

$$V(t) \approx V(0)e^{(G/2C)t}, \qquad (3.2-24)$$

whereas for $t \to \infty$

$$V(t) \approx V_0 \qquad (3.2-25)$$

In physical terms we can say that for small amplitude we have the exponential growth corresponding to a linear negative conductance equal to $-G$. As the amplitude of the oscillation increases, the magnitude of the effective negative conductance, given by (3.2-13), decreases. At a voltage amplitude equal to V_0 the effective negative conductance is zero and so is the growth rate from (3.2-19). The voltage amplitude V_0 represents a stationary amplitude for the system. In Fig. 3-3 is plotted from (3.2-23) the *fraction of maximum amplitude*

$$F = \frac{V}{V_0} \qquad (3.2-26)$$

as a function of the *normalized argument*

$$\eta = \frac{G}{2C} t \qquad (3.2-27)$$

for a value of F equal to 0.1 at $\eta = 0$.

It is important to remember the assumptions upon which (3.2-23) is based. The primary assumption was that the tank voltage was *almost sinusoidal* with a *slowly varying amplitude*. Equation 3.2-16 *must* therefore be satisfied for our solution to be realistic. If (3.2-16) *is* satisfied, then we

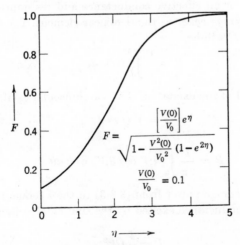

Fig. 3-3 Normalized amplitude growth for the simple oscillator.

have found a simple differential equation, (3.2-22), for the slowly varying amplitude the solution of which is (3.2-23). Our solution neglects all harmonics of the fundamental oscillation frequency.

The exact equation which describes the tank circuit in Fig. 3-2*b* is

$$i(v) + C\frac{dv}{dt} + \frac{1}{L}\int v \, dt = 0. \tag{3.2-28}$$

Assuming $i(v)$ as in Fig. 3-2*a* and differentiating with respect to time yields the differential equation

$$\frac{d^2v}{dt^2} - \frac{G}{C}\left(1 - \frac{4v^2}{V_0{}^2}\right)\frac{dv}{dt} + \frac{v}{LC} = 0. \tag{3.2-29}$$

This is *van der Pol's equation*, one of the most thoroughly studied of all nonlinear differential equations. We have determined an approximate solution which is valid for $G \ll \sqrt{C/L}$. A more general solution is discussion in the following chapter.

3.3. EQUAL POWER INTERPRETATION OF EQUIVALENT CONDUCTANCE AND RESISTANCE

The effective conductance and resistance for a given NLC and NLR respectively are obtained in the last section as that linear (but amplitude dependent) element which would develop the *same response amplitude and phase at the fundamental frequency* as the nonlinear element does.

Let us now ask for an effective conductance and resistance which would absorb the *same average power* as the nonlinear element. The average power absorbed by an NLC will be

$$P = \frac{1}{T}\int_0^T i(v)v \, dt, \tag{3.3-1}$$

where T is a period of the excitation. For the sinusoidal excitation given by

$$v = V \cos \omega t \tag{3.3-2}$$

we have

$$P = \frac{1}{2\pi}\int_0^{2\pi} i(V \cos \theta)V \cos \theta \, d\theta. \tag{3.3-3}$$

If we equate the average power from (3.3-3) to the average power from an equivalent linear conductance excited by the sinusoidal voltage of (3.3-2),

$$P = \frac{1}{2}\tilde{G}V^2, \tag{3.3-4}$$

we find that the effective conductance is again

$$\tilde{G} = \frac{1}{\pi V} \int_0^{2\pi} i(V \cos \theta) \cos \theta \, d\theta, \qquad (3.3\text{-}5)$$

just as in (3.2-6). A similar argument is easily carried through for an NLR.

Thus we have the interesting result that *the equivalent linear element for equal fundamental harmonic response is equal to the equivalent linear element for equal power if the excitation is a sinusoid.*

Equivalent linearization or quasiharmonic analysis is therefore a technique of analysis which is valid if the currents and voltages in a circuit are all approximately sinusoidal at the same frequency. It can be considered as a technique for using linear circuit theory to balance currents and voltages (i.e., satisfy Kirchhoff's laws) at the fundamental frequency which does not violate the conservation of energy. This technique can be used to develop differential equations for the growth rates of normal modes for a circuit, but the initial assumption that voltages and currents be approximately sinusoidal requires that the growth be only a small fraction during one period of the oscillation.

The equal power interpretation of quasiharmonic analysis is particularly convenient for determining stationary levels of oscillation and also for rapidly estimating whether the equivalent linearization procedure is valid. Consider for example the system shown in Fig. 3-4a. The resistor R_2 represents passive losses in the tank circuit while R_1 is an output load. If we are to use

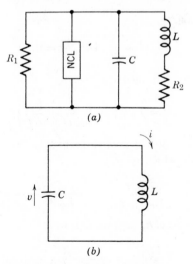

(a)

(b)

Fig. 3-4 A quasiharmonic oscillator.

quasiharmonic analysis, the voltages and currents must be approximately sinusoidal. We can determine their relative amplitude and phase from the simplified, linear, lossless system in Fig. 3-4b. Evidently

$$v = V \cos \omega t,$$

and   (3.3-6)

$$i = I \sin \omega t.$$

The relation between the voltage amplitude and the current amplitude can be determined from the condition that the maximum electrical stored energy equals the maximum magnetic stored energy or

$$\tfrac{1}{2}CV^2 = \tfrac{1}{2}LI^2,$$ (3.3-7)

so

$$V = \left(\frac{L}{C}\right)^{\!\frac{1}{2}} I.$$

Suppose now that the NLC has the $i(v)$ characteristic shown in Fig. 3-2a so the effective negative conductance is given by (3.2-13):

$$\tilde{G} = -G\left(1 - \frac{V^2}{V_0^{\,2}}\right).$$ (3.2-13)

For a stationary oscillation the power injected into the oscillation by the NLC must equal the power absorbed by R_1 and R_2. Thus the level of oscillation can be determined from the equation

$$\tfrac{1}{2}\tilde{G}V^2 + \frac{1}{2R_1}V^2 + \tfrac{1}{2}R_2 I^2 = 0,$$ (3.3-8)

or with the use of (3.3-7)

$$\tilde{G} + \frac{1}{R_1} + R_2 \frac{C}{L} = 0,$$

so from (3.2-13) we have immediately

$$V^2 = V_0^{\,2}\left[1 - \left(\frac{1}{R_1 G} + \frac{R_2 C}{GL}\right)\right].$$ (3.3-9)

We can now find the value of load resistor R_1 which will absorb maximum power. The power absorbed by R_1 is

$$P_L = \frac{1}{2}\frac{V^2}{R_1} = \frac{V_0^{\,2}}{2}\left[\frac{1 - (R_2 C/GL)}{R_1} - \frac{1}{R_1^{\,2}G}\right].$$ (3.3-10)

From the condition $dP_L/dR_1 = 0$ we obtain

$$R_1\big|_{\text{opt}} = \frac{2/G}{1 - (R_2 C/GL)},$$ (3.3-11)

which implies a *maximum* power into R_1 of

$$P_L\big|_{\max} = \frac{GV_0^2}{8}\left(1 - \frac{R_2C}{GL}\right)^2.$$ (3.3-12)

If R_1 is made very much smaller than the optimum, the system will not oscillate; if it is made very much larger it will absorb little power.

3.4. NONLINEAR CAPACITANCE AND INDUCTANCE

The method of equivalent linearization devised by Kryloff and Bogoliuboff is also useful in dealing with nonlinear energy storage elements. For a *nonlinear capacitor* it is usually possible to specify the charge as a single valued function of the terminal voltage,

$$Q = Q(v).$$ (3.4-1)

For a *nonlinear inductor* it is sometimes possible to specify the flux as a single valued function of the terminal current,

$$\Phi = \Phi(i).$$ (3.4-2)

Equation 3.4-1 and 3.4-2 evidently assume that hysteresis loops are not present. For a sinusoidal voltage of the form given by

$$v = V \cos \omega t,$$ (3.4-3)

we expect the charge to be an even periodic function with a frequency equal to ω. It can therefore be expressed as the Fourier cosine series

$$Q(t) = Q_0 + Q_1 \cos \omega t + Q_2 \cos 2\omega t + Q_3 \cos 3\omega t + \cdots.$$ (3.4-4)

For quasiharmonic analysis to be appropriate we must have Q_1 large compared with the other coefficients in (3.4-4). Q_1 can be evaluated as

$$Q_1 = \frac{1}{\pi} \int_0^{2\pi} Q(V \cos \theta) \cos \theta \, d\theta.$$ (3.4-5)

We then *approximate*

$$Q(t) \approx Q_1 \cos \omega t,$$ (3.4-6)

for which we have the corresponding current

$$i = \frac{dQ}{dt}$$

$$= -\omega Q_1 \sin \omega t;$$ (3.4-7)

for an equivalent linear capacitor the current would be

$$i = \tilde{C}\frac{dv}{dt}$$

$$= -\omega\tilde{C}V \sin \omega t. \tag{3.4-8}$$

Thus the value of an equivalent linear capacitor is found from (3.4-5), (3.4-7) and (3.4-8) to be

$$\tilde{C} = \frac{1}{\pi V}\int_0^{2\pi} Q(V \cos \theta) \cos \theta \, d\theta, \tag{3.4-9}$$

which is of the same form as the expression for equivalent conductance given in (3.2-6).

In a similar way if we assume a sinusoidal current in (3.4-2)

$$i = I \cos \omega t, \tag{3.4-10}$$

the equivalent linear inductor is

$$\tilde{L} = \frac{1}{\pi I}\int_0^{2\pi} \Phi(I \cos \theta) \cos \theta \, d\theta. \tag{3.4-11}$$

Evidently for Taylor series expansions of $Q(v)$ and $\Phi(i)$ we can carry through exactly the same term by term numerical evaluation of C and L as was previously outlined for G and R. Thus for

$$Q(v) = \sum_{n=0}^{\infty} a_n v^n, \tag{3.4-12}$$

$$\tilde{C} = \sum_{n=0}^{\infty} 2\langle\cos^{2(n+1)}\theta\rangle a_{2n+1}V^{2n}; \tag{3.4-13}$$

and for

$$\Phi(i) = \sum_{n=0}^{\infty} b_n i^n, \tag{3.4-14}$$

$$\tilde{L} = \sum_{n=0}^{\infty} 2\langle\cos^{2(n+1)}\theta\rangle b_{2n+1}I^{2n}. \tag{3.4-15}$$

It is important to bear in mind, however, that the restrictions on the nonlinearity of $Q(v)$ and $\Phi(i)$ for validity of the quasiharmonic analysis are more severe than the restrictions on $i(v)$ of an NLC or on $v(i)$ of an NLR. This is because the basic requirement for the quasiharmonic analysis to be appropriate is that the entire circuit be oscillating approximately in a sinusoidal manner. If the *shape* of $Q(v)$ in a simple nonlinear tank circuit deviates greatly from linearity, other frequency components will appear in appreciable magnitude [in (3.4-4)] which will not be taken into account by the analysis. For the simple tank circuit of Fig. 3-2 in which L and C are both linear, on the other hand, it is only necessary to require that the current through the NLC be small compared with the current through the capacitor in order to insure an approximately sinusoidal voltage. This requirement is satisfied essentially by (3.2-16). It is *not* necessary for $i(v)$ to be nearly linear. We can think of the NLC as a small perturbation to the linear, lossless tank circuit which squirts a little energy in during each cycle. The amount of energy injected is correctly calculated by equivalent linearization formula for an $i(v)$ characteristic of arbitrary shape as long as the voltage is approximately sinusoidal.

3.5. QUASIHARMONIC TRAVELING WAVE AMPLIFICATION

In the spirit of the quasiharmonic analysis let us now consider the simple nonlinear transmission line of Fig. 3-5*a* which has a shunt current per unit length of

$$j(v) = -g\left(v - \frac{4}{3}\frac{v^3}{V_0{}^2}\right) \tag{3.5-1}$$

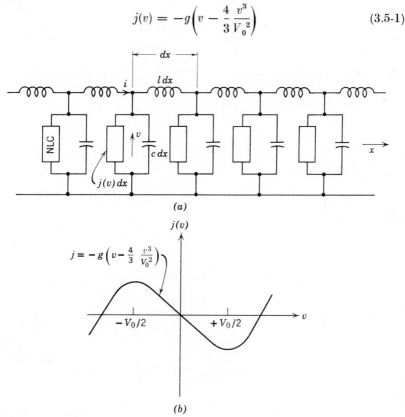

(a)

(b)

Fig. 3-5   (*a*) A simple nonlinear transmission line. (*b*) A simple nonlinear conductance.

shown in Fig. 3-5b. We suppose that the line is excited at $x = 0$ with a sinusoidal source as indicated in Fig. 3-6. Assuming a stable, steady amplitude traveling wave is eventually attained along the line, we should expect that amplitude to vary with x somewhat as in Fig. 3-6. Initially the amplitude $V(x)$ is small compared with V_0 and the growth is approximately exponential. Since the effective shunt conductance corresponding to (3.5-1) is

$$\tilde{g} = -g\left(1 - \frac{V^2}{V_0{}^2}\right), \tag{3.5-2}$$

we expect the spatial growth rate to decrease and eventually to become zero as the amplitude of the wave approaches V_0. This limiting effect is often referred to as *saturation*.

We can calculate the shape of the saturation curve by quasiharmonic analysis as follows. From the *linear* analysis in Chapter I

$$
\begin{aligned}
v(x, t) &= V(0)e^{\alpha x}\cos(\omega t - \beta x) \\
&= V(x)\cos(\omega t - \beta x),
\end{aligned} \tag{3.5-3}
$$

where, if we assume $g \ll \omega c$,

$$\alpha = \tfrac{1}{2}g\left(\frac{l}{c}\right)^{\!\!\frac{1}{2}} \quad \text{and} \quad \beta = \omega\sqrt{lc}.$$

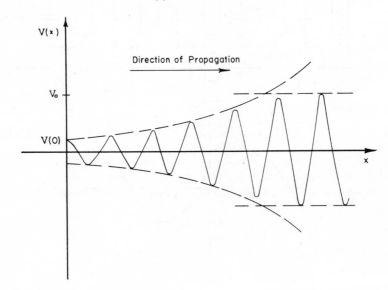

Fig. 3-6   Saturation of a traveling wave.

Equation 3.5-3 implies that the amplitude $V(x)$ obeys the differential equation

$$\frac{dV}{dx} = \alpha V. \tag{3.5-4}$$

Now in the *nonlinear* case we start with the differential equation (3.5-4) but use the quasiharmonic approximation for α

$$\alpha = \tfrac{1}{2}g\left(\frac{l}{c}\right)^{\frac{1}{2}}\left(1 - \frac{V^2}{V_0{}^2}\right). \tag{3.5-5}$$

This leads to the relation

$$\frac{dV}{V(1 - V^2/V_0{}^2)} = \frac{g}{2}\left(\frac{l}{c}\right)^{\frac{1}{2}}dx. \tag{3.5-6}$$

Equation 3.5-6 is formally identical to (3.2-22) which was previously derived to determine the temporal growth of a mode on the active tank circuit in Fig. 3-2. The solution is therefore given by [Vo 2]

$$V(x) = \frac{V(0)e^{(g/2)\sqrt{(l/c)}x}}{\sqrt{1 - [V^2(0)/V_0{}^2](1 - e^{g\sqrt{(l/c)}x})}}. \tag{3.5-7}$$

Equation 3.5-7 has already been plotted in normalized form in Fig. 3-3, where

$$F = \frac{V(\eta)}{V_0}, \tag{3.5-8}$$

and in this case

$$\eta = \frac{g}{2}\left(\frac{l}{c}\right)^{\frac{1}{2}}x. \tag{3.5-9}$$

Our final quasiharmonic solution is therefore

$$v(x, t) = V(x)\cos(\omega t - \beta x), \tag{3.5-10}$$

where $V(0)$ and ω are determined by the source generator and $\beta = \omega\sqrt{lc}$. The basic requirement for validity of the quasiharmonic analysis is that the energy input per cycle must be a small fraction of the total stored energy or

$$\frac{\tilde{g}}{\omega c} \ll 1. \tag{3.5-11}$$

From (3.5-3) this implies

$$\alpha \ll \beta; \tag{3.5-12}$$

that is to say, the growth in a wavelength must also be a small fraction.

In some cases we may be interested in using quasiharmonic analysis simply to determine the wave amplitude at which saturation occurs. A *necessary* condition for wave saturation is evidently

$$\alpha(V) = 0, \tag{3.5-13}$$

but (3.5-13) is not sufficient because the constant amplitude wave might be unstable. A technique for detecting such an instability is discussed in the next section.

3.6. THE STABILITY OF SATURATED TRAVELING WAVES [Sc4]

An amplifying line upon which a traveling wave is propagating with maximum amplitude is said to be *saturated*. Evidently one can seek saturation amplitudes in the quasiharmonic approximation by calculating first the gain constant, α, as a function of the *linear* negative conductance (or resistance), substituting the amplitude dependent *effective* negative conductance (or resistance), then setting α equal to zero and solving for the amplitude. This procedure leaves open the question of whether the resulting constant amplitude traveling wave will be stable.

As an introduction to a general approach to the stability question let us investigate the properties of the partial differential equations which are represented by Fig. 3-7. These are

$$\frac{\partial v}{\partial x} = -l \frac{\partial i}{\partial t},$$

$$c \frac{\partial v_1}{\partial t} + j(v_1) = i_1,$$

$$v = v_1 + i_1 r + l_1 \frac{\partial i_1}{\partial t}, \tag{3.6-1a,b,c,d}$$

$$\frac{\partial i}{\partial x} = -i_1 - c_1 \frac{\partial v}{\partial t}.$$

When a traveling wave is saturated, it will be moving with constant velocity and wave shape. All line voltages and currents can then be written as functions of the variable

$$\xi = x - ut, \tag{3.6-2}$$

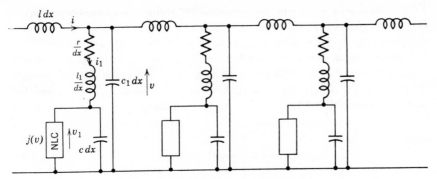

Fig. 3-7   A more complex active line.

where u is the velocity of the steady propagation of the saturated wave. The partial derivatives in (3.6-1) are then related by

$$\frac{d}{d\xi} = \frac{\partial}{\partial x} = -\frac{1}{u}\frac{\partial}{\partial t}. \tag{3.6-3}$$

Thus, if we *assume* steady propagation, (3.6-1) reduces to the ordinary differential equations

$$\frac{dv}{d\xi} = lu\frac{di}{d\xi},$$

$$-cu\frac{dv_1}{d\xi} + j(v_1) = i_1,$$

$$v = v_1 + i_1 r - l_1 u \frac{di_1}{d\xi}, \tag{3.6-4a,b,c,d}$$

$$\frac{di}{d\xi} = -i_1 + c_1 u \frac{dv}{d\xi}.$$

The solutions of (3.6-4) (if any) will represent waves traveling in the $+x$-direction with unchanging shape at velocity u; (3.6-4a) is redundant from a dynamical point of view, since it implies that the line voltage and line current must have the same waveform except for an arbitrary constant which could be a dc bias voltage or bias current. Equations 3.6-4a–d can therefore be written in the form

$$\frac{dv}{d\xi} = \frac{-lui_1}{1 - lc_1 u^2}$$

$$\frac{dv_1}{d\xi} = \frac{j(v_1) - i_1}{cu}, \tag{3.6-5a,b,c}$$

$$\frac{di_1}{d\xi} = \frac{v_1 - v + i_1 r}{l_1 u}$$

Equations 3.6-5a–c are *autonomous* ordinary differential equations, that is, the rate of change of the vector (v, v_1, i_1) with ξ is a unique function of position in (v, v_1, i_1) space. This point of view leads to a fairly general procedure for investigating steady propagation on nonlinear lines which will be considered in detail in the following chapter. If we limit our interest to those frequencies for which we can make the quasi-harmonic approximation, (3.6-5) can be written as the linear matrix equation

$$\frac{d}{d\xi}\begin{bmatrix} v \\ v_1 \\ i_1 \end{bmatrix} = [B] \times \begin{bmatrix} v \\ v_1 \\ i_1 \end{bmatrix}, \tag{3.6-6}$$

where

$$[B] = \begin{bmatrix} 0 & 0 & -l'u \\[6pt] 0 & +\dfrac{\tilde{g}}{cu} & -\dfrac{1}{cu} \\[10pt] -\dfrac{1}{l_1 u} & \dfrac{1}{l_1 u} & \dfrac{r}{l_1 u} \end{bmatrix} \tag{3.6-7}$$

and

$$l' = \frac{l}{1 - lc_1 u^2}, \tag{3.6-8}$$

and $\tilde{g}$ is the effective conductance of the NLC.

The nature of the solution to (3.6-6) is determined by the eigenvalues of the matrix $[B]$ or the roots of the characteristic equation

$$\det\left[[B] - \gamma[I]\right] = 0, \tag{3.6-9}$$

where $[I]$ is the identity matrix; or,

$$\gamma^3 - \left(\frac{\tilde{g}}{cu} + \frac{r}{l_1 u}\right)\gamma^2 + \left[\frac{1 + \tilde{g}r}{l_1 cu^2} - \frac{l'}{l_1}\right]\gamma + \frac{l'}{l_1}\frac{\tilde{g}}{cu} = 0 \tag{3.6-10}$$

If these roots are $(-\alpha_1 \pm j\beta)$ and $(-\alpha_2)$, the characteristic equation may be written in the form

$$\gamma^3 + (2\alpha_1 + \alpha_2)\gamma^2 + (2\alpha_1\alpha_2 + \alpha_1^2 + \beta^2)\gamma + \alpha_2(\alpha_1^2 + \beta^2) = 0, \tag{3.6-11}$$

and the voltages and currents along the line will be linear combinations of the functions $e^{-\alpha_2\xi}$, $e^{-\alpha_1\xi}\sin\beta\xi$, and $e^{-\alpha_1\xi}\cos\beta\xi$. The solution will be a stable limit cycle if $\alpha_1 = 0$ and $\alpha_2 < 0$, for then $e^{-\alpha_2\xi}$ will be negligible after a sufficient time (i.e., for ξ large enough and negative). The voltages and currents will then be steady sinusoids with arguments of

$$\beta\xi = \beta(x - ut). \tag{3.6-12}$$

The saturation condition is reached when the amplitude of the voltage across the NLC has increased to such a level that the average negative conductance is small enough to make $\alpha_1 = 0$. From comparison of (3.6-10) and (3.6-11), it is evident that if $\alpha_1 = 0$,

$$\frac{\alpha_2(\alpha_1{}^2 + \beta^2)}{(2\alpha_1 + \alpha_2)} = 2\alpha_1\alpha_2 + \alpha_1{}^2 + \beta^2 \qquad (3.6\text{-}13)$$

or

$$u^2 = \frac{1}{l'c}\left(1 + \frac{l_1\tilde{g}}{rc}\right)(1 + \tilde{g}r), \qquad (3.6\text{-}14)$$

and

$$\beta^2 = \frac{1 + \tilde{g}r}{l_1cu^2} - \frac{l'}{l_1}. \qquad (3.6\text{-}15)$$

Now from (3.6-12) the frequency of excitation is equal to

$$\omega = \beta u. \qquad (3.6\text{-}16)$$

So (3.6-14) and (3.6-15) give the value of effective conductance for which $\alpha_1 = 0$, as

$$\tilde{g} = \frac{-1}{2r}\,[1 - \sqrt{1 - 4(\omega rc)^2}\,]. \qquad (3.6\text{-}17)$$

Also from comparison of (3.6-10) and (3.6-11) under the assumption that $\alpha_1 = 0$, we find that

$$\alpha_2 = -\left(\frac{\tilde{g}}{cu} + \frac{r}{l_1u}\right), \qquad (3.6\text{-}18)$$

which means once again that the quasiharmonic propagating wave is stable only if

$$\alpha_2 < 0 \qquad (3.6\text{-}19)$$

or

$$\left|\frac{l_1\tilde{g}}{rc}\right| < 1. \qquad (3.6\text{-}20)$$

It is interesting to notice that (3.6-20) is also the condition that the linearized characteristic impedance be positive as discussed in Section 2.1. To see this observe that the linearized series impedance per unit length and shunt admittance per unit length are

$$z_{se} = ls \qquad (3.6\text{-}21)$$

and

$$y_{sh} = c_1s + \frac{cs + \tilde{g}}{l_1cs^2 + (rc + l_1\tilde{g})s + (1 + r\tilde{g})}, \qquad (3.6\text{-}22)$$

where $\tilde{g}$ is the effective linear conductance corresponding to $j(v_1)$. If we assume that $rg < 1$, y_{sh} has a pair of complex RHP poles unless (3.6-20) is satisfied.

It is important to be aware that we can say nothing about the sufficiency of stability condition (3.6-20) for two reasons.

1. In limiting our attention to waves with constant velocity and shape we have ignored the possibility of instabilities which might vary independently with time.

2. In the quasiharmonic approach we have neglected all harmonics of the excitation frequency.

Techniques of nonlinear stability analysis which overcome these objections will be discussed in the following chapter.

3.7. SATURATION POWER FLOW [Sc4]

The power flow at any point on an active transmission line will be given in terms of the shunt voltage, v, and the series current, i, by

$$P(x) = \frac{\omega}{2\pi} \int_0^{2\pi/\omega} v(x, t)i(x, t)\, dt. \tag{3.7-1}$$

If the line is saturated, the power flow will be independent of x and equal to

$$P_s = \frac{1}{\lambda} \int_\xi^{\xi+\lambda} v(\xi)i(\xi)\, d\xi, \tag{3.7-2}$$

where λ is the wavelength of the periodic wave. For lines in which the series impedance is simply an inductor (like those of Figs. 3-5a and 3-7), the line voltage and current in saturation will be related by

$$\frac{dv}{d\xi} = lu\frac{di}{d\xi} \tag{3.7-3}$$

as in (3.6-4a). Therefore,

$$i(\xi) = \frac{1}{lu}v(\xi) + \text{const.}, \tag{3.7-4}$$

so the saturation power flow is

$$P_s = \frac{1}{lu\lambda} \int_0^\lambda v^2\, d\varepsilon. \tag{3.7-5}$$

For the simple line of Fig. 3-5a, the saturation voltage level is independent of frequency. The saturation power level is then simply a constant

$$P_s = \frac{1}{2}\left(\frac{c}{l}\right)^{\frac{1}{2}} V_0{}^2. \tag{3.7-6}$$

For the line in Fig. 3-7, the saturation power flow can be calculated by noting from (3.6-5) that in saturation the squared amplitude of v will be related to the squared amplitude of v_1 by

$$\frac{|V|^2}{|V_1|^2} = \frac{(l'u/\beta)^2}{r^2 + (l_1\beta + l'/\beta)^2 u^2}. \tag{3.7-7}$$

Assuming the simple volt-ampere characteristic for the NLC shown in Fig. 3-5b, the saturation power flow can be calculated from (3.7-5) as

$$\frac{P_s}{P_{sm}} = \left(1 + \frac{\tilde{g}}{g}\right)(1 + \tilde{g}r)^{\frac{1}{2}}\left(1 + \frac{l_1\tilde{g}}{rc}\right)^{\frac{3}{2}}\left[\frac{1 + (c_1/c)(1 + l_1\tilde{g}/rc)(1 + \tilde{g}r)}{1 + c_1/c}\right]^{\frac{1}{2}}, \tag{3.7-8}$$

where

$$P_{sm} = \frac{1}{2}\left(\frac{c + c_1}{l}\right)^{\frac{1}{2}} v_0{}^2 \tag{3.7-9}$$

is the maximum (low frequency) saturation power flow. Saturation power flow is determined as a function of frequency, since $\tilde{g}$ is given as a function of frequency by (3.6-17). A plot of (3.7-8) is presented in Fig. 3-8 for the

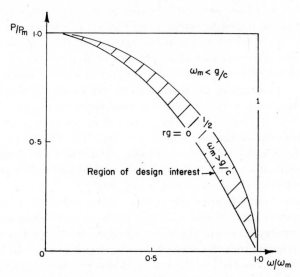

Fig. 3-8   Normalized plot of saturation power versus frequency for the line of Fig. 3-7.

case $l_1 = 0$ and $c_1 = 0$. P_s equals zero at the frequency

$$\omega_m = \frac{g}{c}\left(\frac{1}{rg} - 1\right)^{\frac{1}{2}}.$$ (3.7-10)

It is interesting to notice that for $rg < \frac{1}{2}$; the saturation power flow normalized to P_{sm} is essentially a function only of the frequency normalized to ω_m.

3.8. THE QUASIHARMONIC DISTRIBUTED OSCILLATOR [Sc6]

It is noted in the previous chapter that active transmission lines are rather difficult to stabilize; this tendency favors the application of active lines to oscillators. In the quasiharmonic approximation we can consider the oscillatory mode as a traveling wave which is reflected from the termination at the right end, travels with gain to the left end, is reflected again and finally reinforces itself with the proper gain and phase. Several interesting devices can oscillate in this manner, including the laser, the large area tunnel junction and the traveling wave tube.

We begin our examination of the distributed oscillator by considering the system shown in Fig. 3-9. This oscillator makes use of the simple transmission line shown in Fig. 3-5a. The right end of the line is terminated with a resistor, R_L, which represents the load. To the left end is connected a bias supply which, in effect, places a bias voltage of $-I_B R_B$ in series with each of the differential nonlinear conductors (NLC's). The bias resistor should be made quite small so that waves are reflected from the left hand end of the line with essentially no loss of amplitude. In a practical case it is often necessary to take the inductance of a very small resistor into consideration so a parasitic inductance, L_B, is included in series with the bias resistor.

The shunt voltage and series current amplitudes on the line are sketched in Fig. 3-9b. If R_B and L_B are zero, there will be a current maximum and a voltage minimum at the left end of the line. The line will oscillate at a frequency for which the length is just one quarter of a wavelength, for then the phase shift of a wave which travels from right end to left end and back and is reflected by the short circuit is just 360°.

In the quasiharmonic approximation we assume that the energy supplied by the negative conductance during a cycle is small compared with the oscillatory energy stored in the shunting capacitance. Since a steady state oscillation requires that the power being developed in the NLC's is equal to the power being absorbed in the load and bias resistors, the quasiharmonic assumption is essentially that the oscillation is "high Q" or sinusoidal. The

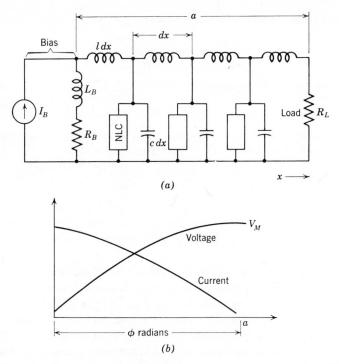

Fig. 3-9 (*a*) A simple distributed oscillator. (*b*) Voltage and current amplitude.

shunt voltage on the line can thus be taken as a sinusoidal function of time multiplied by a spatially dependent amplitude.

$$v(x, t) = V(x) \cos \omega t. \tag{3.8-1}$$

The frequency of this oscillation can be approximately determined by assuming that the circuit is lossless. All NLC's and small resistors are assumed to be zero and all large resistors, infinite. The characteristic impedance and phase constant of a traveling wave are then given by

$$Z_0 = \left(\frac{l}{c}\right)^{\frac{1}{2}}, \tag{3.8-2}$$

$$\beta = \omega\sqrt{lc}, \tag{3.8-3}$$

and the impedance looking to the right from the bias terminals in Fig. 3-9*a* is $Z_0 \coth j\beta a$. At an oscillation frequency this must be the negative of the reactance of the bias circuit, $j\omega L_B$. Thus the frequency of oscillation is given by the root of the transcendental equation

$$\frac{l}{L_B} = \omega\sqrt{lc}\,\tan{(\omega\sqrt{lc}\,a)}. \tag{3.8-4}$$

The angular length of the transmission line

$$\phi = \omega\sqrt{lc}\,a \tag{3.8-5}$$

is plotted as a function of the ratio of bias inductance L_B to total diode inductance al in Fig. 3-10. In the limiting case for which

$$\frac{L_B}{al} \ll 1, \qquad \omega = \frac{\pi/2}{a\sqrt{lc}}, \tag{3.8-6}$$

and for

$$\frac{L_B}{al} \gg 1, \qquad \omega = \frac{1}{\sqrt{L_B ca}}. \tag{3.8-7}$$

That is to say when the bias inductance is less than about $0.05al$ the oscillator is fully distributed and a quarter wave long. When $L_B > 5al$, the oscillator appears to be "lumped." The oscillation then consists of an interchange of energy between the distributed capacitance and the bias inductance.

There are two ways to calculate the steady level of oscillation. The first is to equate the power being absorbed in the load to the power being generated along the line. The voltage amplitude is ϕ radians of a cosine function with an amplitude of V_M volts at the load end as shown in Fig. 3-9b. If we assume

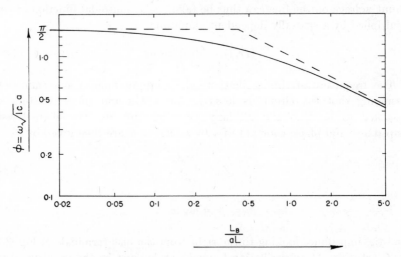

Fig. 3-10 Frequency (angular length) of the distributed oscillator versus ratio of bias inductance to distributed inductance.

the NLC to have the simple cubic volt-ampere characteristic shown in Fig. 3-5b, the total power developed on the line will be

$$P = \frac{1}{2} \int_0^a g \left(1 - \frac{V^2}{V_0^2} \right) V^2 \, dx, \qquad (3.8\text{-}8)$$

where

$$V = V_M \cos \frac{\phi x}{a}. \qquad (3.8\text{-}9)$$

The power absorbed in the load is

$$P = \frac{1}{2} \frac{V_M^2}{R_L}. \qquad (3.8\text{-}10)$$

Equating the right-hand sides of (3.8-8) and (3.8-10) gives an expression for output power which is a function of the load resistance, R_L. The output power has a maximum when the load resistance is

$$R_L|_{\max} = \frac{2}{ag} F_1(\phi) \qquad (3.8\text{-}11)$$

of

$$P|_{\max} = \frac{agV_0^2}{8} F_2(\phi), \qquad (3.8\text{-}12)$$

where

$$F_1(\phi) = \frac{2}{1 + (\sin 2\phi)/2\phi} \qquad (3.8\text{-}13)$$

and

$$F_2(\phi) = \frac{\frac{2}{3}[1 + (\sin 2\phi/2\phi)]^2}{1 + (\sin 2\phi)/2\phi + \frac{2}{3}(\cos^3 \phi \sin \phi)/\phi}$$

are plotted in Fig. 3-11.

Equations 3.8-4, 3.8-11 and 3.8-12 allow a convenient comparison of the quarter wave distributed oscillator ($L_B = 0$ and $\phi = \pi/2$) with the lumped or van der Pol oscillator ($L_B/al \gg 1$ and $\phi = 0$). Suppose two oscillators are constructed with the same total inductance, capacitance and negative conductance; but in one, these elements are distributed along a transmission line while in the other they are lumped in parallel as in Fig. 3-4. The distributed oscillator will have $\frac{2}{3}$ times the power output at $\pi/2$ times the frequency of the lumped oscillator. Maximum output power for the distributed oscillator will be developed into twice the load resistance. There is, therefore, no *disadvantage* in terms of power frequency product in distributing oscillator parameters, but rather the *advantage* of a slightly higher optimum load impedance level.

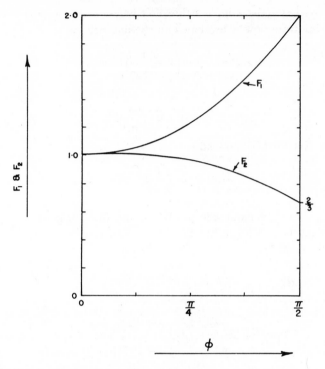

Fig. 3-11   Load resistance factor (F_1) and power output (F_2) as a function of angular length of the distributed oscillator.

3.9. THE GAIN CONDITION

A second approach to determine the steady level of oscillation is to impose the condition that the magnitude of the total gain (as the wave travels in both directions and is reflected from both ends) be unity. This *gain condition* can be written

$$|\rho_B| \, |\rho_L| \exp \left[2 \int_0^a \tilde{\alpha} \, dx \right] = 1, \tag{3.9-1}$$

where $|\rho_B|$ and $|\rho_L|$ are respectively the magnitudes of the voltage reflection coefficients at the bias and load ends, a is the length of the distributed oscillator, and $\tilde{\alpha}$ is the *effective* gain constant of a traveling wave.

We must be careful as we calculate $\tilde{\alpha}$ to consider how the growth constant of a wave traveling in one direction is affected by the presence of a wave traveling in the opposite direction. To determine this effect consider the quasiharmonic ladder line shown in Fig. 3-12 and for which

$$\tilde{z}_{se} = \tilde{r}(I^2) + j\omega l,$$

$$\tilde{y}_{sh} = \tilde{g}(V^2) + j\omega c, \tag{3.9-2a,b}$$

where

$$\tilde{r} \ll \omega l$$

and

$$\tilde{g} \ll \omega c. \tag{3.9-3a,b}$$

Quite a general system may be described in this manner since $\tilde{r}$, l, $\tilde{g}$, and c can all be functions of frequency. The dispersion equation is

$$\gamma^2 = (\tilde{r} + j\omega l)(\tilde{g} + j\omega c), \tag{3.9-4}$$

from which, to the quasiharmonic approximation of (3.9-3), the growth constant for a *solitary* wave is

$$\alpha = -\frac{1}{2}\left(\frac{\tilde{r}}{Z_0} + \tilde{g}Z_0\right). \tag{3.9-5}$$

In the quasiharmonic approximation the characteristic impedance is

$$Z_0 = \left(\frac{\tilde{r} + j\omega l}{\tilde{g} + j\omega c}\right)^{1/2} \approx \left(\frac{l}{c}\right)^{1/2}. \tag{3.9-6}$$

The power flow in a solitary wave is

$$P = \tfrac{1}{2}Z_0 I^2$$

$$= \frac{1}{2}\frac{V^2}{Z_0}, \tag{3.9-7a,b}$$

where I and V are the amplitudes of current and voltage respectively.

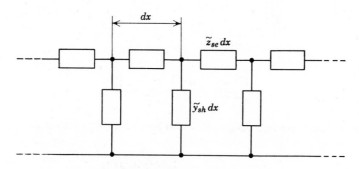

Fig. 3-12   Quasiharmonic ladder line.

The power *gain* per unit length is the *negative* of the dissipation in $\tilde{r}$ and $\tilde{g}$. Thus

$$\frac{dP}{dx} = -(\tfrac{1}{2}\tilde{r}I^2 + \tfrac{1}{2}\tilde{g}V^2) \tag{3.9-8}$$

$$= -\left(\frac{\tilde{r}}{Z_0}P + \tilde{g}Z_0 P\right)$$

$$= 2\alpha P. \tag{3.9-9}$$

Now let us suppose that we have two waves, the first traveling in the $+x$ direction

$$v_1 = V_1(x)\cos(\omega t - \beta x), \quad i_1 = I_1(x)\sin(\omega t - \beta x), \tag{3.9-10a}$$

and the second traveling in the $-x$ direction

$$v_2 = V_2(x)\cos(\omega t + \beta x), \quad i_2 = I_2(x)\sin(\omega t + \beta x). \tag{3.9-10b}$$

The voltage and current amplitudes are related by

$$V_1 = Z_0 I_1 \quad \text{and} \quad V_2 = -Z_0 I_2. \tag{3.9-11a,b}$$

The squared amplitude of the voltage with both waves present is

$$V^2 = V_1^2 + V_2^2 + 2V_1 V_2 \cos 2\beta x, \tag{3.9-12a}$$

and the squared amplitude of the current is

$$I^2 = I_1^2 + I_2^2 + 2I_1 I_2 \sin 2\beta x. \tag{3.9-12b}$$

Both waves are being amplified by the same transmission line so they will have the same effective gain constant. Thus

$$\frac{dP_1}{dx} = 2\tilde{\alpha}P_1,$$

$$\frac{dP_2}{dx} = 2\tilde{\alpha}P_2, \tag{3.9-13a,b}$$

so

$$\frac{dP_1/dx}{dP_2/dx} = \frac{P_1}{P_2} = \frac{V_1^2}{V_2^2} = \frac{I_1^2}{I_2^2}. \tag{3.9-14}$$

The power gain per unit length will still be given by (3.9-8) thus

$$\frac{dP_1}{dx} + \frac{dP_2}{dx} = -\tfrac{1}{2}[\tilde{r}I^2 + \tilde{g}V^2]. \tag{3.9-15}$$

Combining (3.9-14) with (3.9-15) and using (3.9-12) yields

$$\frac{dP_1}{dx} = -\left[\frac{\tilde{r}}{Z_0}\left(1 + \frac{2I_1I_2 \sin 2\beta x}{I_1^{\ 2} + I_2^{\ 2}}\right) + Z_0 g\left(1 + \frac{2V_1V_2 \cos 2\beta x}{V_1^{\ 2} + V_2^{\ 2}}\right)\right]P_1$$

$$= 2\tilde{\alpha}P_1. \qquad (3.9\text{-}16)$$

Therefore

$$\tilde{\alpha} = -\frac{1}{2}\left[\frac{\tilde{r}(I^2)}{Z_0}\left(1 + \frac{2I_1I_2 \cos 2\beta x}{I_1^{\ 2} + I_2^{\ 2}}\right) + Z_0 \tilde{g}(V^2)\left(1 + \frac{2V_1V_2 \cos 2\beta x}{V_1^{\ 2} + V_2^{\ 2}}\right)\right].$$

$$(3.9\text{-}17)$$

It is this value of $\tilde{\alpha}$ which must be used in (3.9-1) in order to apply the gain condition.

As a simple example consider the simple distributed oscillator of Fig. 3-9 with $L_B = R_B = 0$ so $\phi = \pi/2$. Equation 3.9-1 becomes

$$\left|\frac{R_L - Z_0}{R_L + Z_0}\right| \exp\left[2\int_0^a \tilde{\alpha}(x)\,dx\right] = 1. \qquad (3.9\text{-}18a)$$

In the quasiharmonic approximation we must have $R_L \gg Z_0$ in order not to lose a significant fraction of the stored energy during a cycle. Thus

$$\int_0^a \tilde{\alpha}(x)\,dx \approx \frac{Z_0}{R_L} = \frac{1}{R_L}\left(\frac{l}{c}\right)^{1/2}. \qquad (3.9\text{-}18b)$$

The gain constant for a *solitary* wave is given by (3.5-3)

$$\alpha = \tfrac{1}{2}g\left(\frac{l}{c}\right)^{1/2}\left(1 - \frac{V^2}{V_0^{\ 2}}\right), \qquad (3.5\text{-}3)$$

where

$$V^2 = V_M^{\ 2} \cos^2\left(\frac{\pi x}{2a}\right) = V_M^{\ 2} \cos^2\beta x.$$

If the standing wave is considered to be composed of two oppositely directed traveling waves, these must have the same amplitude. Thus from (3.9-12)

$$\tilde{\alpha} = \alpha(1 + \cos 2\beta x)$$

$$= \tfrac{1}{2}g\left(\frac{l}{c}\right)^{1/2}\left[1 - \frac{V_M^{\ 2}}{V_0}\cos^2\beta x\right](1 + \cos 2\beta x). \qquad (3.9\text{-}19)$$

Noting that $\cos^2\beta x = \tfrac{1}{2}(1 + \cos 2\beta x)$ we can write (3.9-19) as

$$\tilde{\alpha} = g\left(\frac{l}{c}\right)^{1/2}\left[\cos^2\beta x - \frac{V_M^{\ 2}}{V_0^{\ 2}}\cos^4\beta x\right]. \qquad (3.9\text{-}20)$$

Substitution of (3.9-20) into (3.9-18) yields

$$R_L ga \left(\frac{1}{2} - \frac{3}{8} \frac{V_M^2}{V_0^2} \right) = 1$$

or

$$\frac{V_M^2}{V_0^2} = \frac{4}{3} \left(1 - \frac{2}{R_L ga} \right).$$

Now the useful power delivered to the load is

$$P_L = \frac{1}{2} \frac{V_M^2}{R_L}$$

$$= \tfrac{2}{3} V_0^2 \left(\frac{1}{R_L} - \frac{2}{R_L^2 ga} \right),$$

so the optimum load resistor is

$$R_L \big|_{\text{opt}} = 4/ga,$$

for which we obtain a maximum output power of

$$P_L \big|_{\max} = \frac{gaV_0^2}{12}. \tag{3.9-21}$$

Note that these results are in agreement with (3.8-11) and (3.8-12) (for $\phi = \pi/2$) which were obtained from the power balance condition.

For a quarter wave oscillator the gain condition has no particular advantage over the power balance condition because the *shape* of the mode [i.e., $V(x)$] is known. Consider, however, the *symmetrical* system shown in Fig. 3-13a. At the series resonance of $l_1 c_1$ or at

$$\omega_1 = \frac{1}{\sqrt{l_1 c_1}} \tag{3.9-22}$$

the gain will be a maximum and the line will oscillate. In this case the gain per wavelength can still be small, satisfying the requirements of the quasi-harmonic approximation, and the mode shape can be completely unknown. Envelope functions, $V_1(x)$ and $V_2(x)$, for the forward and reverse traveling waves which constitute the mode are indicated schematically in Fig. 3-13b,c. The critical parameter is V_T or the amplitude of a traveling wave as it reaches one end. The power absorbed in one load resistor is evidently

$$P_L = \frac{1}{2} \left(\frac{c}{l} \right)^{1/2} V_T^2 (1 - |\rho|^2), \tag{3.9-23}$$

where

$$\rho = \frac{R_L - Z_0}{R_L + Z_0} \tag{3.9-24}$$

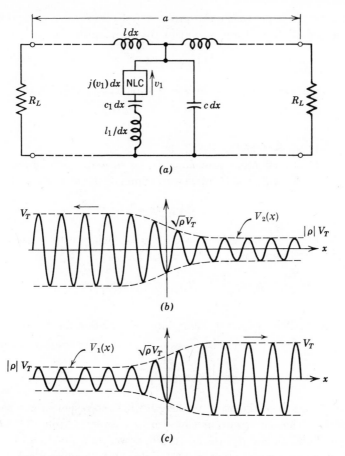

Fig. 3-13   Interaction of forward and reverse traveling waves.

is the voltage reflection coefficient at the end. From (3.9-17) the effective growth constant at ω_1 is a function of both $V_1(x)$ and $V_2(x)$

$$\tilde{\alpha} = -\tfrac{1}{2}\tilde{g}(V^2)\left(\frac{l}{c}\right)^{\!\frac{1}{2}}\left[1 + \frac{2V_1 V_2 \cos 2\beta x}{V_1{}^2 + V_2{}^2}\right]. \tag{3.9-25}$$

But V_1 and V_2 are related by $\tilde{\alpha}$ since

$$\frac{dV_1}{dx} = \tilde{\alpha}V_1 \quad \text{and} \quad \frac{dV_2}{dx} = -\tilde{\alpha}V_2, \tag{3.9-26a,b}$$

so that

$$\frac{dV_1}{V_1} + \frac{dV_2}{V_2} = 0. \tag{3.9-27}$$

Equation 3.9-27 implies that the product $V_1 V_2$ must be a constant. From our definition of V_T and ρ it is evident that this constant is

$$V_1 V_2 = |\rho| \, V_T{}^2. \tag{3.9-28}$$

We know from symmetry that at $x = 0$ V_1 is equal to V_2. Thus

$$V_1(0) = \sqrt{|\rho|} \, V_T. \tag{3.9-29}$$

These results are sketched in Fig. 3-13.

In (3.9-25) the effective gain constant, $\tilde{\alpha}$ is a function of V_1, V_2 and $\cos 2\beta x$. With the aid of (3.9-28) we can eliminate V_2 to obtain

$$\tilde{\alpha} = \tilde{\alpha}(V_1, \cos 2\beta x). \tag{3.9-30}$$

If the number of wavelengths is large, the average growth constant over a cycle can be computed as

$$\langle \tilde{\alpha} \rangle = \frac{1}{2\pi} \int_0^{2\pi} \tilde{\alpha}(V_1, \cos 2\beta x) \, d(2\beta x). \tag{3.9-31}$$

Then from (3.9-26a) we can write an integral equation for V_T as

$$\int_{\sqrt{\rho} \, V_T}^{V_T} \frac{dV_1}{\langle \tilde{\alpha} \rangle V_1} = \frac{a}{2}. \tag{3.9-32}$$

Equation 3.9-32 gives the oscillator length which corresponds to a particular value of V_T. The power output can also be calculated from (3.9-23) if V_T is known. Thus we can determine output power as a function of oscillator length by choosing appropriate values of V_T and solving both (3.9-32) and (3.9-23).

For the *nonsymmetrical* case we must define reflection coefficients, ρ_1 and ρ_2, and wave amplitudes, V_{T1}, and V_{T2}, for both ends. Equation 3.9-28 can still be derived so we have

$$V_1 V_2 = |\rho_1| \, V_{T1}{}^2$$
$$= |\rho_2| \, V_{T2}{}^2. \tag{3.9-33}$$

We do not know the wave amplitudes at $x = 0$, however, at $x = -a/2$, $V_1 = \sqrt{|\rho_1| \, |\rho_2|} \, V_{T1}$. Thus we can write an integral equation analogous to (3.9-32) in the form

$$\int_{\sqrt{|\rho_1||\rho_2|} \, V_{T1}}^{V_{T1}} \frac{dV_1}{\langle \tilde{\alpha} \rangle V_1} = a. \tag{3.9-34}$$

3.10. POWER OUTPUT LIMIT FOR A LONG QUARTER WAVE OSCILLATOR [Sc6]

The relation which has been derived for the power output of the prototype distributed oscillator (3.8-12) indicates a linear increase in maximum output power with the length of the line. It is of interest to ask how long the oscillator can be made before the power output ceases to increase. We should certainly expect when the output power calculated from (3.8-12) becomes equal to the saturation power flow for one way transmission calculated from (3.7-6) no further increase in output power will be possible.

To get a rough idea of what to expect in this situation, let us assume once again the simple prototype line of Fig. 3-9a with the cubic nonlinearity of Fig. 3-5b describing the negative conductors. Let us further assume that the amplitudes of the forward and reverse waves are approximately equal for a long line, so we can write

$$V_1 \approx V_2, \tag{3.10-1}$$

and from (3.9-18) the gain condition is

$$\frac{R_L - Z_0}{R_L + Z_0} = \exp\left[-ag\left(1 - \frac{3}{4}\frac{V_M^2}{V_0^2}\right)Z_0\right]. \tag{3.10-2}$$

For a long line we cannot assume $R_L \gg Z_0$; we will want to make $R_L \approx Z_0$ in order to draw a large amount of power. Thus we solve for V_M^2 as

$$V_M^2 = \tfrac{4}{3}V_0^2\left(\frac{1}{agZ_0}\log\frac{R_L - Z_0}{R_L + Z_0} + 1\right) \tag{3.10-3}$$

so the output power becomes

$$P_0 = P_s F\left(\frac{Z_0}{R_L}, agZ_0\right), \tag{3.10-4}$$

where

$$F = \frac{4}{3}\frac{Z_0}{R_L}\left[\frac{1}{agZ_0}\log\left(\frac{1 - Z_0/R_L}{1 + Z_0/R_L}\right) + 1\right] \tag{3.10-5}$$

and

$$P_s = \frac{1}{2}\frac{V_0^2}{Z_0} \tag{3.10-6}$$

is the saturation power flow as indicated in (3.7-6). The optimum value of R_L has been determined graphically as a function of agZ_0 and is plotted in Fig. 3-14. The value of F_{max} which corresponds to this optimum value of load resistance is plotted in Fig. 3-15.

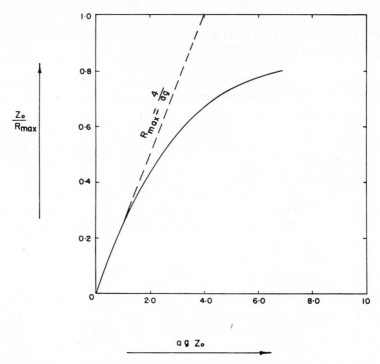

Fig. 3-14 Optimum load resistance for a long line oscillator—calculated from the quasiharmonic approximation.

The plotted curve of $F_{\max}$ versus agZ_0 has been checked experimentally [Sc 6] by measuring both the maximum oscillator power output and the saturation power flow for a tunnel diode transmission line. The quotient of these quantities is plotted versus agZ_0 in Fig. 3-15. We find fairly good agreement for

$$agZ_0 < 2. \tag{3.10-7}$$

When the line is made longer, the power output remains constant.

This difficulty is anticipated in the previous chapter. We show in (2.2-10) that if

$$a < \frac{\pi}{g}\left(\frac{c}{l}\right)^{1/2}$$

the oscillation is no longer sinusoidal, but instead it assumes the character of a multivibrator or "blocking" oscillation. To put the matter into other terms, note that since frequency is related to line length by

$$\omega\sqrt{lc}\,a = \frac{\pi}{2} \tag{3.10-8}$$

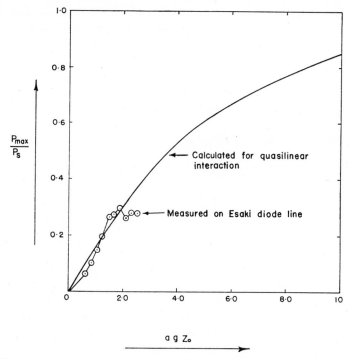

Fig. 3-15 Measured and calculated ratio of maximum oscillator power output to saturation power flow versus line length.

Equation (3.10-7) is equivalent to

$$g < \frac{4}{\pi}\,\omega c,$$

which is the quasiharmonic condition. Thus the real limit on power output for long lines of the type considered is not saturation of a traveling wave, but rather that the oscillation frequency becomes so low that the line no longer appears quasiharmonic. The concept of weakly interacting forward and reverse traveling waves then becomes a very poor approximation to reality.

3.11. MULTIMODE OSCILLATIONS [Sc17]

In Sections 8, 9 and 10 we analyze the distributed oscillator of Fig. 3-9 under the assumption that only one of the possible modes of excitation is excited. In this section we suppose that more than one mode is excited on a distributed oscillator and inquire whether there exists a set of stationary amplitudes which is stable. Our principle result is that such multimode oscillations are possible on oscillator structures with two or more spatial dimensions.

To begin let us consider a square shaped oscillator constructed from the two-dimensional unit cells shown in Fig. 3-16. In the spirit of the quasi-harmonic analysis we focus our attention on the corresponding lossless structure for which a unit cell is sketched in Fig. 3-17. This system is described by the difference differential equations

$$v_{ij} - v_{(i-1)j} = -L\frac{\partial i_{xij}}{\partial t},$$

$$v_{ij} - v_{i(j-1)} = -L\frac{\partial i_{yij}}{\partial t}, \qquad (3.11\text{-}1a,b,c)$$

$$i_{x(i+1)j} - i_{xij} + i_{yi(j+1)} - i_{yij} = -C\frac{\partial v_{ij}}{\partial t}.$$

Since the system is assumed to be linear, elementary solutions will obey Floquet's theorem [Br 7], which we write in the form

$$v_{(i+1)j} = e^{jB_x}v_{ij} \quad \text{and} \quad v_{i(j+1)} = e^{jB_y}v_{ij},$$

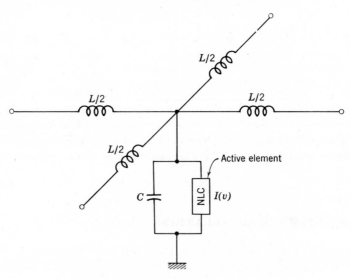

Fig. 3-16   A two dimensional unit cell.

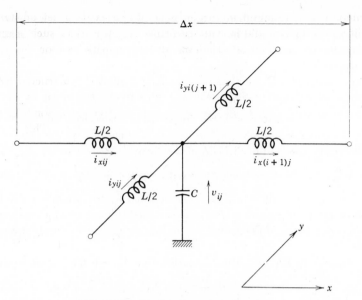

Fig. 3-17   The lossless approximation.

and likewise for the current variables. It is then not difficult to show that for time dependence of the form e^{jwt}

$$\sin^2 \left(\frac{B_x}{2} \right) + \sin^2 \left(\frac{B_y}{2} \right) = \frac{\omega^2 LC}{4}. \tag{3.11-2}$$

Equation 3.11-12 relates the phase shift per section in the x-direction (B_x) and the phase shift per section in the y-direction (B_y) to the frequency (ω) for an elementary solution on the large system.

If $\omega^2 LC \ll 1$, (3.11-2) becomes approximately

$$B_x^2 + B_y^2 \approx \omega^2 LC, \tag{3.11-3}$$

and for a section length equal to Δx (see Fig. 3-17) we can define the distributed parameters

$$\beta_x = \frac{B_x}{\Delta x}, \qquad \beta_y = \frac{B_y}{\Delta x},$$

$$l = L, \qquad c = \frac{C}{(\Delta x)^2}.$$

The dispersion equation (3.11-3) becomes in the distributed approximation

$$\beta_x^2 + \beta_y = \omega^2 lc. \tag{3.11-4}$$

The fundamental requirement which must be satisfied for this distributed approximation to be valid is that the phase shift per section be small compared with a radian. If this is the case, (3.11-1) implies the pde

$$\frac{\partial^2 v}{\partial x^2} + \frac{\partial^2 v}{\partial y^2} - lc\frac{\partial^2 v}{\partial t^2} = 0. \tag{3.11-5}$$

For a square oscillator with the edges either open circuit or short circuit (i.e., rectangular boundary conditions) the voltage of a single mode will be an elementary solution of (3.11-5) of the form

$$v = V \cos \beta_x x \cos \beta_y y \cos (\omega t + \phi), \tag{3.11-6}$$

where the allowed values of β_x and β_y are fixed by the boundary conditions and the corresponding value of ω is determined from (3.11-4). Corresponding equations for a one dimensional oscillator are obtained simply by setting $\beta_y = 0$.

We suppose in the first approximation that n such modes are excited so

$$v = v_1 \cos \theta_1 + v_2 \cos \theta_2 + \cdots + v_n \cos \theta_n, \tag{3.11-7}$$

where

$$v_i(x, y) = V_i \cos \beta_{xi} x \cos \beta_{yi} y,$$
$$\theta_i = \omega_i t + \phi_i. \tag{3.11-8a,b}$$

To determine whether several modes can be stably excited, we must calculate the average power into each mode as a function of all the mode amplitudes. We assume a volt-ampere characteristic for the active element in Fig. 3-16 of the form

$$I(v) = -G\left(v - \frac{4}{3}\frac{v^3}{V_0^2}\right), \tag{3.11-9}$$

which in the distributed approximation becomes a conduction current per unit area

$$i(v) = \frac{I(v)}{(\Delta x)^2}$$
$$= -g\left(v - \frac{4}{3}\frac{v^3}{V_0^2}\right), \tag{3.11-10}$$

where $g = G/(\Delta x)^2$.

Substitution of (3.11-7) into (3.11-10) gives an expression for the shunt conduction current per unit area which is multiply periodic in the variables θ_i. This can be expressed as the multiple Fourier cosine series

$$i(v) = I_1 \cos \theta_1 + I_2 \cos \theta_2 + \cdots + I_n \cos \theta_n$$
$$+ \text{ higher harmonics.} \tag{3.11-11}$$

In the quasiharmonic approximation we write

$$i(v) \approx I_1 \cos \theta_1 + I_2 \cos \theta_2 + \cdots + I_n \cos \theta_n \qquad (3.11\text{-}12)$$

and define for each mode an effective conductance per unit area given by

$$\tilde{g}_i = I_i / v_i. \qquad (3.11\text{-}13)$$

Assuming a square oscillator of length a on each side, the power *into* each mode will be

$$P_i = -\int_{-a/2}^{+a/2} \int_{-a/2}^{+a/2} \tfrac{1}{2} \tilde{g}_i v_i^2 \, dx \, dy. \qquad (3.11\text{-}14)$$

If we suppose that no two of the n mode frequencies [the ω_i in (3.11-8b)] have a rational ratio, it is a simple matter to substitute (3.11-7) into (3.11-10) and average to obtain the effective conductance per unit area for the first mode as

$$\tilde{g}_1 = -g\left[1 - \frac{v_1^2 + 2(v_2^2 + \cdots + v_n^2)}{V_0^2}\right]. \qquad (3.11\text{-}15)$$

The effective conductances for the other modes are obtained by rotating the indices in (3.11-15). Substitution of (3.11-15) into (3.11-14) now yields the following expression for the power into the first mode as a function of the mode amplitudes:

$$P_1 = \frac{gAV_1^2}{8}\left[1 - \frac{\tfrac{9}{8}V_1^2 + (V_2^2 + \cdots + V_n^2)}{2V_0^2}\right], \qquad (3.11\text{-}16)$$

where $A = a^2$ is the total area of the oscillator. In deriving (3.11-16) it has been assumed that β_x and β_y are different for all the excited modes.

The energy in the ith mode is related to the mode amplitude by

$$U_i = \frac{cA}{8} V_i^2. \qquad (3.11\text{-}17)$$

Furthermore the power input to a mode is the rate of change of this mode energy with time. Thus

$$\frac{dU_i}{dt} = P_i, \qquad (3.11\text{-}18)$$

and we can write

$$\frac{dU_1}{d\tau} = U_1\{1 - \alpha[\tfrac{9}{8}U_1 + (U_2 + \cdots + U_n)]\}, \qquad (3.11\text{-}19)$$

where $\tau = gt/c$ and

$$\alpha = \frac{4}{cAV_0^2}. \qquad (3.11\text{-}20)$$

For n excited modes we have a set of n equations similar to (3.11-19) for the rates of change of the mode energies as functions of the mode energies. These equations are nonlinear but autonomous. Stationary values for the energies are found by supposing

$$\frac{dU_i}{d\tau} = 0$$

for all n modes and setting

$$U_1 = U_2 = \cdots = U_n \equiv U_0.$$

Then U_0 is found to be

$$U_0 = \frac{1}{(n + \frac{1}{8})\alpha}. \tag{3.11-21}$$

This energy is a stationary value for all the modes. The stability of n modes at this stationary level can be determined by introducing small deviations in mode energy. Thus we assume that

$$U_i = U_0 + \Delta_i, \tag{3.11-22}$$

where $\Delta_i \ll U_0$. The Δ_i obey permutations of the linear differential equation

$$\frac{-1}{\alpha U_0} \frac{d\Delta_1}{d\tau} = \tfrac{9}{8}\Delta_1 + \Delta_2 + \cdots + \Delta_n. \tag{3.11-23}$$

If we assume a solution in the form

$$\Delta_i \sim \exp{(\alpha U_0 s\tau)}, \tag{3.11-24}$$

s is a root of the equation

$$\det \begin{bmatrix} z & 1 & 1 & \cdots & 1 \\ 1 & z & 1 & \cdots & 1 \\ 1 & 1 & z & \cdots & 1 \\ . & . & . & \cdots & . \\ 1 & 1 & 1 & \cdots & z \end{bmatrix} = 0, \tag{3.11-25}$$

where

$$z = s + \tfrac{9}{8}. \tag{3.11-26}$$

Equation 3.11-25 can be written in the factored form [Ho 6]

$$(z - 1)^{n-1}(z + n - 1) = 0. \tag{3.11-27}$$

Since the zeros of (3.11-27) all lie in the LHP, n-mode excitation will be stable on the square oscillator. Let us briefly recapitulate the assumptions made in deriving this result.

1. The mode frequencies are high enough so the quasiharmonic approximation is valid.

2. The modes are nonresonant; that is, "mode locking" does not occur.

3. The edges are either open circuit or short circuit (rectangular boundary conditions) so the individual modes have the sinusoidal form indicated in (3.11-6).

4. All n modes have different values of β_x and β_y.

A similar procedure may be used to determine the stability of n modes on a structure of N spatial dimensions. The characteristic equation remains as in (3.11-25) or (3.11-27) but in general (3.11-26) becomes

$$z = s + \frac{3^N}{2^{N+1}}. \tag{3.11-28}$$

Thus for two or more spatial dimensions multimode oscillation should be possible; for one dimension it should not.

A rough experimental confirmation of this result has been obtained on a 16-cell (4×4) square oscillator and a 4-cell line oscillator employing germanium Esaki diodes as the active elements. Circuit diagrams of the unit cells are shown in Fig. 3-18. These oscillators differ from the theoretical model examined above in several important respects.

1. The experimental oscillators contain relatively few elements and cannot be considered distributed for the modes of higher frequency.

2. The presence of the biasing resistor (R in Fig. 3-18) tends to reduce the effective conductance seen by the higher frequency modes.

3. The elements in the unit cells are not precisely equal; they are chosen from random samples with about 10% tolerances.

In spite of these reservations, however, it is readily demonstrated that the square oscillator can support several multimode combinations, some of which are nonresonant. The waveforms in Figs. 3-19 and 3-20, for example, were taken from an oscillator with the following element values:

$L = 10\ \mu h\ (Q = 8\ \text{at }100\ \text{kc})$,

$C = 0.068\ \mu f\ (Q = 80\ \text{at }100\ \text{kc})$ in parallel with $0.01\ \mu f$ ceramic ($Q = 300$ at 100 kc) to suppress high frequency parasitics,

T.D. $= \text{GE } 714\ (I_p = 2.2\ \text{ma})$,

$R = \frac{1}{2}$ ohm.

Two adjacent edges were short circuit and the other two open circuit. Figs. 3-19a and 3-20a are waveforms of two states measured at the corner

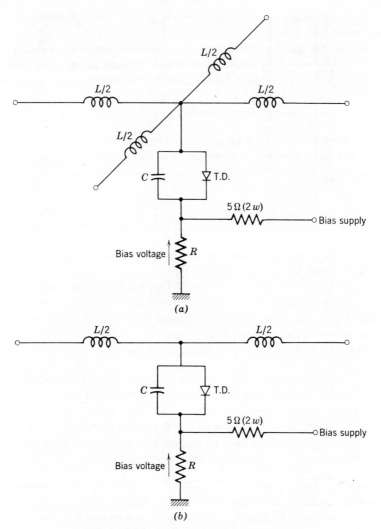

Fig. 3-18 Experimental oscillator circuits.

cell between the shorted sides. Figures 3-19*b* and 3-20*b* are corresponding Lissajous figures observed between the above mentioned vertex corner and the corner opposite. The circuit can be switched into or out of these states by "tickling" with an external audio oscillator. Figure 3-19 shows a resonant multimode oscillation and Fig. 3-20 shows a nonresonant multimode oscillation.

No such multimode or multistate phenomena has been observed on the line oscillator of Fig. 18*b* or [Sc 6].

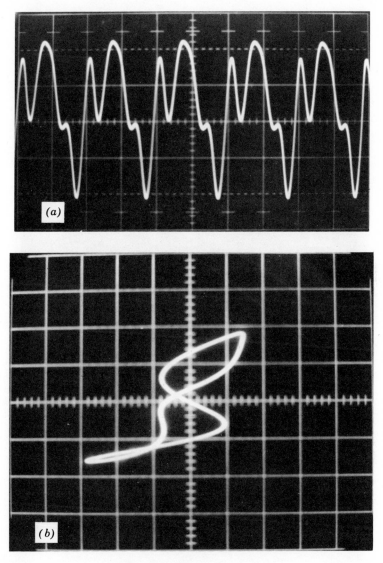

Fig. 3-19 Resonant multimode oscillation, Bias = 0.088 volts. (a) Waveform: V — 2 mv/div, H — 5 μsec/div. (b) Lissajous figure: V — 50 mv/div, H — 2 mv/div.

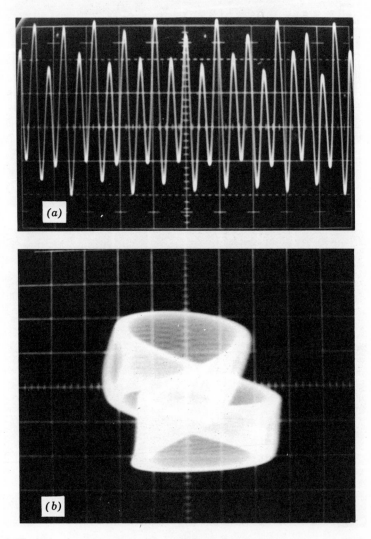

Fig. 3-20 Nonresonant multimode oscillation, Bias = 0.088 volts. (a) Waveform: V — 1 mv/div, H — 5 μsec/div. (b) Lissajous figure: V — 5 mv/div, H — 1 mv/div.

3.12. THE LASER OSCILLATOR [Os1, Sc14]

The simple laser oscillator model to be considered in this section is shown in Fig. 3-21a. Two parallel, partially reflecting mirrors with amplitude reflection coefficient ρ are separated by a distance L and filled with the four layer laser medium shown in Fig. 3-21b. The stimulated transitions in this laser medium take place between an upper level at U_2 and a lower level at U_1. The atomic population at level U_1 is assumed to be maintained at zero by rapid transition to a ground level at U_0. The notation to be used is as follows:

N_2 = number of atoms per unit volume in energy level U_2.

I_p = number of atoms pumped into energy level U_2 per unit time and per unit volume.

τ_s = lifetime for spontaneous emission of an atom in energy level U_2.

M = number of electromagnetic modes per unit volume within the frequency range of the spontaneous emission. It is equal to $8\pi f^2 \, \Delta f / c^3$ where f is the mode frequency, Δf is the band width for spontaneous emission, and c is the velocity of light in the laser medium.

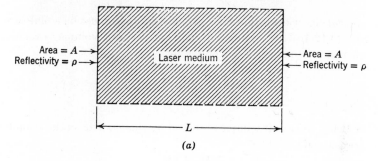

(a)

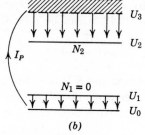

(b)

Fig. 3-21 A simple laser model.

n = number of photons per unit volume in the excited mode. It is assumed that only one electromagnetic mode is excited.

τ_p = lifetime of a photon in the laser medium.

The number of atoms per unit volume and per unit time which make spontaneous transitions from U_2 to U_1 is N_2/τ_s, and this must be equal to the total number of photons emitted per unit volume and per unit time. The fraction of this total spontaneous photon emission which is absorbed by a single mode is $N_2/\tau_s M$. Referring to (2.12-13) and noting that $N_1 = 0$ we have the interesting and important result that *the stimulated emission into a mode is equal to the spontaneous emission into that mode times the number of photons in the mode* [Sl 1, pp. 98–101]. On a per unit volume basis this implies that the stimulated emission into the excited mode is $N_2 n/\tau_s M$. Thus *rate equations* for N_2 and n can be written as

$$\frac{dN_2}{dt} = I_p - \frac{N_2}{\tau_s}\left(1 + \frac{n}{M}\right),$$

$$\frac{dn}{dt} = \frac{N_2(n+1)}{\tau_s M} - \frac{n}{\tau_p}. \tag{3.12-1a,b}$$

For *steady-state* laser operation both dN_2/dt and dn/dt must be equal to zero. Then from (3.12-1a) the stimulated emission per unit volume is related to the number of photons per unit volume by

$$\frac{N_2 n}{\tau_s M} = \frac{I_p n/M}{1 + n/M}, \tag{3.12-2}$$

so that the power per unit volume absorbed by the mode from the stimulated atomic transitions is

$$p = \frac{hfn\, I_p/M}{1 + n/M}, \tag{3.12-3}$$

where h is Planck's constant and f is the frequency. If the atomic transitions are assumed to be caused by the action of the electric field, the number of photons per unit volume in (3.12-3) can be related to the electric energy density by

$$nhf = \tfrac{1}{2}\varepsilon E^2, \tag{3.12-4}$$

where ε is the dielectric constant and E is the electric field amplitude. From (3.12-3) and (3.12-4) the power per unit volume absorbed by the mode can be expressed in terms of a negative conductivity, σ_-, as

$$p = \tfrac{1}{2}\sigma_- E^2, \tag{3.12-5}$$

where σ_- depends upon the electric field amplitude as

$$\sigma_- = \frac{\sigma_{0-}}{1 + E^2/E_0^{\,2}} , \tag{3.12-6}$$

where

$$\sigma_{0-} = \frac{\varepsilon I_p}{M} \tag{3.12-7}$$

and

$$E_0^{\,2} = \frac{2hfM}{\varepsilon} . \tag{3.12-8}$$

Note from (3.12-5) and (3.12-6) the power per unit volume absorbed by the mode in the limit of large electric field amplitude is $\frac{1}{2}\sigma_{0-}E_0^{\,2}$ which from (3.12-7) and (3.12-8) is equal to hfI_p.

We now use (3.12-6) together with the concepts outlined in Section 3.9 to calculate the efficiency of a laser oscillator. In particular we shall determine the *outside quantum efficiency* or the rate at which photons leave the laser divided by the pump rate ALI_p.

If the electric field amplitude of a wave incident on an end mirror is called E_T, the amplitude of a reflected wave is ρE_T and the power transmitted from both ends (the output power) is

$$P_0 = (1 - \rho^2)A\left(\frac{\varepsilon}{\mu}\right)^{\!1/2} E_T^{\,2}. \tag{3.12-9}$$

For a solitary wave traveling in the $+x$ direction the gain constant can be written

$$\alpha = \tfrac{1}{2}(\sigma_- - \sigma_+)\left(\frac{\mu}{\varepsilon}\right)^{\!1/2}$$
$$= \frac{1}{2}\left(\frac{\sigma_{0-}}{1 + E^2/E_0^{\,2}} - \sigma_+\right)\left(\frac{\mu}{\varepsilon}\right)^{\!1/2}. \tag{3.12-10}$$

The laser oscillation implies both a forward and a reverse wave for which the electric field amplitudes can be represented as

$$E_f = E_1(x) \cos(\beta x - \omega t),$$
$$E_r = E_2(x) \cos(\beta x + \omega t), \tag{3.12-11a,b}$$

where E_1 and E_2 are undetermined functions of x with the same general form as the voltage waves in Fig. 3-13. The total electric field amplitude is related to E_1 and E_2 by

$$E^2 = E_1^{\,2} + E_2^{\,2} + 2E_1E_2 \cos 2\beta x, \tag{3.12-12}$$

so that together with (3.9-17) the effective gain constant is

$$\tilde{\alpha} = \frac{1}{2}\sqrt{\frac{\mu}{\varepsilon}}\left[\frac{\sigma_{0-}}{1 + E^2/E_0{}^2} - \sigma_+\right]\left(1 + \frac{2E_1 E_2}{E_1{}^2 + E_2{}^2}\cos 2\beta x\right). \quad (3.12\text{-}13)$$

Just as in (3.9-28) we can show that the product of the forward and reverse wave amplitudes is the constant

$$E_1 E_2 = \rho E_T{}^2. \quad (3.12\text{-}14)$$

Equation 3.12-14 can be used to eliminate E_2 from (3.12-13) which allows us to write a single differential equation for E_1 as

$$\frac{dE_1}{dx} = \tilde{\alpha}(E_1, \cos 2\beta x)E_1. \quad (3.12\text{-}15)$$

In the quasiharmonic approximation the change in amplitude over a wave length must be by a small fraction. The $\cos 2\beta x$ dependence can therefore be removed from (3.12-15) by averaging over a wavelength with a fixed value of E_1. The result is a differential equation which involves the amplitude of E_1 alone.

$$\frac{dE_1}{dx} = E_1 \frac{\sigma_+}{2}\left(\frac{\mu}{\varepsilon}\right)^{1/2}\left\{\left(\frac{\sigma_{0-}/\sigma_+}{(E_1{}^2/E_0{}^2) + (R^2 E_T{}^4/E_0{}^2 E_1{}^2)}\right)\right.$$

$$\times \left[1 - \frac{1}{[1 + (E_1{}^2/E_0{}^2) + (R^2 E_T{}^4/E_0{}^2 E_1{}^2)^2 - (4R^2 E_T{}^4/E_0{}^4)]^{1/2}}\right] - 1\right\}$$

$$(3.12\text{-}16)$$

If we write (3.12-16) in the form

$$\frac{dE_1}{dx} = f(E_1),$$

the electric field amplitude impinging upon an end mirror is determined implicitly as a function of laser length [just as in (3.9-32)] from the integral

$$\int_{\sqrt{\rho}E_T}^{E_T} \frac{dE_1}{f(E_1)} = \tfrac{1}{2}L. \quad (3.12\text{-}17)$$

This integration has been carried out on a digital computer for several values of reflectivity and pumping level. We normalize the pumping rate to the value I_0 for which σ_{0-} in (3.12-7) is equal to σ_+. Thus

$$I_0 = \frac{M\sigma_+}{\varepsilon}. \quad (3.12\text{-}18)$$

We also normalize laser length to the value L_0 for which the threshold pumping rate is just twice the minimum value for an infinitely long laser, thus

$$L_0 = \frac{2}{\sigma_+} \left(\frac{\varepsilon}{\mu}\right)^{1/2} \log\left(\frac{1}{\rho}\right). \tag{3.12-19}$$

Furthermore we define the outside quantum efficiency to be

$$\eta_0 \equiv \frac{P_0}{A L I_p h f}, \tag{3.12-20}$$

where P_0 is determined by (3.12-9). Results of the integration of (3.12-17) are presented in Figs. 3-22 and 3-23 as plots of η_0 versus L/L_0 and I_p/I_0 for $\rho = 0.99$ and for $\rho = 0.1$. It is interesting to note that these plots are almost identical.

The results of this section have been derived using the quasiharmonic assumption. This implies that negative conduction current density in the laser medium is small compared with displacement current density or

$$\sigma_{0-} \ll 2\pi f \varepsilon. \tag{3.12-21}$$

From (3.12-7) this implies the analysis is valid only for pumping rates below.

$$I_p \ll 2\pi f M$$

$$\ll \frac{16\pi^2 \Delta f}{\lambda^3}, \tag{3.12-22}$$

where λ is the electromagnetic wavelength within the laser cavity.

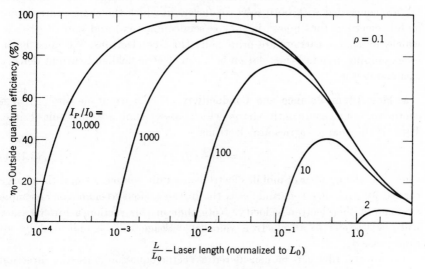

Fig. 3-22 Efficiency vs. normalized laser length ($\rho = 0.1$).

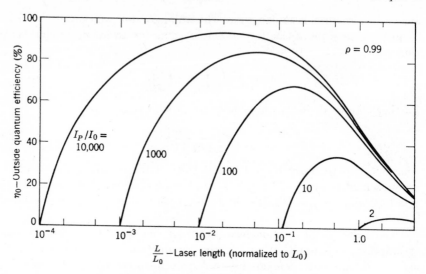

Fig. 3-23   Efficiency vs. normalized laser length ($\rho = 0.99$).

3.13. PLASMA WAVE PROPAGATION

In this section we briefly introduce some of the ideas basic to an understanding of wave propagation in a plasma. Plasma waves are essentially electromagnetic waves which are coupled to mobile charges of a conductor. We are concerned with both *solid conductors* in which the charge carriers are mobile electrons (or "holes" in p-type semiconductors) and *ionized gases* in which the charge carriers are principally the free electrons. We must begin by examining in detail the relation between electric field and current density in a conductor.

a. Momentum Balance and Conductivity.   The current density, J, in a conductor is a measure of the charge which crosses a unit area in a unit of time. Thus, if the charge carries are electrons,

$$J = n(-e)\langle v \rangle, \tag{3.13-1}$$

where n is the number of mobile electrons per unit volume, $(-e)$ is the charge carried by each electron, and $\langle v \rangle$ is the instantaneous average (or ensemble average) of the electron velocity. Note that in this section a lower case v will always refer to an electron velocity; voltage will be indicated by an upper case V.

Equation 3.13-1 can be considered a vector equation since the direction of charge flow will be in the direction of the average velocity. In order to determine the way in which current density depends upon electric field, we must investigate the dependence of average velocity upon electric field.

If no electric field is applied to a conductor, the electrons will undergo rapid random thermal motion with no average displacement as indicated in Fig. 3-24a. The direction of this motion will change abruptly as the electron collides with ions (in a gas) or with sound waves or crystalline imperfections in a solid conductor. The average time lapse between collisions is called the *collision time*, τ_c. Upon application of a steady electric field there is a relatively slow average velocity as indicated in Fig. 3-24b. The way that the average velocity depends upon electric field can be determined from the *momentum balance condition*.

$$(-e)E = \frac{m\langle v \rangle}{\tau_c} + m\frac{d\langle v \rangle}{dt} . \tag{3.13-2}$$

The term on the left-hand side of this equation is the force applied to an electron by the electric field. Since

$$\text{impulse} = \int (\text{force}) \, dt$$

is a measure of the net momentum imparted to a massive object, $(-eE)$ is the *rate* at which momentum is being supplied to each electron. Equation 3.13-2 states that this must be equal to the rate at which average momentum is being destroyed by collisions $(m\langle v \rangle / \tau_c)$ plus the rate at which the average

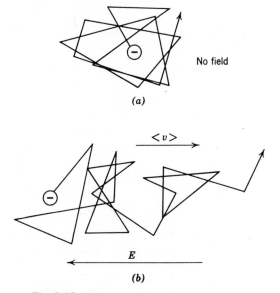

(a)

(b)

Fig. 3-24   Electron motion in a conductor.

momentum is increasing $(md\langle v\rangle/dt)$. Thus from (3.13-1) and (3.13-2) we can write the relation between current density and electric field as

$$\tau_c \frac{dJ}{dt} + J = \frac{ne^2\tau_c}{m} E. \tag{3.13-3}$$

It is customary to use the notation

$$\sigma_0 = \frac{ne^2\tau_c}{m}, \tag{3.13-4}$$

where σ_0 is the *conductivity* or the ratio of *steady* current density to *steady* electric field. By a steady electric field we mean that the percent change is small during a time τ_c. If a step of electric field (of amplitude E_1) is applied at time $t = 0$ the current density response given by (3.13-3),

$$J = \sigma_0 E_1 (1 - e^{-t/\tau_c}), \tag{3.13-5}$$

as indicated in Fig. 3-25. From a physical point of view the current density is zero at $t = 0^+$ because the electrons have not yet gained average velocity in the direction of the field. After a time of the order of τ_c a new equilibrium is established and steady current flows.

b. Plasma Oscillation.   Consider a rectilinear piece of conducting material bounded between perfect conductors as shown in Fig. 3-26*a*. The total current flow through the external terminals will be the sum of the conduction current and the displacement current. Thus

$$\frac{I}{A} = J + \varepsilon \frac{dE}{dt}, \tag{3.13-6}$$

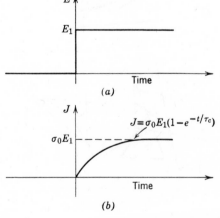

Fig. 3-25   Current response to voltage step in a conductor.

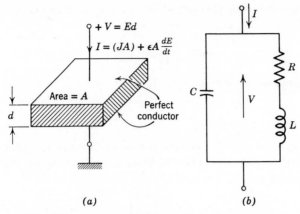

Fig. 3-26   Lumped equivalent circuit for a plasma.

where $E = V/d$ is the internal electric field. The relation between external current and voltage is given by the two equations

$$I = JA + \frac{\varepsilon A}{d}\frac{dV}{dt},$$

$$\left(\frac{\sigma_0 A}{d}\right)V = JA + \tau_c\frac{d(JA)}{dt}.$$

$$(3.13\text{-}7a,b)$$

The conductor in Fig. 3-26a can therefore be described by the equivalent circuit in Fig. 3-26b, where

$$C = \frac{\varepsilon A}{d},$$

$$R = \frac{d}{\sigma_0 A},$$

$$L = \frac{d\tau_c}{\sigma_0 A}.$$

$$(3.13\text{-}8a,b,c)$$

Figure 3-26b indicates the possibility of *plasma oscillations* which involve a pulsating interchange of energy between electrostatic energy stored in the dielectric and kinetic energy of the charge carriers. Such oscillations can take place within the bulk of the conductor. One condition for plasma oscillations to occur is that the circuit of Fig. 3-26b must be "high Q." In terms of circuit theory this requires that the inductive relaxation time

$$\frac{L}{R} = \tau_c$$

$$(3.13\text{-}9)$$

be large compared with the period of the resonant frequency or *plasma frequency*

$$\omega_p = \frac{1}{\sqrt{LC}} = \left(\frac{\sigma_0}{\tau_c \varepsilon}\right)^{1/2}. \tag{3.13-10}$$

Thus for plasma oscillations we must have

$$\tau_c \gg \frac{\varepsilon}{\sigma_0}. \tag{3.13-11}$$

Note that ε/σ_0 is the *dielectric relaxation time* or the time necessary for charge in a conductor to disperse. From (3.13-4) and (3.13-10) we can write the plasma frequency as

$$\omega_p = \left(\frac{ne^2}{\varepsilon m}\right)^{1/2}. \tag{3.13-12}$$

Another requirement for plasma oscillations to occur comes about because there is a limitation upon the rate at which the potential in a conductor can vary with distance. This effect puts a lower limit upon the *size* of the conductor in which oscillation will be observed. To see this suppose we have an infinite plasma with potential V chosen to be equal to zero where the plasma is neutral. For a gas and for a nondegenerate semiconductor the electron concentration will be related to V by the Boltzmann ratio. Thus the charge density will be

$$\rho = n(-e)(\varepsilon^{eV/kT} - 1). \tag{3.13-13}$$

This equation says the charge density due to electrons will rise above the neutralizing positive background charge (because of ions in a gas or to fixed lattice charge in a solid) by the factor $\exp(eV/kT)$. The charge density is related to the potential through Poisson's equation

$$\nabla^2 V = -\frac{\rho}{\varepsilon}. \tag{3.13-14}$$

Thus

$$\nabla^2 V = \frac{ne}{\varepsilon}(\varepsilon^{eV/kT} - 1)$$

$$\approx \frac{ne^2}{\varepsilon kT} V \quad \text{for} \quad \frac{eV}{kT} < 1 \tag{3.13-15}$$

is the differential equation which the potential must satisfy. Thus for oscillations of small amplitude ($V < kT/e$) the potential cannot change greatly in distances of the order

$$\lambda_D = \left(\frac{\varepsilon kT}{ne^2}\right)^{1/2}. \tag{3.13-16}$$

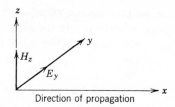

Fig. 3-27   Coordinates for TEM propagation.

This distance is called the *Debye length* for the plasma. If the dimensions of the plasma are small compared with λ_D there can be no potential variation and therefore no electric field and therefore no plasma oscillation.

c. Transverse Plasma Waves.   In the sinusoidal steady-state Maxwell's equations become

$$\text{curl } \mathbf{E} = -j\omega\mu\mathbf{H},$$
$$\text{curl } \mathbf{H} = j\omega\varepsilon\mathbf{E} + \mathbf{J}, \qquad (3.13\text{-}17a,b)$$

where from (3.13-3)

$$\mathbf{J} = \frac{\sigma_0}{1 + j\omega\tau_c} \mathbf{E}. \qquad (3.13\text{-}18)$$

We begin our consideration of wave propagation in a plasma with **TEM** waves. If we take the electric field in the y-direction, the magnetic field in the z-direction, and the x-axis as the direction of propagation (see Fig. 3-27), (3.13-7) becomes

$$\frac{\partial E_y}{\partial x} = -j\omega\mu H_z,$$

$$\frac{\partial H_z}{\partial x} = -\left(j\omega\varepsilon + \frac{\sigma_0}{1 + j\omega\tau_c}\right)E_y. \qquad (3.13\text{-}19a,b)$$

These equations can be represented by the equivalent circuit shown in Fig. 3-28.

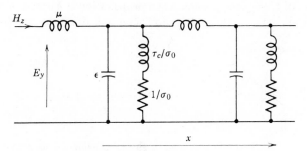

Fig. 3-28   Equivalent circuit for transverse plasma waves.

The propagation constant for the transmission system of Fig. 3-28 is of particular interest in the case $\omega\tau_c \gg 1$ for then many swings of the oscillatory excitation occur before a mobile charge is scattered out of the wave. In this case

$$\gamma^2 = j\omega\mu\left(j\omega\varepsilon + \frac{\sigma_0}{1 + j\omega\tau_c}\right) \qquad (3.13\text{-}20)$$

is approximately equal to

$$\gamma^2 \approx (j\omega)^2\mu\varepsilon\left[\left(1 - \frac{\omega_p{}^2}{\omega^2}\right) - \frac{j\omega_p{}^2}{\omega^3\tau_c}\right], \qquad (3.13\text{-}21)$$

so the real and imaginary parts of the propagation constant are

$$\alpha \approx \frac{\omega_p{}^2\sqrt{\mu\varepsilon}}{2\tau_c\omega^2\sqrt{1 - \omega_p{}^2/\omega^2}}, \qquad (3.13\text{-}22)$$

$$\beta \approx \omega\sqrt{\mu\varepsilon(1 - \omega_p{}^2/\omega^2)}. \qquad (3.13\text{-}23)$$

Equation 3.13-22 can be inverted to give

$$\omega = \left(\frac{\beta^2}{\mu\varepsilon} + \omega_p{}^2\right)^{\!\frac{1}{2}}. \qquad (3.13\text{-}24)$$

This lossless despersion relation is plotted in Fig. 3-29. The group velocity of a wave packet

$$u_g = \frac{d\omega}{d\beta}$$

$$= \frac{\beta}{\omega\mu\varepsilon} \qquad (3.13\text{-}25)$$

increases from zero where $\omega = \omega_p$ to $1/\sqrt{\mu\varepsilon}$ for $\omega \gg \omega_p$.

If a pulse of transverse plasma wave propagation is formed of component frequencies close to ω, the pulse amplitude will decay as $\exp(-\alpha x)$ or as

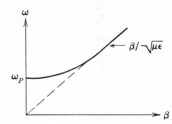

Fig. 3-29 Dispersion equation for transverse plasma waves.

$\exp\left(-\alpha u_g t\right)$. The pulse *energy* will then decay exponentially with a time constant

$$\tau = \frac{1}{2\alpha u_g}$$

$$= \frac{\omega^2}{\omega_p^2} \tau_c. \tag{3.13-26}$$

Thus the energy of a stationary plasma oscillation ($\beta = 0$ and $\omega = \omega_p$) will decay with a time constant equal to the collision time τ_c. This makes sense physically because the stationary plasma oscillation involves a periodic interchange between electric field energy and kinetic energy of the mobile charge carriers. Since *all* the energy of oscillation is kinetic energy of charge carriers at one instant of each cycle, the oscillation energy will decay at the same rate that charge carriers are scattered. At higher frequencies ($\omega > \omega_p$ and $\beta > 0$) the plasma oscillation involves a periodic interchange between electric field energy and a *combination* of the kinetic energy of charge carriers and magnetic field energy. Thus a smaller fraction of the total energy of the packet is lost upon the scattering of a charge carrier.

d. Longitudinal Plasma Waves. [Bo 3] An electromagnetic wave traveling in a vacuum or in a nondispersive dielectric medium must have the electric and magnetic fields perpendicular to the direction of propagation. If we consider electromagnetic propagation in the presence of mobile charge, a *longitudinal* electric field (i.e., an electric field in the direction of propagation) can exist and interchange energy with charge carriers moving in the direction of propagation. To investigate this phenomena we must describe the electronic motion more precisely than by an average velocity because electrons traveling with approximately the same speed as the wave will interact much more strongly with the wave than faster or slower electrons.

In order to determine the dispersion relation for constant amplitude small signal longitudinal plasma wave propagation, we shall assume a sinusoidal traveling wave potential function of the form

$$V = V_0 \cos\left[\beta(x - ut)\right]. \tag{3.13-27}$$

This is a wave with a longitudinal component of electric field ($E_x = -dV/dx$) traveling with velocity u. The potential function is sketched in Fig. 3-30 where we have used (as in Section 3.6) the notation

$$\xi = x - ut \tag{3.13-28}$$

for distance in the direction of propagation for a coordinate system moving with the wave. We shall determine the charge distribution which results from such a potential and equate it to the charge necessary to produce the

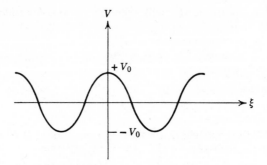

Fig. 3-30   The longitudinal potential.

potential. This "self consistant field" requirement yields the dispersion relation for longitudinal waves.

The velocity of an electron in laboratory coordinates is called v. The velocity of an electron with respect to the wave is then

$$v' = v - u. \tag{3.13-29}$$

The kinetic energy of an electron in the wave coordinates is then given by

$$\tfrac{1}{2}m(v')^2 = eV + \text{const}$$

or

$$(v')^2 - (v_0')^2 = \frac{2e}{m} V, \tag{3.13-30}$$

where v_0' is the velocity of the electron in wave coordinates at points at which $V(\xi) = 0$.

There are two ways that the potential wave can accumulate electric charge.

1. *Electron trapping.* An electron will be "trapped" in a peak of the sinusoidal potential function if $(v')^2 < 0$ when $V(\xi) = -V_0$. Thus the condition for trapping is

$$(v_0')^2 < \frac{2e}{m} V_0. \tag{3.13-31}$$

This electron trapping will contribute to growth or decay of the wave amplitude. To see this let us define $nf(v)\,dv$ to be the number of electrons per unit volume with x component of velocity in the range v to $v + dv$. Then the wave propagation will be active if $f(v)$ is an increasing function of v (for $v = u$) because more electrons which are traveling faster than the wave will be trapped than are traveling slower than the wave. Thus the wave will receive a net gain of kinetic energy. Conversely, if $f(v)$ is a decreasing function of v (for $v = u$) net energy will be lost because of trapping. Evidently a non-equilibrium velocity distribution is required for active wave propagation as indicated in Fig. 3-31. We will neglect this effect for the moment and concentrate our attention upon the other mechanism by which the wave accumulates charge, namely by

2. *Slowing of Electrons.* The electrons are slowed down near the troughs of the potential function [from (3.13-30)] so there the electron density will be higher. The number of electrons per unit volume will be inversely proportional to particle speed. Thus if dn is the number of electrons per unit volume with wave coordinate velocity between v' and $v' + dv'$

$$dn = \frac{v_0'}{v'} nf(v') \, dv'$$

$$= \frac{nf(v) \, dv}{\sqrt{1 + 2eV(\xi)/m(v_0')^2}} \, . \tag{3.13-32}$$

The total charge density at any point is equal to $+ne$ (the positive ion or lattice charge) *minus* the total electronic charge of

$$e \int dn,$$

thus

$$\rho(\xi) = ne\left[1 - \int_{-\infty}^{\infty} \frac{f(v) \, dv}{\sqrt{1 + 2eV(\xi)/m(v_0')^2}}\right]. \tag{3.13-33}$$

This charge density must support the potential $V(\xi)$ through Poisson's equation,

$$\frac{d^2V}{d\xi^2} = -\rho/\varepsilon. \tag{3.13-34}$$

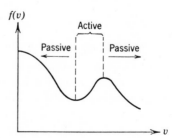

Fig. 3-31 Active range of velocity distribution.

In the small signal case we assume

$$\frac{2eV}{m(v_0')^2} \ll 1,$$

so that

$$\int_{-\infty}^{\infty} \frac{f(v)\,dv}{\sqrt{1 + 2eV/m(v_0')^2}} \approx 1 - \frac{eV}{m}\int_{-\infty}^{\infty} \frac{f(v)\,dv}{(v_0')^2}.$$

Then Poisson's equation (3.13-34) becomes

$$\frac{d^2V}{d\xi^2} = -\left(\frac{ne^2}{\varepsilon m}\right)V\int_{-\infty}^{\infty} \frac{f(v)\,dv}{(v-u)^2}. \qquad (3.13\text{-}35)$$

This is a linear propagation equation for V with a sinusoidal solution as was originally assumed. Noting the definition of the plasma frequency (3.13-12) and also from (3.13-27) that

$$\frac{d^2V}{d\xi^2} = -\beta^2 V,$$

Equation 3.13-35 becomes

$$\beta^2 = \omega_p{}^2 \int_{-\infty}^{\infty} \frac{f(v)\,dv}{(v-u)^2}.$$

Since $u = \omega/\beta$, this is the *dispersion relation*

$$\frac{\omega^2}{\omega_p{}^2} = \int_{-\infty}^{\infty} \frac{f(v)\,dv}{(1 - v/u)^2}. \qquad (3.13\text{-}36a)$$

Neglecting the trapped electrons is equivalent to assuming $f(u) = 0$ so we can make the series expansion

$$\frac{\omega^2}{\omega_p{}^2} = \int_{-\infty}^{\infty}\left(1 + 2\frac{v}{u} + 3\left(\frac{v}{u}\right)^2 + \cdots\right)f(v)\,dv. \qquad (3.13\text{-}36b)$$

Now by definition,

$$\int_{-\infty}^{\infty} f(v)\,dv = 1. \qquad (3.13\text{-}37)$$

For an isotropic plasma medium

$$\int_{-\infty}^{\infty} v f(v)\,dv = 0. \qquad (3.13\text{-}38)$$

Also,

$$\int_{-\infty}^{\infty} v^2 f(v)\,dv = \langle v^2 \rangle, \qquad (3.13\text{-}39)$$

the mean square velocity in the x-direction. For a classical electron gas

$$\langle v^2 \rangle = \frac{kT}{m}. \tag{3.13-40}$$

By arguments similar to those advanced for (3.13-38) and (3.13-39) we can also write

$$\int_{-\infty}^{\infty} v^3 f(v)\, dv = 0, \tag{3.13-41}$$

$$\int_{-\infty}^{\infty} v^4 f(v)\, dv = \langle v^4 \rangle. \tag{3.13-42}$$

In evaluating (3.13-36) we shall neglect the fourth order term which means we are assuming

$$\frac{5\beta^4}{\omega^4} \langle v^4 \rangle \ll 1$$

or

$$\frac{\beta^4}{\omega^4} \langle v^2 \rangle^2 \ll 1. \tag{3.13-43}$$

The dispersion relation (3.13-36) can then be written

$$\frac{\omega^2}{\omega_p{}^2} \approx 1 + \frac{3\beta^2}{\omega^2} \langle v^2 \rangle. \tag{3.13-44}$$

The approximation (3.13-43) which was made in order to truncate the series of (3.13-36) at the second term implies that $3\beta^2\langle v^2\rangle/\omega^2 \ll 1$ or $\omega^2 \approx \omega_p{}^2$. Thus (3.13-44) can be written finally as

$$\boxed{\omega^2 \approx \omega_p{}^2 + 3\langle v^2 \rangle \beta^2.} \tag{3.13-45}$$

This dispersion relation is only valid for a small range of frequency slightly greater than ω_p as indicated in Fig. 3-32. This appears at first to be a rather severe restriction. That it is not can be seen by writing the inequality of

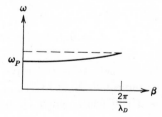

Fig. 3-32 Dispersion equation for longitudinal waves.

(3.13-43) for a classical gas as

$$\frac{\beta^2}{\omega_p^2} \frac{kT}{m} \ll 1,$$

which implies that

$$\lambda \gg \lambda_D,$$

where λ_D is the Debye length given by (3.13-16). For wavelengths smaller than the Debye length plasma propagation will not be possible because the potential function cannot change over a distance smaller than λ_D. Thus our dispersion relation (3.13-45) is valid over just the range of wavelengths for which propagation will occur.

We have so far ignored trapping and scattering which introduce gain and loss mechanisms and have investigated only the effect of slowing of electrons by a sinusoidal potential function. A self consistent field requirement has given (3.13-45) the dispersion relation for constant amplitude propagation.

e. Gain and Loss Mechanisms for Longitudinal Plasma Waves [Bo 3].   We now consider how to generalize (3.13-45) to take gain and loss mechanisms into account. One gain mechanism is associated with the trapping of electrons by the potential wave and is positive or negative as df/dv is positive or negative. Losses will also arise because of electron scattering just as for transverse plasma waves.

Our previous assumption that no trapping occurs is equivalent to the assumption that $f(v)$ is equal to zero in the vicinity of $v = u$. We can put the matter somewhat more precisely by dividing $f(v)$ into two components as

$$f(v) = f_1(v) + f_2(v), \tag{3.13-46}$$

where

$$f_1 = f(v) \quad \text{and} \quad f_2 = 0 \quad \text{for} \quad \begin{cases} v < u - \left(\dfrac{2eV_0}{m}\right)^{1/2} \\[2ex] v > u + \left(\dfrac{2eV_0}{m}\right)^{1/2} \end{cases}$$

and

$$f_1 = 0, f_2 = f(v) \text{ for } u - \sqrt{2eV_0/m} < v < u + \sqrt{2eV_0/m}.$$

Here $\sqrt{2eV_0/m}$ is the wave system velocity below which trapping occurs as indicated by (3.13-31). The development of (3.13-45) assumed that $f_1(v)$ is a sufficiently good approximation to $f(v)$ for calculation of the charge density due to slowing of electrons. If we now include consideration of the electrons being trapped, (3.13-36a) becomes

$$\frac{\omega^2}{\omega_p^{\,2}} = u^2 \int_{-\infty}^{\infty} \frac{f_1 \, dv}{(v-u)^2} + u^2 \int_{-\infty}^{\infty} \frac{f_2 \, dv}{(v-u)^2}$$

$$\approx 1 + \frac{3\beta^2}{\omega_p^{\,2}} \langle v^2 \rangle + u^2 \int_{-\infty}^{\infty} \frac{f_2 \, dv}{(v-u)^2}. \tag{3.13-47}$$

Thus we wish to evaluate the integral

$$\int_{-\infty}^{\infty} \frac{f_2 \, dv}{(v-u)^2} = -\left. \frac{f_2}{v-u} \right|_{-\infty}^{\infty} + \int_{-\infty}^{\infty} \frac{f_2' \, dv}{v-u}.$$

The second term of this integration by parts is from the definition of f_2

$$\int_{-\infty}^{\infty} \frac{f_2' \, dv}{v-u} = \int_{u-\sqrt{2eV_0/m}}^{u+\sqrt{2eV_0/m}} \frac{f_2' \, dv}{v-u}. \tag{3.13-48}$$

If we consider that $f_2 = f$ over a circular region in the complex v-plane which includes the restricted limits of integration of (3.13-48) (see Fig. 3-33), then the integral of (3.13-48) will be just $\frac{1}{2}$ of the integral around a complete circular path just within the shaded region. By Cauchy's integral theorem, however, this is just equal to $2\pi j f'$. Since $f_2'(u) = f'(u)$ (3.13-47) becomes

$$\frac{\omega^2}{\omega_p^{\,2}} = 1 + \frac{3\beta^2}{\omega_p^{\,2}} \langle v^2 \rangle + j\pi f' u^2. \tag{3.13-49}$$

The second and third terms on the right hand side of this equation are both

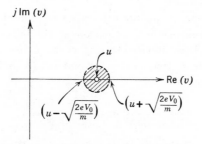

Fig. 3-33   Integration of (3.13-48).

assumed small compared with unity so we can write

$$\frac{\omega}{\omega_p} \approx 1 + \frac{3}{2}\frac{\beta^2}{\omega_p^2}\langle v^2 \rangle + j\frac{\pi}{2}f'u^2 \qquad (3.13\text{-}50a)$$

or

$$\frac{s}{\omega_p} = -\frac{\pi}{2}f'(u)u^2 + j\left(1 + \frac{3}{2}\frac{\beta^2}{\omega_p^2}\langle v^2 \rangle\right). \qquad (3.13\text{-}50b)$$

To include the effects of electron scattering we need only recall that longitudinal plasma waves oscillate only at $\omega \approx \omega_p$ and, as previously noted, this involves an energy interchange between electrostatic energy and kinetic energy of the charge carriers. Thus the energy of the oscillation will decay as $\exp(-t/\tau_c)$ or the amplitude as $\exp(-t/2\tau_c)$. This effect can be included in (3.13-50) by adding $j/2\tau_c$ to the frequency. The result is

$$\frac{s}{\omega_p} = -\left[\frac{\pi}{2}\frac{\omega_p^2}{\beta^2}f'(u) - \frac{1}{2\omega_p\tau_c}\right] + j\left[1 + \frac{3}{2}\frac{\beta^2}{\omega_p^2}\langle v^2 \rangle\right] \qquad (3.13\text{-}51)$$

Thus the condition for a growing oscillation is

$$f' > \frac{\beta^2}{\pi\omega_p^3\tau_c}. \qquad (3.13\text{-}52)$$

Evidently this condition will be more difficult to satisfy as the wavelength becomes shorter.

One way to obtain the nonequilibrium electron velocity distribution necessary for active wave propagation (see Fig. 3-31) is to shoot an electron beam into the plasma. In this case we can consider the plasma and the beam separately in the integration of (3.13-36a) to obtain the dispersion relation [La 3]

$$\omega^2 = \omega_p^2\left(1 + \frac{3\beta^2}{\omega^2}\langle v^2 \rangle\right) + \frac{\omega_b^2}{(1 - \beta v_b/\omega)^2} \qquad (3.13\text{-}53)$$

Here ω_b is the plasma frequency calculated for the electrons of the beam alone and v_b is the velocity of the electrons in the beam.

For a system of two interpenetrating electron beams with velocities v_1 and v_2 and with plasma frequencies ω_1, and ω_2, (3.13-36a) indicates immediately the dispersion relation

$$\frac{\omega_1^2}{(\omega - \beta v_1)^2} + \frac{\omega_2^2}{(\omega - \beta v_2)^2} = 1. \qquad (3.13\text{-}54)$$

f. Quasiharmonic Estimate of the Saturation Wave Amplitude [Bo 2, Bo 3].   We now estimate the level to which the amplitude of a longitudinal plasma wave can grow. This estimate is made by balancing the rate at which energy is received from the electrons being trapped and the rate at which energy is lost due to electron scattering. This is essentially a quasiharmonic calculation for we suppose a sinusoidal potential wave to be propagating with the dispersion relation given by (3.13-45).

As discussed previously (3.13-31), an electron is trapped by the potential wave when its velocity lies within the range

$$(v - u)^2 < \frac{2eV_0}{m}, \tag{3.13-31}$$

where u is the wave velocity. If we assume that the trapped electron will eventually move with the wave velocity, it must give up an energy of

$$\tfrac{1}{2}m(v^2 - u^2) = \frac{m}{2}(v - u)(v + u)$$

$$\approx mu(v - u). \tag{3.13-55}$$

In the steady state the rate at which electrons are trapped must equal the rate at which they are scattered due to collisions. In the velocity range between v and $v + dv$ this rate is

$$\frac{nf(v)\,dv}{\tau_c}.$$

Thus the steady state power input to the wave (per unit volume)

$$P_T = \int_{u-\sqrt{2eV_0/m}}^{u+\sqrt{2eV_0/m}} mu(v - u)\frac{nf(v)}{\tau_c}\,dv. \tag{3.13-56}$$

By writing $f(v)$ as a Taylor series about $v = u$

$$f(v) = f(u) + (v - u)f'(u) + \tfrac{1}{2}(v - u)^2 f''(u) + \cdots, \tag{3.13-57}$$

and assuming that the contribution to (3.13-33) of the second (and higher) order terms can be neglected

$$P_T = \frac{2}{3}\frac{munf'(u)}{\tau_c}\left(\frac{2eV_0}{m}\right)^{3/2}. \tag{3.13-58}$$

The steady state rate at which energy per unit volume is lost through collisions is equal to the energy density divided by the collision time. The energy density is

$$\tfrac{1}{2}\varepsilon E^2 = \tfrac{1}{2}\varepsilon\beta^2 V_0^2,$$

so that the power loss per unit volume is

$$P_c = \frac{1}{2} \frac{\varepsilon \beta^2 V_0^2}{\tau_c}.$$
(3.13-59)

Equating P_T and P_c gives for the saturation wave amplitude

$$V_0\Big|_{\text{sat}} = \frac{128}{9} \frac{mu^6}{e} (f'(u))^2.$$
(3.13-60)

This amplitude is proportional to the square of $f'(u)$ so the saturation power flow will be proportional to the fourth power of $f'(u)$.

Suppose now that the plasma density *decreases* in the direction of propagation. The simple dispersion relation

$$\beta^2 = \frac{(\omega^2 - \omega_p^2)}{3\langle v^2 \rangle}$$
(3.13-45)

indicates that for a constant frequency of excitation both the wavelength $(2\pi/\beta)$ and the wave velocity (ω/β) will decrease in the direction of propagation. We have here the possibility of trapping high velocity electrons and forcing them slowly to give *all* their energy to the wave as the wave slows down. Under these conditions the energy given up by an electron would be approximately $mu^2/2$ so the wave would absorb energy at the rate

$$P_T \approx \frac{mu^2 nf(u)}{\tau_c} \left(\frac{2eV_0}{m}\right)^{1/2}.$$
(3.13-61)

Equating this to the rate of energy loss because of collisions [P_c in (3.13-59)] gives an amplitude

$$V_0 = \frac{2m}{e} \left(u^4 f(u)\right)^{2/3}.$$
(3.13-62)

Since the amplitude is proportional to $f^{2/3}$, this situation should be important for low density plasmas. This effect has been suggested as a possible cause of the high acceleration of cosmic ray particles [Bo 2].

PROBLEMS

1. Will the high frequency parasitic inductance (capacitance) postulated in Fig. 3-1 *always* represent magnetic (electric) energy storage?
2. Verify (3.2-8).

3. For the series loaded tank circuit of Fig. P3-1 where $v(i)$ is given by (3.1-2) assume that quasiharmonic analysis is appropriate.
   (a) Find the differential equation for the slowly varying current amplitude.
   (b) What are the requirements on the b_i's for quasiharmonic analysis to be valid?
   (c) What is a sufficient condition on the b_i's for a nonzero oscillation of stationary amplitude?

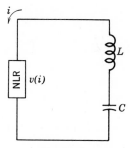

Fig. P3-1

4. In the circuit of Fig. P3-1 assume that the coefficients describing the NLR are
   $$b_0 = b_2 = b_4 = \text{etc} = 0,$$
   $$b_1 = -R, b_3 = +\tfrac{4}{3}R/3!, b_5 = -\tfrac{8}{5}R/5!, b_7 = +\tfrac{64}{35}R/7! \text{ etc.}$$

   (a) Find all of the oscillations of stationary amplitude.
   (b) Which of these oscillations of stationary amplitude are unstable?

5. Assume that the NLC shown in Fig. 3-1a is connected in shunt with a bias current source equal to I_B as indicated in Fig. P3-2.
   (a) Sketch the new characteristic which appears between terminals a–a'.
   (b) How are the Taylor series coefficients for the new characteristic related to those for the original NLC?

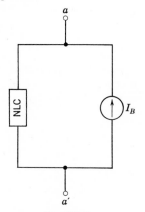

Fig. P3-2

6. Repeat Problem 5 for the three bias arrangements indicated in Fig. P3-3.

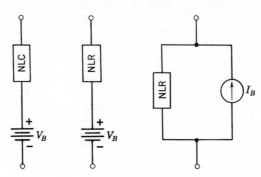

Fig. P3-3

7. Discuss with the aid of sketches the effect of the following:
   (a) putting a resistor in series with an NLR.
   (b) putting a resistor in shunt with an NLR.
   (c) putting a resistor in shunt with an NLC.
   (d) putting a resistor in series with an NLC.

8. What is a simple way to tell whether an NLC or an NLR contains internal energy sources?

9. Show that the effective conductance for the $I(v)$ characteristic shown in Fig. P3-4 is

$$\tilde{G} = G\left(1 - \frac{4}{\pi}\frac{V_0}{V}\right).$$

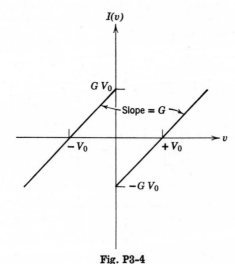

Fig. P3-4

10. Demonstrate by direct integration of (3.2-22) that (3.2-23) is the solution.

11. State requirements for validity of the quasiharmonic analysis in terms of restrictions on the positions of natural frequencies in the s-plane.

12. For the nonlinear tank circuit shown in Fig. P3-5 the inductor has a flux which is related to the current i by

$$\Phi = L_0(i + \tfrac{4}{3}bi^3),$$

and the capacitor has a charge which is related to the voltage v by

$$Q = C_0(v - \tfrac{4}{3}av^3).$$

(a) What are the requirements on a, b, and the current and voltage amplitudes for quasiharmonic analysis to be valid.

(b) Use quasiharmonic analysis to calculate the resonant frequency as a function of the voltage amplitude.

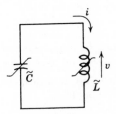

Fig. P3-5

13. Use quasiharmonic analysis to calculate the resonant frequency of a pendulum as a function of the maximum angle. Over what range of angle amplitude do you expect this expression to be useful?

14. Suppose for the simple nonlinear transmission line of Fig. 3-5a that the shunt current per unit length is given by

$$j(v) = -g\left[v - \frac{4/3}{3!}v^3 + \frac{8/5}{5!}v^5 - \frac{64/35}{7!}v^7 + \cdots \text{etc}\right].$$

(a) Find all the stationary amplitudes for traveling waves.

(b) Which of these stationary solutions are unstable.

15. For the active nonlinear transmission of Fig. P3-6 the distributed current is given by

$$j(v) = -gv\left(1 - \frac{4}{3}\frac{v^2}{V_0^2}\right).$$

Use the condition $\alpha = 0$ to find the amplitude of v which corresponds to a saturated traveling wave as a function of the excitation frequency, ω.

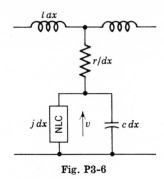

Fig. P3-6

16. Use the results of Section 2.6 to show that the gain per section of a traveling wave in a quarter wave oscillator of N sections will increase over that for the fully distributed case in the ratio

$$\frac{A}{a} = \sec\frac{\pi}{4N}.$$

17. How will the frequency times maximum power output of a lumped quarter wave oscillator depend upon the number of sections?

18. Show that a laser of length L_0 given in (3.12-19) has just twice the threshold pump level for an infinitely long laser.

19. Show from (3.12-17) that $\eta_0 \to 1$ as $L/L_0 \to 0$ and $I_p/I_0 \to \infty$.

20. Show that the condition for nonresonant multimode stability in an N-dimensional oscillator of the type described in Section 3.11 is

$$\frac{3^N}{2^{N+1}} > 1.$$

21. Plot the current density response to (a) a unit impulse of electric field, (b) a unit ramp.

22. Calculate the electron densities in gaseous plasmas necessary for plasma frequencies of 3 kmc, 10 kmc and 35 kmc. Assuming one electron per ion and an ion temperature of $300°K$, find the corresponding pressures. Assuming an electron temperature sufficient to ionize hydrogen (kT/e is 13.5 electron volts), determine the corresponding Debye lengths.

23. The conduction electron density in a metal is about 10^{23} per cm^3. Calculate the plasma frequency (use the free electron mass for the conduction electrons). Over what range of collision times will plasma effects be observed?

24. Conduction electrons in the semiconductor indium antimonide (InSb) have an "effective mass" of about 0.013 times the free electron mass. Calculate and sketch the plasma frequency as a function of electron concentration between 10^{16} and 10^{19} per cm^3.

25. Sketch the attenuation constant for transverse electromagnetic propagation over a range from $\omega\tau_c \ll 1$ to $\omega\tau_c \gg 1$.

26. Show that only transverse waves are allowed for electromagnetic propagation in a nondispersive dielectric.

27. Assuming τ_c to be infinite, what is the partial differential equation satisfied by E_y and H_z for transverse plasma wave propagation?

28. The differential equation obtained in Problem 27 is often called the "Klein-Gordon" equation. It was suggested shortly after the development of wave mechanics as the simplest differential equation which (upon being quantized) yields particles obeying special relativity. The relation between energy and momentum from relativity theory is

$$E = \sqrt{p^2 c^2 + m_0{}^2 c^4}.$$

(a) "Quantize" the dispersion relation for the equation of Problem 27 by substituting $E/\hbar$ for ω and $p/\hbar$ for β.
(b) What is the rest mass of a "transverse plasmon?"
(c) What physical interpretation can you give to this result?

29. What is the group velocity of a longitudinal plasma wave? How does it depend upon temperature?

30. For a Maxwellian velocity distribution over v (velocity in the direction of propagation)

$$f(v) = \left(\frac{m}{2\pi kT}\right)^{\!\frac{1}{2}} e^{-mv^2/2kT},$$

show that the dispersion relation for longitudinal plasma waves becomes

$$s = \omega_p \left[\frac{1}{8\pi} \frac{\lambda^2 u}{\lambda_D{}^2} f(u) + \frac{1}{2\omega_p \tau_c} \right] + j\omega_p \left(1 + \frac{3}{2} \frac{kT}{m} \frac{\beta^2}{\omega_p{}^2} \right).$$

31. Show from the stability criteria of Chapter II that the dispersion relation for the double electron stream (3.13-54) indicates instability. Is this instability absolute or convective?

32. Discuss the physical origin of each term in (3.13-51).

33. Bohm and Gross [Bo 2] suggest that the high energy of cosmic ray particles may be due to acceleration of ions in the low density plasmas of intergalactic space. Assuming the growth is because of propagation in the direction of decreasing plasma density, estimate the limiting voltage amplitude of the wave and the corresponding particle energy. Make the calculations for electrons and hydrogen ions with a density of 1 per cm^3 and a mean thermal energy of 5 electron volts.

IV

NONLINEAR ACTIVE PROPAGATION

As the frequency of excitation of a nonlinear line is decreased, it eventually becomes unrealistic to assume lossless propagation in the first approximation with energy exchange mechanisms included as a small perturbation. The quasiharmonic assumption is then no longer valid, and the range of possible behavior of the line is greatly enhanced. There is necessarily a corresponding increase in the difficulty of analyzing such a line. The engineer should view this difficulty optimistically as the price one must pay for the understanding of transmission lines with enlarged design possibilities. The human brain, which is perhaps the most impressive example of electrochemical technology, makes extensive use of transmission lines (the nerve axons) which are not at all quasiharmonic.

In this chapter we shall be primarily concerned with techniques for determining possible "waves of permanent profile" which travel with constant shape and velocity. There are many physical examples of this phenomena

165

including propagation on the dynamite fuse, the candle, the grass fire, traveling domains in a Gunn diode, the neuristor (or artificial nerve axon), and, of course, the nerve axon itself. The analytic approach is essentially to take advantage of the translational symmetry of the system in order to reduce the number of independent variables from two to one. Partial differential equations are then reduced to ordinary differential equations which can be solved in the phase space of the dependent variables. Since this approach leans heavily upon the classical techniques of phase space solutions for ordinary differential equations, these techniques are briefly reviewed in Sections 4.1 through 4.4.

4.1. VAN DER POL'S EQUATION AGAIN
[An 1, ch. 1; Mi 6, ch. 4; Po 2]

Let us begin by considering again the simple nonlinear oscillator of Fig. 4-1*a* without making the quasiharmonic approximation. The state of the system is exactly described by the voltage across the capacitor and the current through the inductor which in turn must obey the ordinary differential equations

$$\frac{di}{dt} = \frac{v}{L},$$

$$\frac{dv}{dt} = -\frac{i + I(v)}{C}. \tag{4.1-1a,b}$$

These equations are nonlinear if the shunting conductance $I(v)$ is nonlinear. To obtain an exact solution we can consider (v, i) to be a *position vector* or *phase point* in a *v-i phase plane* and interpret (4.1-1) as an expression for the *velocity vector* $(dv/dt, di/dt)$ of the phase point as a function of its position in the phase plane. At any point in the phase plane (4.1-1) implies that a solution path or *trajectory* must have the slope

$$\frac{di}{dv} = \frac{-v(C/L)}{i + I(v)}, \tag{4.1-2}$$

which is a unique function of (v, i). It is then a relatively simple matter to sketch directions for the trajectories and to determine the nature of possible solutions.

For example let us take $I(v)$ to be the active nonlinear conductance indicated in Fig. 4-1*b*. Then for $v = 0$ the trajectories must all be horizontal from (4.1-2) and from (4.1-1*b*) they will be directed in the $-v$-direction for i positive and in the $+v$-direction for i negative. Similar considerations

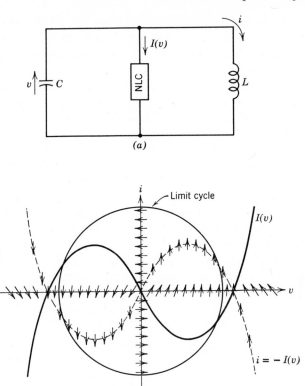

Fig. 4-1 Simple van der Pol oscillator.

indicate vertical trajectories along the (dotted) curve $i + I(v) = 0$. Along the v-axis ($i = 0$) and the slope is $-v/I$ which is also easily sketched. Thus very rapidly it is possible to gain a qualitative appreciation for the form of the solution trajectories. Note in particular if the initial condition is that v and/or i are very large, the solution trajectory winds inward with increasing time. On the other hand, if the initial condition is $v = i = 0$, the solution trajectory winds outward. Both solutions approach in an asymptotic manner a *limit cycle* shown in Fig. 4-1b which in turn describes the *steady state oscillation* of the system.

The key property of (4.1-1) which permits the construction of solutions in the manner described above is that the derivatives dv/dt and di/dt are independent of time. A set of first order ordinary differential equations for which the derivatives are not functions of the independent variable are said to be *autonomous*. Evidently the solution of equations which are not autonomous is considerably more difficult to effect. It is also important that the nonlinear element $I(v)$ is a *single valued* function of the phase plane variable v. If the NLC were in series with the inductor, its voltage would be a multi-valued function of the inductor current and a phase plane of several layers would be necessary.

4.2. MULTIDIMENSIONAL PHASE SPACE SYSTEMS

It is a straightforward matter to apply these techniques to the general nonlinear circuit shown in Fig. 4-2. Here we have singled out the energy storage elements and exhibited them at terminals external to the "nonlinear constraint without energy storage." This nonlinear constraint is simply all the rest of the system excluding the energy storage elements. We can immediately define a phase space for the vector $(v_1, \ldots, v_n, i_1, \ldots, i_m)$. Note that the dimension of this phase space is just equal to the number of energy storage elements for which the energy can be independently specified. An analysis of the nonlinear constraint will then permit calculation of the current through the capacitors and the voltage across the inductors. We

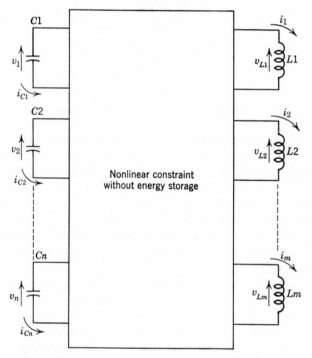

Fig. 4-2   A system with many degrees of freedom.

suppose the capacitors can be described as charges $Q_i(v_i)$ which are single-valued functions of voltages as indicated by (3.4-1). Then if i_{Ci} is the current through one of these capacitors,

$$\frac{dv_i}{dt} = \frac{i_{Ci}}{dQ_i/dv_i}.$$ (4.2-1)

Likewise if the inductors can be described as fluxes which are single valued functions of their currents,

$$\frac{di_i}{dt} = \frac{v_{Li}}{d\Phi/di_i}.$$ (4.2-2)

Thus the velocity vector $(dv_1/dt \cdots dv_n/dt, di_1/dt \cdots di_m/dt)$ can be calculated as a function of the position in phase space. This function will be *unique* if the nonlinear constraint gives the capacitor currents and inductor voltages $(i_{C1}, \ldots, i_{Cn}, v_{L1}, \ldots, v_{Lm})$ as a *single-valued function* of the capacitor voltages and inductor currents $(v_1, \ldots, v_n, i_1, \ldots, i_m)$. The resulting system of equations will then be autonomous.

4.3. PROPERTIES OF THE PHASE SPACE [Hu 3]

For the systems described in the previous sections we found that the state of a system could be described by specifying the instantaneous values of phase space coordinates and the velocity of the phase point could then be calculated. With certain restrictions on the properties of the system this phase space velocity is a unique function of position. We can then think of the phase space as being described by the allowed trajectories of the phase point. Evidently no trajectories can cross if velocity is a unique function of position, that is, if the system is autonomous.

As we have already noted in Fig. 4-1*b*, the phase space can have *limit cycles* which correspond to oscillatory behavior of the system. Limit cycles may be either *stable* if the system will return to the limit cycle after a small perturbation or *unstable* if a small perturbation from the limit cycle will grow with time.

Also of interest are *singular points* at which the velocity vector is equal to zero. These points evidently correspond to stationary behavior of the system and again can be classified as stable or unstable depending upon whether a small perturbation decays or grows with time. The singular points can be further classified in terms of the behavior of trajectories in the vicinity of the point. To see this let us consider first the phase plane. We can for convenience, transform the origin to the singular point and expand in a Taylor series as

$$\frac{dv}{dt} = av + bi + \text{higher order terms,}$$

$$\frac{di}{dt} = cv + di + \text{higher order terms,}$$

or in vector notation

$$\frac{d}{dt}\begin{bmatrix} v \\ i \end{bmatrix} \approx \begin{bmatrix} a & b \\ c & a \end{bmatrix} \times \begin{bmatrix} v \\ i \end{bmatrix}, \tag{4.3-1}$$

where we have written the position vector (v, i) as a column vector

$$(v, i) \equiv \begin{bmatrix} v \\ i \end{bmatrix}. \tag{4.3-2}$$

Now let us suppose that the position vector varies with time as

$$(v, i) = [V \exp (st), I \exp (st)]. \tag{4.3-3}$$

Equation 4.3-1 becomes

$$\begin{bmatrix} (a - s) & b \\ c & (d - s) \end{bmatrix} \times \begin{bmatrix} V \\ I \end{bmatrix} = 0, \tag{4.3-4}$$

which is only satisfied for nonzero values of V and I if

$$\det \begin{bmatrix} a - s & b \\ c & d - s \end{bmatrix} = 0, \tag{4.3-5a}$$

or

$$\frac{b}{a - s} = \frac{d - s}{c}, \tag{4.3-5b}$$

or

$$s_+ \cdot s_- = \tfrac{1}{2}[(a + d) \pm \sqrt{(a + d)^2 - 4(ad - bc)}]. \tag{4.3-5c}$$

For each of the roots of (4.3-5), the ratio of V to I must be chosen such that (4.3-4) is satisfied. Thus we can define for $s = s_+$

$$\frac{V}{I} \equiv Z_+$$

$$= \frac{b}{s_+ - a} = \frac{s_+ - d}{c}, \tag{4.3-6a}$$

and for $s = s_-$

$$\frac{V}{I} \equiv Z_-$$

$$= \frac{b}{s_- - a} = \frac{s_- - d}{c}. \tag{4.3-6b}$$

From (4.3-5c) we can write

$$Z_+, Z_- = \frac{1}{2c}\left[(a - d) \pm \sqrt{(a + d)^2 - 4(ad - bc)}\right]. \tag{4.3-7}$$

Thus, if s_+ and s_- are a complex conjugate pair, Z_+ and Z_- will also be a complex conjugate pair.

A general trajectory in the vicinity of a singular point will therefore be the linear combination

$$(v, i) = \left(V_+ e^{s_+ t} + V_- e^{s_- t}, \frac{V_+}{Z_+} e^{s_+ t} + \frac{V_-}{Z_-} e^{s_- t}\right). \tag{4.3-8}$$

For s_+ and s_- real we can therefore consider the vector (v, i) to be composed of a "+ component" along the direction specified by (4.3-6a) which varies as $\exp(s_+ t)$, and a "− component" along the direction specified by (4.3-6b) which varies as $\exp(s_- t)$. If s_+ and s_- have positive (negative) sign then all trajectories will be directed away (toward) the origin as is illustrated in Fig. 4-3a. This singularity is called an unstable (stable) *node*. If s_+ and s_- have opposite signs, the component of (v, i) along the Z_+ direction will increase with time while the component along the Z_- direction will decrease with time. This singularity is called a *saddle point* and is illustrated in Fig. 4-3b.

If s_+ and s_- are the complex conjugate pair

$$s_+, s_- = \sigma_0 \pm j\omega_0.$$

v and i will be of the form

$$v \sim e^{\sigma_0 t} \cos(\omega_0 t),$$

$$i \sim e^{\sigma_0 t} \cos(\omega_0 t + \phi).$$

This trajectory winds outward (inward) from (to) the origin if σ_0 is positive (negative). The singularity is called an *unstable* (stable) *focus* and is illustrated in Fig. 4-3c. For $\sigma_0 = 0$ the singularity has a family of closed cycles in its vicinity. It is then called a *center* and is illustrated in Fig. 4-3d. Detailed behavior depends upon the higher order terms.

For higher dimensional phase spaces the classification of singularities becomes more difficult. For a three dimensional vector equation corresponding to (4.3-1) with a cubic characteristic equation corresponding to (4.3-5),

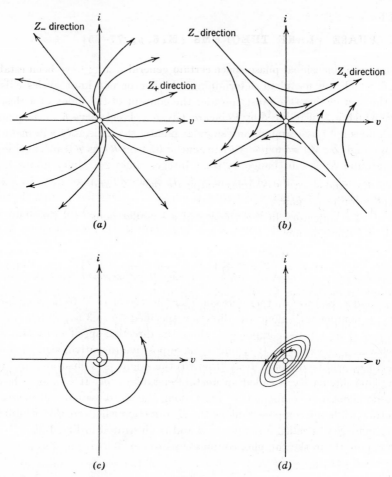

Fig. 4-3 Trajectories near a phase plane singularity: (*a*) node, (*b*) saddle, (*c*) focus, (*d*) center.

the following singular points can be defined according to the roots of the cubic [Ha 13, pp. 44–45; Me 2].

1. *Node.* Three roots real with the same sign.

2. *Saddle point.* Real roots but not of the same sign.

3. *Focal point.* One real root and a c.c. pair with real parts all of the same sign.

4. *Saddle focus.* One real root with opposite sign as the real part of a c.c. pair.

5. *Center.* Real root zero and imaginary pair; detailed behavior depends upon higher order terms.

4.4. PHASE PLANE THEOREMS [Mi 6, pp. 77–85]

In the two dimensional phase space certain general results have been established which are useful in determining whether or not limit cycles exist. For the first of these we must consider the concept of the index of a closed curve which was introduced by Poincaré. Given a closed curve K in the plane which does not pass through any singular points, the trajectory will make a certain angle θ with a tangent to K at each point on K. As a point is moved once around K, θ will change by some integer times 2π. Unity minus this integer is called the *index* of the curve K. It is not difficult to show by construction that (a) the index is zero if K contains no singular points, (b) the index is $+1$ if K contains a focus, a node or a center, and (c) the index is -1 if K contains a saddle point. Thus in general the index of a curve K is

$$\text{index } (K) = N + F + C - S, \tag{4.4-1}$$

where N, F, C and S are the number of nodes, foci, centers and saddle points enclosed, respectively. If the phase plane has a closed trajectory, an intuitively obvious but most useful result is that the index of the closed trajectory must equal $+1$. Thus a closed trajectory or limit cycle must surround at least one singular point.

We now discuss a criterion for the nonexistence of limit cycles which was established by Bendixson. Consider the general two dimensional autonomous system

$$\frac{dv}{dt} = F_1(v, i), \qquad \frac{di}{dt} = F_2(v, i). \tag{4.4-2}$$

By Green's theorem (i.e., the divergence theorem in two dimensions) the integral of $(\partial F_1/\partial v + \partial F_2/\partial i)$ over a region of the plane bounded by the curve K is

$$\int_{\substack{\text{surface enclosed by } K}} \left(\frac{\partial F_1}{\partial v} + \frac{\partial F_2}{\partial i} \right) dv\, di = \oint_K (F_1\, di - F_2\, dv). \tag{4.4-3}$$

But if the curve K is a closed trajectory or limit cycle

$$\oint_K (F_1\, di - F_2\, dv) = \oint \left(\frac{dv}{dt}\frac{di}{dt} - \frac{di}{dt}\frac{dv}{dt} \right) dt = 0.$$

Thus *Bendixson's negative criterion* can be summarized by the

Statement. *If the expression $(\partial F_1/\partial v + \partial F_2/\partial i)$ does not change sign or vanish identically within a region of the phase plane, that region has no closed trajectory.*

Finally we have the Poincaré-Bendixson theorem which is recorded without proof as the

Statement. *If a trajectory remains in a finite region of the phase plane without approaching any singularities, it is either a closed trajectory or approaches such a trajectory.*

4.5. WAVES OF PERMANENT PROFILE

We now turn our attention to an investigation of a nonlinear transmission line for which the quasiharmonic approximation is not appropriate. In general the line will be described by a set of nonlinear partial differential equations which can be very difficult to solve in detail. The process of solution can be simplified, however, by seeking solutions of a certain form or character. One set of special solutions are, of course, the stationary solutions for which $\partial/\partial x = 0$ and $\partial/\partial t = 0$. These correspond to *equilibrium states* of the transmission line.

Another and more interesting class of special solutions are the *waves of permanent profile* which propagate with constant velocity and unchanging shape. For steady propagating waves the dynamical variables will be functions only of the argument $(x - ut)$ where u is an *assumed* velocity of propagation. If we denote this argument by

$$\xi = x - ut, \tag{4.5-1}$$

the partial derivatives will be related by

$$\frac{\partial}{\partial x} = \frac{d}{d\xi} = -\frac{1}{u}\frac{\partial}{\partial t}. \tag{4.5-2}$$

Thus the original partial differential equations in the independent variables x and t can be reduced to ordinary differential equations in the variable ξ. The solutions to these ordinary differential equations, if they exist at all, will be possible modes of steady propagation. Note carefully that the ordinary differential equations depend parametrically upon the assumed velocity u.

As an elementary example of the application of this technique consider the simple telegraph line of Fig. 1-1. The partial differential equations are $\partial v/\partial x = -(l)\,\partial i/\partial t$ and $\partial i/\partial x = -(c)\,\partial v/\partial t$ or

$$\frac{\partial^2 v}{\partial x^2} = lc\,\frac{\partial^2 v}{\partial t^2}. \tag{4.5-3}$$

Upon substitution of (4.5-2) this reduces to the simple condition that $u^2 = 1/lc$ for an *arbitrary* waveform. In more complex situations we will find that only particular waves of permanent profile are allowed.

We can consider (4.5-1) to imply that we have transformed our spatial coordinate system to one which is moving with respect to the wave medium. The solutions which we seek are *stationary in the moving coordinate system.* Thus this analytic technique is sometimes called dynamic steady state (dss) analysis and the resulting waves of permanent profile are sometimes called dss solutions [Sc 3, Sc 13].

4.6. THE SIMPLE AUTONOMOUS TRANSMISSION LINE

Consider now the nonlinear transmission system shown in Fig. 4-4. The shunt current per unit length is the sum of a conductive current $j(v)$ amps/meter and a capacitive current $dQ(v)/dt = c(v)\,dv/dt$ amps/meter where $c(v) = dQ/dv$ is a differential nonlinear capacitance. Likewise the series voltage per unit length is the sum of a resistive voltage $w(i)$ V/meter and an inductive voltage $l(i)\,di/\partial t$ V/m where $l(i) = d\Phi/di$. The partial differential equations which describe the line are therefore

$$\frac{\partial v}{\partial x} = -w(i) - l(i)\frac{\partial i}{\partial t},$$

$$\frac{\partial i}{\partial x} = -j(v) - c(v)\frac{\partial v}{\partial t}. \tag{4.6-1}$$

Upon substitution of (4.5-2) these become the ordinary differential

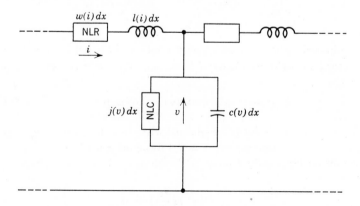

Fig. 4-4 The simple autonomous transmission line.

equations which determine possible modes of steady propagation

$$\frac{dv}{d\xi} = -w(i) + ul(i)\frac{di}{d\xi},$$

$$\frac{di}{d\xi} = -j(v) + uc(v)\frac{dv}{d\xi},$$

or

$$\frac{dv}{d\xi} = -\frac{w(i) + uj(v)l(i)}{1 - u^2l(i)c(v)},$$

$$\frac{di}{d\xi} = -\frac{j(v) + uw(i)c(v)}{1 - u^2l(i)c(v)}. \tag{4.6-2a}$$

Equations 4.6-2a are evidently autonomous nonlinear differential equations the solutions for which will be facilitated by taking advantage of the phase plane techniques discussed in the first four sections of this chapter. We shall sometimes refer to this phase space as "ξ-space." Let us consider first the asymptotic behavior in the vicinity of a singular point. We translate the singular point to the origin and expand in the Taylor series as

$$\frac{dv}{d\xi} = av + bi + \text{higher order terms},$$

$$\frac{di}{d\xi} = cv + di + \text{higher order terms}, \tag{4.6-2b}$$

where

$$a = -\frac{ul\,dj/dv}{1 - u^2lc}, \qquad b = -\frac{dw/di}{1 - u^2lc},$$

$$c = -\frac{dj/dv}{1 - u^2lc}, \qquad d = -\frac{uc\,dw/di}{1 - u^2lc} \tag{4.6-3}$$

are all evaluated at the singular point under consideration. For behavior of the vector (v, i) of the form $\exp(\gamma\xi)$ in the vicinity of the singular point, γ must satisfy

$$\gamma^2 - (a + d)\gamma + (ad - bc) = 0. \tag{4.6-4}$$

The singularity is a node for the roots real with the same sign, a saddle point. for the roots real with opposite sign, and a focus for complex conjugate roots.

The condition for a saddle point is therefore $ad - bc < 0$ or from (4.6-3)

$$\frac{1}{1 - lcu^2}\left(\frac{dj}{dv}\right)\left(\frac{dw}{di}\right) > 0. \tag{4.6-5}$$

Since the singularities of (4.6-2) occur only at points in the v-i phase plane where $j(v)$ and $w(i)$ are both equal to zero, these singularities correspond to equilibrium states of the line; that is, enough steady series current is flowing so the series voltage is zero and enough steady shunt voltage is present so the shunt current per unit length is zero. Equation 4.6-5 says that if the product of the differential series resistance and the differential shunt conductance is positive for an equilibrium state and if $u\sqrt{lc} < 1$, the corresponding singularity in the phase plane will be saddle point. But if $c(v)$ is positive at a particular *stable* equilibrium state, dj/dv must also be positive; otherwise a shunt voltage instability with temporal variation as $\exp(-tc^{-1}\,dj/dv)$ would develop. Likewise if $l(i)$ is positive, dw/di must be positive at a stable equilibrium state of the line. These considerations can be summarized by the following

Statement. *If both the differential capacitance and the differential inductance are positive at a stable equilibrium state of the system in Fig. 4-4 and if $u\sqrt{lc} < 1$, the corresponding singularity of (4.6-2) in the v-i phase plane is a saddle point.*

All of the phase plane trajectories correspond to waves of permanent profile, but on a uniform transmission line which is infinite in extent only those waves which are *bounded* will correspond to physically realizable solutions. Thus our attention will be focused upon two types of trajectories: (a) *closed cycles* which correspond to waves which are *periodic functions* of ξ and (b) *open trajectories* which emerge from one singular point at large negative values of ξ and proceed toward (possibly) another as ξ approaches $+\infty$ and which correspond to the propagation of a *localized disturbance* representing a transition from one equilibrium to another.

It is convenient that stable equilibrium states correspond to saddle points in the ξ-plane for it will usually allow us to fix a definite value for pulse velocity. Consider, for example, the situation shown in Fig. 4-5 where the singular points are saddle points. As the *assumed* value of u is changed, the trajectories change. There is a particular value of u for which one of the trajectories leaving ① becomes a trajectory approaching ② and this is the velocity at which a dss transition between these singular points is possible. It is important to notice in Fig. 4-5 that a trajectory which leaves ① at $\xi = -\infty$ and approaches ② as $\xi \to +\infty$ represents a temporal transition from state ② to state ①. This is evident from (4.5-1) since $t \to +\infty$ as $\xi \to -\infty$.

Several possible trajectory configurations in the ξ-plane are sketched in Fig. 4-6 and the corresponding waveforms on the transmission line are shown in Fig. 4-7. Figure 4-6a indicates a family of closed trajectories which implies

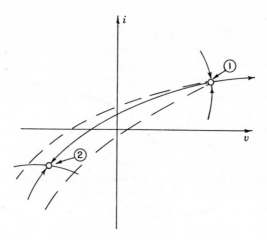

Fig. 4-5   Connection of two saddle points by a trajectory for a unique value of assumed propagation velocity.

the family of periodic waves shown in Fig. 4-7a. This situation arises on lossless nonlinear lines and will be considered more in detail in the following chapter. Figure 4-6b indicates isolated closed trajectories or limit cycles which correspond to the isolated periodic traveling wave in Fig. 4-7b. Finally Fig. 4-6c indicates a temporal transition from state ② to state ①. The corresponding pulse voltage waveform is shown in Fig. 4-7c.

Note in Fig. 4-6b that the limit cycle ② is *unstable* because neighboring trajectories diverge as $t \to +\infty$ and as $\xi \to -\infty$. Cycle ① on the other hand is *possibly* stable since neighboring trajectories converge as $t \to +\infty$ ($\xi \to -\infty$). However it is extremely important to remember that investigation of trajectories in ξ-space cannot yield sufficient conditions for stability of the corresponding dss waveforms. This is because we are primarily concerned with stability of the original partial differential equations (4.6-1) and in ξ-space we have only information related to the dss equations (4.6-2). There is a vast range of possible non dss solutions to (4.6-1) (bumps that grow and flutter and wiggle) which could contribute to instability. We shall consider this problem in more detail in Section 4.10.

It may be well to close this section with a simple, concrete example of the system shown in Fig. 4-4. Consider the long tunnel diode junction of Fig. 4-8a with a distributed bias supply of j_B amps per meter and the nonlinear junction current of $j_d(v)$ amps per meter. The corresponding equivalent circuit is shown in Fig. 4-8b where r is a constant series resistance per unit length, c is a constant shunt capacitance of the junction per unit length and the total nonlinear shunt current per unit length is $j(v) = j_d(v) - j_B$. The

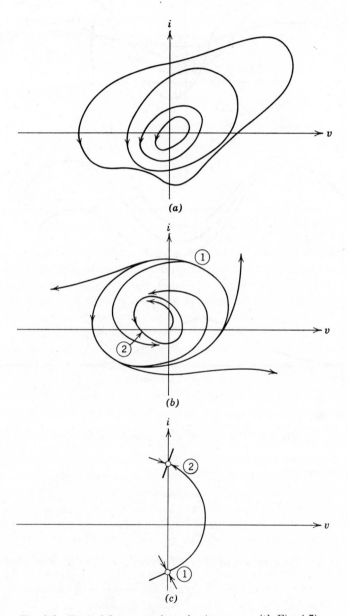

Fig. 4-6 Typical ξ-space trajectories (compare with Fig. 4-7).

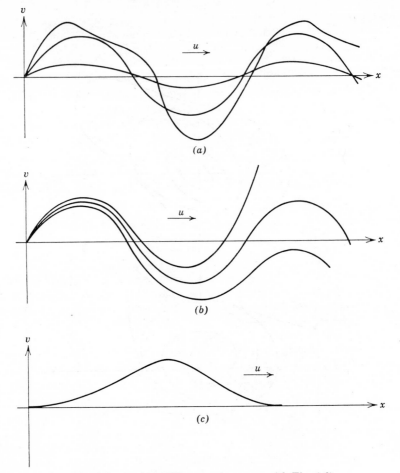

Fig. 4-7   Typical DSS waves (compare with Fig. 4-6).

pd equations are

$$\frac{\partial v}{\partial x} = -ri,$$

$$\frac{di}{\partial x} = -j(v) - c\frac{\partial v}{\partial t},$$

(4.6-6a,b)

and with the substitution of (4.5-2) the corresponding dss equations are

$$\frac{dv}{d\xi} = -ri,$$

$$\frac{di}{d\xi} = -j(v) - rcui.$$

(4.6-7a,b)

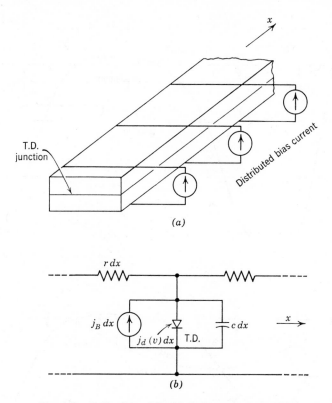

Fig. 4-8   A distributed Esaki diode transmission line.

The nature of the trajectories for various values of assumed propagation velocity are sketched in Fig. 4-9. There are three singular points at which both i and $j(v)$ are equal to zero. The roots of (4.6-4) in the neighborhood of these singular points are

$$\gamma_{1,2} = \frac{rcu}{2}\left[-1 \pm \left(1 + \frac{4r\,dj/dv}{(rcu)^2}\right)^{1/2}\right] \tag{4.6-8}$$

Thus points ① and ③ for which $dj/dv > 0$ are saddle points while ② is an inward node or focus for $dj/dv < 0$. The *inward* node or focus evidently corresponds to an *unstable* bias state of the line because $t \to +\infty$ as $\xi \to -\infty$.

As the assumed propagation velocity, u, is increased, the trajectories develop as shown in Fig. 4-9. A possible solution of (4.6-6) is determined by finding the value of u for which a trajectory proceeds from ① to ③ as ξ goes from $-\infty$ to $+\infty$. This solution represents a pulse which discharges the line from its stable equilibrium in the high voltage region ③ to its stable equilibrium in the low voltage region ①.

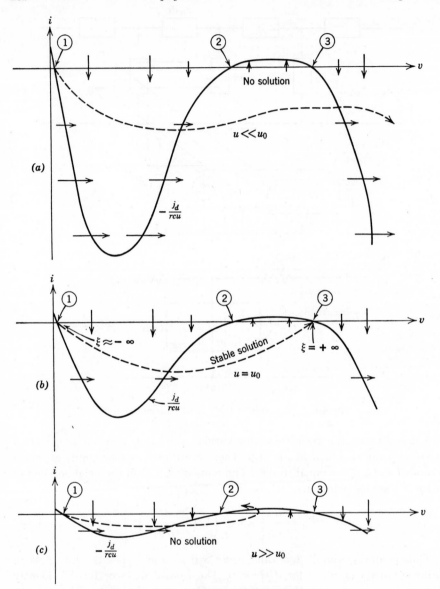

Fig. 4-9 ξ-space trajectories for line of Fig. 4-8.

4.7. THE GENERAL AUTONOMOUS LADDER LINE

In this section we will briefly consider the generalization of the previous results to the nonlinear ladder line shown in Fig. 4-10a. Both the series and shunt elements are supposed to consist of an arbitrary number of possibly

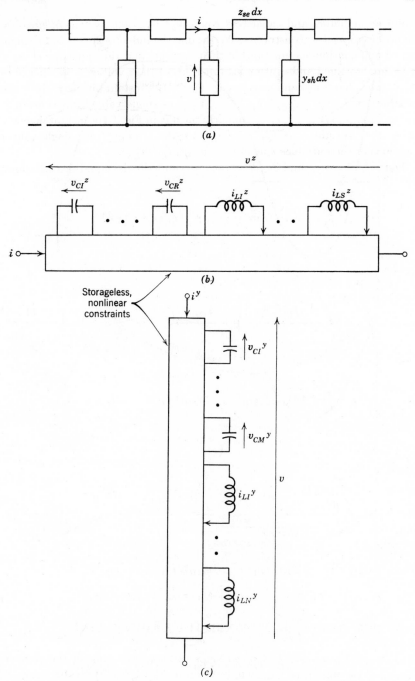

Fig. 4-10 (a) A general nonlinear ladder line, (b) z_{se}, (c) y_{sh}.

nonlinear inductors and capacitors connected by some system of possibly nonlinear storageless constraints. We assume the inductor fluxes to be single valued and continuous functions of their currents and the capacitor charges to be single-valued and continuous functions of their voltages. Furthermore we assume that the nonlinear box in Fig. 4-10b instantaneously gives the variables $v^z, i_{C1}{}^z, \ldots, i_{CR}{}^z, v_{L1}{}^z, \ldots, V_{LS}{}^z$ as single-valued functions of i, $v_{C1}{}^z, \ldots, v_{CR}{}^z, i_{L1}{}^z, \ldots, i_{LS}{}^z$. Similarly the box in Fig. 4-10c instantaneously gives the variables $i^y, i_{C1}{}^y, \ldots, i_{CM}{}^y, v_{L1}{}^y, \ldots, v_{LN}{}^y$ as single-valued functions of the variables $v, v_{C1}{}^y, \ldots, v_{CM}{}^y, i_{L1}{}^y, i_{LN}{}^y$.

Since $\partial i_i / \partial t = v_i / l_i$ and $\partial v_i / \partial t = i_i / c_i$, we can write dss equations as follows

$$\frac{dv_{C1}{}^z}{d\xi} = f_1(i, v_{C1}{}^z, \ldots, v_{CR}{}^z, i_{L1}{}^z, \ldots, i_{LS}{}^z)$$

.

.

.

$$\frac{dv_{CR}{}^z}{d\xi} = f_R(i, v_{C1}{}^z, \ldots, v_{CR}{}^z, i_{L1}{}^z, \ldots, i_{LS}{}^z) \qquad (4.7\text{-}1)$$

$$\frac{di_{L1}{}^z}{d\xi} = f_{R+1}(i, v_{C1}{}^z, \ldots, v_{CR}{}^z, i_{L1}{}^z, \ldots, i_{LS}{}^z)$$

.

.

.

$$\frac{di_{LS}{}^z}{d\xi} = f_{R+S}(i, v_{C1}{}^z, \ldots, v_{CR}{}^z, i_{L1}{}^z, \ldots, i_{LS}{}^z),$$

and

$$\frac{dv_{C1}{}^y}{d\xi} = g_1(v, v_{C1}{}^y, \ldots, v_{CM}{}^y, i_{L1}{}^y, \ldots, i_{LN}{}^y)$$

.

.

.

$$\frac{dv_{CM}{}^y}{d\xi} = g_M(v, v_{C1}{}^y, \ldots, v_{CM}{}^y, i_{L1}{}^y, \ldots, i_{LN}{}^y)$$

$$\frac{di_{L1}{}^{y}}{d\xi} = g_{M+1}(v, v_{C1}{}^{y}, \ldots, v_{CM}{}^{y}, i_{L1}{}^{y}, \ldots, i_{LN}{}^{y}) \qquad (4.7\text{-}2)$$

$$\vdots$$

$$\frac{di_{LN}{}^{y}}{d\xi} = g_{M+N}(v, v_{C1}{}^{y}, \ldots, v_{CM}{}^{y}, i_{L1}{}^{y}, \ldots, i_{LN}{}^{y}).$$

Then since $\partial v / \partial x = -v^{z}$,

$$\frac{dv}{d\xi} = f_{R+S+1}(i, v_{C1}{}^{z}, \ldots, v_{CR}{}^{z}, i_{L1}{}^{z}, \ldots, i_{LS}{}^{z}); \qquad (4.7\text{-}3)$$

and since $\partial i / \partial x = -i^{y}$,

$$\frac{di}{d\xi} = g_{M+N+1}(v, v_{C1}{}^{y}, \ldots, v_{CM}{}^{y}, i_{L1}{}^{y}, \ldots, i_{LN}{}^{y}). \qquad (4.7\text{-}4)$$

Thus in general a set of autonomous equations can be written for the capacitor voltages, the inductor currents and the line voltage and current. In the case where the shunt element has a series *linear* capacitor

$$\frac{di}{d\xi} = cu\,\frac{dv_{C1}{}^{y}}{d\xi}, \qquad (4.7\text{-}5)$$

and one of the variables $v_{C1}{}^{y}$ or i is redundant. Likewise if the series element has a shunt *linear* inductor

$$\frac{dv}{d\xi} = lu\,\frac{di_{L1}{}^{z}}{d\xi}, \qquad (4.7\text{-}6)$$

and again either v or $i_{L1}{}^{z}$ is redundant.

These considerations can be summarized by the

Statement. *The number of independent, autonomous, dss equations describing the system of Fig. 4-10 is equal to the following:*

1. The number of independent energy storage variables in the series and shunt networks.

2. Plus one if the shunt voltage is not already counted and plus one if the series current is not already counted.

3. Minus one if the shunt network has a series linear capacitor and minus one if the series network has a shunt linear inductor.

In the vicinity of a singular point voltages and currents will change slowly with time so we can write truncated Taylor series expansions for the series and shunt elements as

$$z_{se} \approx r + ls,$$
$$y_{sh} \approx g + cs,$$

$$(4.7\text{-}7a,b)$$

which are just the expressions describing the second order system of Fig. 4-4 near a singular point. The projection of the trajectories onto the v-i subplane of ξ-space will be those of a saddle point if the corresponding equilibrium state of the line is stable and if the differential series inductance and shunt capacitance [l and c in (4.7-7)] are positive. Thus once again we expect the dss velocity to be uniquely determined.

4.8. ANALYTIC EXAMPLES

In this section we consider several fairly simple transmission systems for which the dynamic steady state analysis has been carried through in detail. An appreciation of the various approaches which have proved successful in the past should be helpful in attempting future problems.

   a. The Series r, Shunt $j(v)$ — c Line [Ku 3, Ku 4, Na 2, Of 1 Ro 2 Sc 3]. This system has previously been discussed qualitatively in Section 4.6 in relation to Figs. 4-8 and 4-9. It is sketched again in Fig. 4-11 together with some suitable approximations for the nonlinear shunt current per unit length. For convenience we write again the dss equations

$$\frac{dv}{d\xi} = -ri,$$
$$\frac{di}{d\xi} = -j(v) - rcui.$$

$$(4.8\text{-}1a,b)$$

To determine the sorts of trajectories which are possible, consider the application of Bendixson's negative criterion which was discussed in Section 4.4. It states that the function

$$\frac{\partial}{\partial v}\left(\frac{dv}{d\xi}\right) + \frac{\partial}{\partial i}\left(\frac{di}{d\xi}\right) = -rcu$$

$$(4.8\text{-}2)$$

must change sign or vanish identically within a region of the phase plane in order to have a closed trajectory within that region. But $-rcu$ is constant over the entire phase plane so there are no closed trajectories. Thus the only possible waveforms are changes of voltage level between zeroes of $j(v)$.

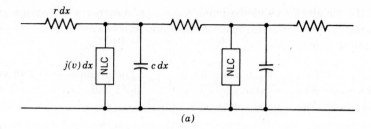

(a)

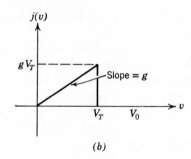

(b)

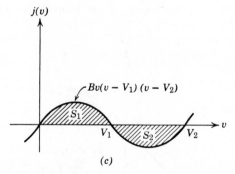

(c)

Fig. 4-11   (a) A nonlinear line; (b) and (c) possible characteristics for the NLC.

Lindgren and Buratti have recently shown that a pulse dss waveform does exist if the line is tapered [Li 7]. This pulse travels only in the direction of increasing resistance. It is, however, unstable in the sense defined in Section 4.10.

Consider first the piecewise linear representation for $j(v)$ shown in Fig. 4-11b. Above a threshold voltage, V_T, $j(v)$ is zero. Below this threshold there is a linear conductance per unit length so $j(v) = gv$. Thus, in general, $v(\xi)$

must satisfy the differential equation

$$\frac{d^2v}{d\xi^2} + rcu\frac{dv}{d\xi} - rgv = 0, \tag{4.8-3}$$

where $g = 0$ for $v > V_T$ but not for $v < V_T$. The problem is to find appropriate linear solutions above and below threshold and then to match them at threshold. The general solution for (4.8-3) is

$$v = Ae^{\gamma_1\xi} + Be^{\gamma_2\xi} + C, \tag{4.8-4}$$

where

$$\gamma_{1,2} = -\frac{rcu}{2}\left[1 \pm \left(1 + \frac{4g}{rc^2u^2}\right)^{1/2}\right]. \tag{4.8-5}$$

The line is assumed initially charged to voltage $V_0 > V_T$. For $v > V_T$ we seek a solution which remains finite and approaches V_0 as $\xi \to +\infty$ and which equals V_T for $\xi = 0$ (see Fig. 4-12). A function of the form of (4.8-4) which satisfies these conditions is evidently

$$v(\xi) = V_0 - (V_0 - V_T)e^{+\gamma_1\xi} \quad (\text{for } v > V_T), \tag{4.8-6}$$

where from (4.8-5) (with $g = 0$)

$$\gamma_1 = -rcu. \tag{4.8-7}$$

Likewise for $v < V_T$ we seek a solution which approaches zero as $\xi \to -\infty$ and which equals V_T for $\xi = 0$. A function of the form of (4.8-4) which

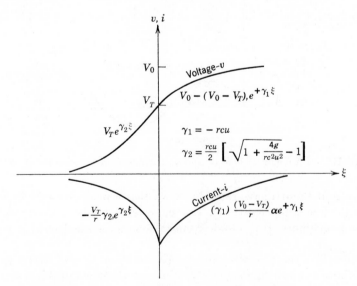

Fig. 4-12 Current and voltage wave forms for line of Fig. 4-11.

satisfies these conditions is

$$v(\xi) = V_T e^{\gamma_2 \xi} \quad (\text{for } v < V_T), \tag{4.8-8}$$

where from (4.8-5) (with $g \neq 0$)

$$\gamma_2 = -\frac{rcu}{2}\left[1 - \left(1 + \frac{4g}{rc^2u^2}\right)^{1/2}\right]. \tag{4.8-9}$$

We also require *continuity of series current* at the threshold because a discontinuity in i at some point would imply an infinite shunt current per unit length and therefore an infinite shunt voltage. From (4.8-1a) and (4.8-6)

$$i(\xi) = +\left(\frac{V_0 - V_T}{r}\right)\gamma_1 e^{+\gamma_1 \xi} \quad (\text{for } v > V_T), \tag{4.8-10}$$

and from (4.8-1a) and (4.8-8)

$$i(\xi) = -\frac{V_T}{r}\gamma_2 e^{\gamma_2 \xi} \quad (\text{for } v < V_T). \tag{4.8-11}$$

Equating (4.8-10) and (4.8-11) at $\xi = 0$ satisfies the condition of series current continuity and establishes the dss velocity as

$$u = \pm\left(\frac{g}{rc^2}\frac{V_T^2}{V_0(V_0 - V_T)}\right)^{1/2}. \tag{4.8-12}$$

Consider next the cubic representation of $j(v)$ which is sketched in Fig. 4-11c.

$$j(v) = Bv(v - V_1)(v - V_2). \tag{4.8-13}$$

From (4.8-1) we can write a differential equation for a solution trajectory as

$$\frac{di}{dv} = cu + \frac{Bv(v - V_1)(v - V_2)}{ri}. \tag{4.8-14}$$

Now with a flash of insight (which Nagumo et al. in [Na 2] ascribe to Huxley), we recognize that (4.8-14) can be satisfied by a trajectory of the form

$$i = Kv(v - V_2), \tag{4.8-15}$$

where K is a constant which upon substitution of (4.8-15) into (4.8-14) is found to equal $\sqrt{B/2r}$. Substitution of (4.8-15) into (4.8-14) also fixes the dss velocity as

$$u = \pm\left(\frac{B}{2rc^2}\right)^{1/2}(2V_1 - V_2). \tag{4.8-16}$$

From (4.8-1a) we have $dv/d\xi = -ri$ so (4.8-15) is integrated to obtain

$$v = \frac{V_2}{2}\left\{1 + \tanh\left[\pm\frac{V_2}{2}\left(\frac{Br}{2}\right)^{1/2}\xi\right]\right\}. \tag{4.8-17}$$

Note that if we take the $+$ sign in (4.8-16) and (4.8-17) then for $V_1 > V_2/2$ the wave velocity from (4.8-16) is positive and (4.8-17) represents a discharge wave from $v = V_2$ to $v = 0$ which is traveling in the $+x$ direction. For $V_1 < V_2/2$, u is negative and (4.8-17) represents a wave traveling in the $-x$ direction for which the voltage rises from $v = 0$ to $v = V_2$. It is easily verified that for $V_1 = V_2/2$

$$\int_0^{V_1} j(v)\,dv = -\int_{V_1}^{2V_1} j(v)\,dv = \frac{V_1^4}{4}.$$

Referring to Fig. 4-11c we can say that if the ratio of areas

$$\frac{S_1}{S_2} > 1 \tag{4.8-18a}$$

the line will support a discharge wave from V_2 to zero. If on the other hand

$$\frac{S_2}{S_1} > 1 \tag{4.8-18b}$$

the line will support a wave for which the voltage on the line rises from $v = 0$ to $v = V_2$.

b. The Series l, Shunt $j(v) - c$ Line [Il 1, Po 4, Sc 3]. This system is sketched in Fig. 4-13a. The nonlinear partial differential equations are

$$\frac{\partial v}{dx} = -l\frac{\partial i}{dt},$$

$$\frac{\partial i}{\partial x} = -c\frac{\partial v}{\partial t} - j(v). \tag{4.8-19a,b}$$

The ξ-space is of one dimension and the dss equation is

$$\frac{dv}{d\xi} = -\frac{luj(v)}{1 - lcu^2}. \tag{4.8-20}$$

Suppose that $j(v)$ is as in Fig. 4-11c. If the dss waveform is to represent a discharge from the stable bias point at V_2 to the stable bias point at zero, we must consider the possibility of $dv/d\xi$ going to zero at V_1 (where $j(v)$

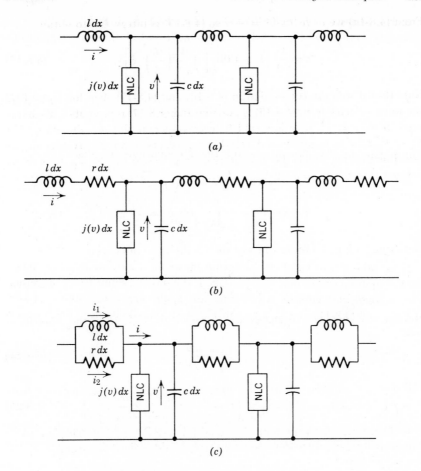

Fig. 4-13   Some nonlinear lines discussed in text.

goes through its intermediate zero), and the solution "hanging up." This difficulty can be avoided if we suppose that

$$u = \frac{1}{\sqrt{lc}}, \tag{4.8-21}$$

but then $dv/d\xi$ is infinite everywhere except at $v = V_1$. Thus we should expect a discontinuous transition from V_2 to zero which propagates at a velocity equal to $1/\sqrt{lc}$. We will find that this tentative conclusion is confirmed when we investigate the problem in greater detail in Section 4.9.

c. The Series $r - l$, Shunt $j(v) - c$ Line [Pe 1, Sc 3, Sc 7, Vo 6]. This system is sketched in Fig. 4-13b. The nonlinear partial differential equations are

$$\frac{\partial v}{\partial x} = -l\frac{\partial i}{\partial t} - ri,$$

$$\frac{\partial i}{\partial x} = -c\frac{\partial v}{\partial t} - j(v). \tag{4.8-22a,b}$$

The ξ-space has two dimensions and the dss equations are

$$\frac{dv}{d\xi} = -\frac{ri + luj(v)}{1 - lcu^2},$$

$$\frac{di}{d\xi} = -\frac{j(v) + curi}{1 - lcu^2}. \tag{4.8-23a,b}$$

If we take $j(v)$ to be of the piecewise linear form indicated in Fig. 4-11b, the dss solution can be obtained just as for the series r, shunt $j(v) - c$ system. The voltage and current waveforms are again given by (4.8-6), (4.8-8), (4.8-10) and (4.8-11) and sketched in Fig. 4-12. The difference in this case is that

$$\gamma_1 = \frac{-rcu}{1 - lcu^2} \tag{4.8-24}$$

and

$$\gamma_2 = -\frac{u(gl + rc)}{2(1 - lcu^2)}\left\{1 - \left[1 + \frac{4rg(1 - lcu^2)}{u^2(gl + rc)}\right]^{1/2}\right\}. \tag{4.8-25}$$

The requirement of current continuity at $\xi = 0$ once again establishes the dss velocity as

$$u = \left[\frac{g}{rc^2}\left(\frac{V_T^2}{V_0(V_0 - V_T)}\right)\left(1 - \frac{gl}{rc}\frac{V_T}{V_0}\right)^{-1}\right]^{1/2}. \tag{4.8-26}$$

Equation 4.8-26 appears at first glance to allow an arbitrarily high velocity as the term (glV_T/rcV_0) approaches unity. However, for $u > 1/\sqrt{lc}$ it is seen from (4.8-24) and (4.8-25) that γ_1 and γ_2 change sign so the waveform will diverge as $\xi \to \pm\infty$. Thus under circumstances for which (4.8-26) indicates a value of u which is greater than $1/\sqrt{lc}$ some non-dss waveform will propagate.

We can get some information from Bendixson's negative criterion by evaluating

$$\frac{\partial}{\partial v}\left(\frac{dv}{d\xi}\right) + \frac{\partial}{\partial i}\left(\frac{dv}{di}\right) = -\frac{lu}{1 - lcu^2}\left[\frac{dj}{dv} + \frac{rc}{l}\right]. \tag{4.8-27}$$

Thus a necessary condition for a closed trajectory in the ξ-plane is that the maximum negative value of dj/dv be greater than rc/l. Pease has shown that a closed trajectory can occur for this system [Pe 1].

d. The Parallel $r - l$, Shunt $j(v) - c$ Line [Pa 2, Pa 6, Sc 10, Yu 1]. This system is sketched in Fig. 4-13c. The nonlinear partial differential equations are

$$\frac{\partial v}{\partial x} = -ri_2.$$

$$\frac{\partial i_1}{\partial x} + \frac{\partial i_2}{\partial x} = -c\frac{\partial v}{\partial t} - j(v), \qquad (4.8\text{-}28a,b,c)$$

$$l\frac{\partial i_1}{\partial t} = ri_2.$$

These lead to the dss equations

$$\frac{dv}{d\xi} = -ri_2.$$

$$\frac{di_1}{d\xi} + \frac{di_2}{d\xi} = -rcui_2 - j(v), \qquad (4.8\text{-}29a,b,c)$$

$$\frac{di_1}{d\xi} = -\frac{r}{lu}i_2.$$

These appear at first to imply a ξ-space of three dimensions, however substitution of (4.8-29c) into (4.8-29b) results in the autonomous pair

$$\frac{dv}{d\xi} = -ri_2,$$

$$\frac{di_2}{d\xi} = -j(v) + \frac{r}{lu}(1 - lcu^2)i_2. \qquad (4.8\text{-}30a,b)$$

In order to apply Bendixson's negative criterion we compute

$$\frac{\partial}{\partial v}\left(\frac{dv}{d\xi}\right) + \frac{\partial}{\partial i_2}\left(\frac{di_2}{d\xi}\right) = \frac{r}{lu}(1 - lcu^2),$$

thus a necessary condition for a closed trajectory is

$$u = \frac{1}{\sqrt{lc}}. \qquad (4.8\text{-}31)$$

If (4.8-31) is satisfied, (4.8-30) implies $dv/di_2 = ri_2/j(v)$ or

$$\tfrac{1}{2}ri_2^{\,2} = \int j(v)\,dv. \qquad (4.8\text{-}32)$$

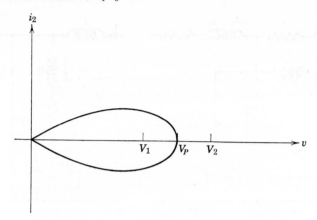

Fig. 4-14 ξ-space trajectory for line of Fig. 4-13c.

If $j(v) = Bv(v - V_1)(v - V_2)$, this equation for the trajectory becomes

$$i_2 = \pm \left(\frac{B}{2r}\right)^{1/2} (v)\sqrt{[v^2 - \tfrac{4}{3}(V_1 + V_2)v + 2V_1 V_2]}. \qquad (4.8\text{-}33)$$

In order for the trajectory to cross the v axis, the roots of the quadratic must be real. In order that the roots of the quadratic be real, it is necessary that

$$[\tfrac{4}{3}(V_1 + V_2)]^2 \geq 4 \times 2V_1 V_2$$

or

$$V_2 \geq 2V_1. \qquad (4.8\text{-}34)$$

The peak voltage of this trajectory is the v axis intercept where $i_2 = 0$ so the amplitude of the resulting pulse voltage waveform is

$$V_P = \tfrac{2}{3}(V_1 + V_2) - \sqrt{\tfrac{4}{9}(V_1 + V_2)^2 - 2V_1 V_2}. \qquad (4.8\text{-}35)$$

Note that $V_1 \leq V_P \leq V_2$. A sketch of the trajectory in the v-i_2 phase plane is given in Fig. 4-14. The shape of the pulse waveform as a function of ξ can be obtained by substituting (4.8-33) into (4.8-30a) and integrating. The result is [Pa 2]

$$v = \frac{4V_1 V_2}{\sqrt{\tfrac{16}{9}(V_1 + V_2)^2 - 8V_1 V_2}\, \cosh \sqrt{(BrV_1 V_2)}\, |\xi| + \tfrac{4}{3}(V_1 + V_2)}. \qquad (4.8\text{-}36)$$

e. Other Systems Which are Discussed in the Literature. The line in Fig. 4-15a permits the return to a resting voltage V_0 after the passage of a discharge pulse in a time of the order of gl [Sc 3]. It has been proposed by Nagumo et al. as an interesting model for the nerve axon and studied carefully both on a computer and experimentally [Na 1, No 1].

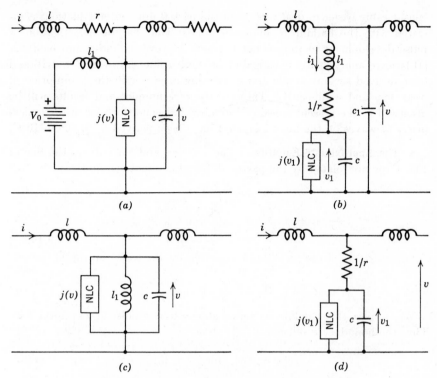

Fig. 4-15   More nonlinear lines which have been studied.

The line in Fig. 4-15*b* has been analyzed in the previous chapter to determine the saturation level for amplification in the quasiharmonic approximation [Sc 4].

The line in Fig. 4-15*c* has been carefully analyzed by Oizuma et al. on a digital computer [Oi 1]. It was demonstrated that a stable pulse waveform would propagate.

The line in Fig. 4-15*d* has been proposed as the equivalent circuit for a very thin Esaki diode [Sc 5], and has been investigated in detail by Vorontsov et al. [Vo 3, Vo 4, Vo 6].

4.9. TRANSIENT ANALYSIS [Il 1]

In the previous discussion we have assumed steady propagation of pulse waveforms. This is a natural restriction because one is often interested primarily in the character of the steady waveforms and also because the ordinary differential equations associated with steady propagation are

considerably easier to deal with than the partial differential equations associated with the buildup or decay of pulses. The analytic investigation of
pulse development in time is not hopeless, however. Il'inova and Kokhlov
[Il 1] have analytically investigated the active line shown in Fig. 4-16 and
have derived several simple and interesting results with the assumption of
weak loss and nonlinearity. These analytic techniques and results will be
discussed in the present section. Note also that conditions for distortionless
decay of waves on the line of Fig. 4-4 have been derived by Bickley [Bi 1].

a. The Approximate Equation.   The voltages and currents on the line of
Fig. 4-16a are related by the partial differential equations

$$\frac{\partial v}{\partial x} = -l\frac{\partial i}{\partial t},$$

$$\frac{\partial i}{\partial x} = -c\frac{\partial v_1}{\partial t} - j(v), \qquad (4.9\text{-}1a,b,c)$$

$$\frac{\partial v_1}{\partial t} = \frac{v - v_1}{rc}.$$

We suppose that the line is excited at $x = 0$ by a pulse of waveform $F(t)$.
Thus the boundary condition is

$$v = F(t) \quad \text{for} \quad x = 0. \qquad (4.9\text{-}2)$$

Equation 4.9-1 can be written in the form

$$\frac{\partial^2 v}{\partial x^2} - lc\frac{\partial^2 v}{\partial t^2} + lrc^2\frac{\partial^3 v_1}{\partial t^3} - l\frac{\partial j(v)}{\partial t} = 0. \qquad (4.9\text{-}3)$$

If r and $j(v)$ were both zero, the line would be lossless and dispersionless
with solution $v = F(t - \sqrt{lc}\ x)$. Let us assume then that the series resistance
of the capacitor and the nonlinear shunt current are both *small* so that the
first two terms on the left of (4.9-3) are dominant. Then we expect the
voltage to be a function of the form

$$v = v(x, t - \sqrt{lc}\ x) = v(x, \tau), \qquad (4.9\text{-}4)$$

where $\tau = (t - \sqrt{lc}\ x)$ and the explicit dependence upon x is weak. The
small term involving v_1 in (4.9-3) can then be approximated by a similar
term involving v since $v \approx v_1$. Thus (4.9-3) becomes

$$\frac{\partial^2 v}{\partial x^2} - lc\frac{\partial^2 v}{\partial t^2} + lrc^2\frac{\partial^3 v}{\partial t^3} - l\frac{\partial j(v)}{\partial t} = 0, \qquad (4.9\text{-}5)$$

or in the variables x and τ, since

$$\frac{\partial v(x, t)}{\partial x} = \frac{\partial v(x, \tau)}{\partial x} + \frac{\partial v(x, \tau)}{\partial \tau} \frac{\partial \tau}{\partial x},$$

we have

$$\frac{\partial^2 v}{\partial x^2} - 2\sqrt{lc} \frac{\partial^2 v}{\partial x \, \partial \tau} + lrc^2 \frac{\partial^3 v}{\partial \tau^3} - l \frac{\partial j(v)}{\partial \tau} = 0. \tag{4.9-6}$$

In the variables x and τ we expect the x dependence of v to be weak compared with the τ dependence which implies that the first term of (4.9-6) can be neglected. Thus the *approximate equation* for $v(x, \tau)$ is

$$\frac{\partial}{\partial \tau} \left[2\sqrt{lc} \frac{\partial v}{\partial x} - lrc^2 \frac{\partial^2 v}{\partial \tau^2} + lj(v) \right] = 0. \tag{4.9-7}$$

Integrating (4.9-7) over τ gives

$$\frac{\partial v}{\partial x} + \frac{1}{2} \left(\frac{l}{c}\right)^{1/2} j(v) = \frac{rc}{2} \sqrt{lc} \frac{\partial^2 v}{\partial \tau^2} + f(x), \tag{4.9-8}$$

where $f(x)$ is an arbitrary function of x which will be zero if the line is initially unexcited.

b. Shock Wave Formation. Suppose now that the series resistance of the capacitor is equal to zero. Then $v(x, \tau)$ is governed by the first order equation

$$\frac{\partial v}{\partial x} = -\frac{1}{2} \left(\frac{l}{c}\right)^{1/2} j(v). \tag{4.9-9}$$

The implications of (4.9-9) are simple and important. If $j(v)$ is positive, $\partial v/\partial x$ is negative and vice-versa. In Fig. 4-16b a possible $j(v)$ curve is sketched together several curves of $v(\tau)$ for specific values of x. As x increases the pulse amplitude will increase in the voltage range for which $j(v)$ is negative and it will decrease in the voltage range for which $j(v)$ is positive. Thus, for large values of x, a rectangular pulse eventually develops if the input pulse is large enough to bring the nonlinear conductance into its negative range.

The effect of the resistance r will be to prohibit the formation of infinitely steep wavefronts. This can be seen by noting that near a steep wavefront $\partial v/\partial x$ will be small compared with $(rc/2)\sqrt{lc}(\partial^2 v/\partial \tau^2)$ so that (4.9-8) becomes approximately

$$\frac{\partial^2 v}{\partial \tau^2} = \frac{1}{rc^2} j(v) \tag{4.9-10}$$

for an initially uncharged line. If (as indicated in Fig. 4-16b) the nonlinear conduction current at the unstable negative bias point, V_1, is approximated

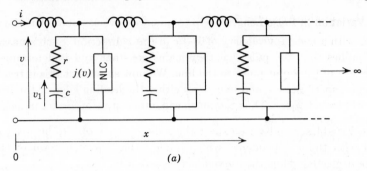

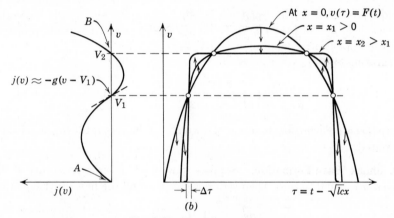

Fig. 4-16 Transient analysis.

by the tangent line

$$j(v) \approx -g(v - V_1),$$ (4.9-11)

then the steep wavefront must occur over a range of τ given by

$$\Delta\tau \sim \left(\frac{rc^2}{g}\right)^{1/2}.$$ (4.9-12)

The line of Fig. 4-16 with the assumptions of small loss and nonlinearity is almost dispersionless. Thus we expect the higher harmonics which are produced to travel approximately in synchronism with the input wave and to contribute to the development of a shock front. However, the dispersion is small only at frequencies for which the shunt admittance looks approximately capacitive. At frequencies with periods smaller than that indicated by (4.9-12), dispersive and dissipative effects prevent synchronous propagation. It is at these higher frequencies that the quasilinear calculations of saturation waveforms which were outlined in the previous chapter would apply.

c. Variation in Pulse Length. Up to now we have assumed that the pulse moves with a constant velocity of $1/\sqrt{lc}$ in the x direction. Such an assumption implies that the pulse length remains constant and is determined by the length of the input pulse to the line. We now show that this is true only in certain special cases, and in general either the leading edge or the trailing edge will travel faster. Thus the pulse will either grow or shrink in length as it travels down the line.

To see this suppose the line has been excited by a long pulse which has settled to the approximately rectangular shape indicated in Fig. 4-16b. Then we can consider both the leading and trailing edges to be in states of steady propagation. The question is whether or not the steady velocities will be the same for both edges. To decide this we write the steady propagation equations corresponding to (4.9-1) as

$$\frac{dv}{d\xi} = lu\frac{di}{d\xi},$$

$$\frac{di}{d\xi} = cu\frac{dv_1}{d\xi} - j(v), \qquad (4.9\text{-}13a,b,c)$$

$$\frac{dv_1}{d\xi} = \frac{v_1 - v}{rcu}.$$

These equations can be combined to yield

$$\frac{dv}{d\xi} = lcu^2\frac{dv_1}{d\xi} - luj(v). \qquad (4.9\text{-}14)$$

Now suppose that the actual velocity of either the leading or the trailing edge differs from $1/\sqrt{lc}$ by an amount specified by the parameter δ through

$$u^2 = \frac{1}{lc} + \delta. \qquad (4.9\text{-}15)$$

Then (4.9-14) becomes

$$\frac{d(v - v_1)}{d\xi} = \delta lc\frac{dv_1}{d\xi} - luj(v), \qquad (4.9\text{-}16)$$

or together with (4.9-13c)

$$d(v_1 - v) + \frac{\delta l}{ru}(v_1 - v)\,d\xi = luj(v)\,d\xi. \qquad (4.9\text{-}17)$$

We can determine δ_L (for the leading edge) by integrating (4.9-17) from point A to point B in Fig. 4-16b. The integral of $d(v_1 - v)$ across the leading edge must be zero since $v_1 = v$ for steady voltage on the line. Thus

$$\frac{\delta_L}{u^2} = \frac{r \int_A^B j(v) \, d\xi}{\int_A^B (v_1 - v) \, d\xi} .$$

(4.9-18a)

Likewise for the trailing edge

$$\frac{\delta_T}{u^2} = \frac{r \int_A^B j(v) \, d\xi}{\int_A^B (v_1 - v) \, d\xi} .$$

(4.9-18b)

Now when v is *increasing* (i.e., on the leading edge) (4.9-13c) indicates that $(v_1 - v)$ is *negative*, while $(v_1 - v)$ is *positive* when v is decreasing (i.e., on the trailing edge). Thus if

$$\int_A^B j(v) \, d\xi \quad \text{and} \quad \int_B^A j(v) \, d\xi$$

are both *positive*, $\delta_L < \delta_T$ and the pulse shrinks. On the other hand if these integrals are both negative, $\delta_L > \delta_T$ and the pulse grows in length as it travels. If we suppose a constant variation of voltage with ξ during the leading and trailing edges, this condition becomes simply

$$\int_A^B j(v) \, dv \quad \begin{matrix} > 0 \Rightarrow \delta_L < \delta_T \\ < 0 \Rightarrow \delta_L > \delta_T \end{matrix} .$$

(4.9-19)

This condition has a rather simple physical interpretation. When the integrals are positive, more of the line length is contributing to loss rather than gain so the pulse length and the associated energy storage must decrease. The condition of (4.9-19) can be stated as implying that the negative area under the $j(v)$ characteristic must exceed the positive area for pulses to grow as they propagate. This conclusion is illustrated in Fig. 4-17. These effects have been verified experimentally by Vorontsov [Vo 3, Vo 4].

d. General Approach to Transient Analysis. The technique of transient analysis discussed in this section can be placed on a somewhat more general foundation. Consider the situation shown in Fig. 4-18a where we have an approximately dss pulse which is moving with velocity u along the line $x = ut$ in the x, t plane. We can effect two transformations of the independent variables; one which directs the new temporal axis along the line $x = ut$ (as in Fig. 4-18b), and one which directs the new spatial axis along that line (as in Fig. 4-18c).

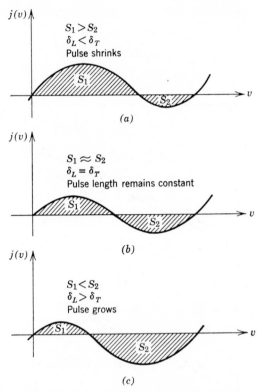

Fig. 4-17 Area condition for pulse growth.

The first of these we designate a (ξ, τ) *transformation* defined by

$$x \to \xi = x - ut,$$
$$t \to \tau = t,$$

(4.9-20a,b)

so that

$$\frac{\partial}{\partial x} \to \frac{\partial}{\partial \xi},$$
$$\frac{\partial}{\partial t} \to \frac{\partial}{\partial \tau} - u \frac{\partial}{\partial \xi}.$$

(4.9-21a,b)

In deriving the dss equations we have effected a (ξ, τ) transformation and then assumed $\partial/\partial\tau = 0$.

The second transformation we call a (ζ, τ) *transformation* defined by

$$x \to \zeta = x,$$
$$t \to \tau = t - \frac{1}{u} x,$$

(4.9-22a,b)

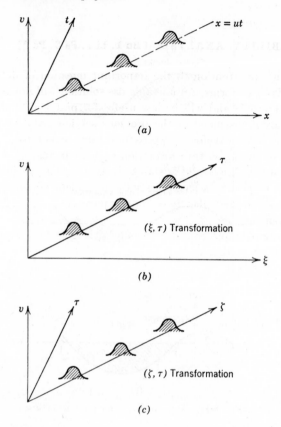

Fig. 4-18 Transformations of independent variables.

so that

$$\frac{\partial}{\partial x} \rightarrow \frac{\partial}{\partial \zeta} - \frac{1}{u}\frac{\partial}{\partial \tau},$$

$$\frac{\partial}{\partial t} \rightarrow \frac{\partial}{\partial \tau}.$$

$$(4.9\text{-}23a,b)$$

This is evidently the transformation which has been employed in this section. It is more convenient when the excitation is specified as a function of time at some position as in (4.9-2). It is important to notice that the basic equations of the dss analysis, (4.5-2), can also be obtained from (4.9-23) if we assume $\partial/\partial \zeta = 0$.

4.10. STABILITY ANALYSIS [Bu 1, Li 7, Pa 3, Pa 5]

We now turn our attention to the important question of determining the stability of dss waveforms. An unstable dss solution will not remain a wave of permanent profile and will be less useful for practical applications. The transient analysis discussed in the previous section gives an indication of stability; for if a waveform approaches some asymptotic shape (with increasing ζ in the (ζ, τ) transformation or with increasing τ in the (ξ, τ) transformation) the waveform is stable. In this section we shall investigate stability with respect to a small spatially dependent perturbation which is introduced at some particular time. For this purpose the (ξ, τ) transformation is more convenient.

As a specific example consider the line in Fig. 4-11a. From (4.6-6) the pde for the shunt voltage is

$$\frac{\partial^2 v}{\partial x^2} - rc \frac{\partial v}{\partial t} - rj(v) = 0. \tag{4.10-1}$$

After a (ξ, τ) transformation, this becomes

$$\frac{\partial^2 v}{\partial \xi^2} - rc \frac{\partial v}{\partial \tau} + rcu \frac{\partial v}{\partial \xi} - rj(v) = 0. \tag{4.10-2}$$

The dss solution $v_0(\xi)$ is a solution of (4.10-2) with the $\partial v/\partial \tau$ assumed equal to zero. Thus

$$\frac{d^2 v_0}{d\xi^2} + rcu \frac{dv_0}{d\xi} - rj(v_0) = 0. \tag{4.10-3}$$

We now suppose that the solution to (4.10-2) is the sum of the dss solution plus a small perturbation $v_p(\xi, \tau)$;

$$v(\xi, \tau) = v_0(\xi) + v_p(\xi, \tau), \tag{4.10-4}$$

where we are prepared to assume $|v_p| \ll |v_0|$. Using (4.10-3), we can write (4.10-2) in the form

$$\frac{\partial^2 v_p}{\partial \xi^2} - rc \frac{\partial v_p}{\partial \tau} + rcu \frac{\partial v_p}{\partial \xi} - r\lfloor j(v_0 + v_p) - j(v_0) \rfloor = 0, \tag{4.10-5}$$

and for small v_p

$$[j(v_0 + v_p) - j(v_0)] \approx \frac{dj}{dv}\bigg|_{v_0} v_p \equiv g(v_0)v_p, \tag{4.10-6}$$

so that (4.10-7) can be written as

$$\frac{\partial^2 v_p}{\partial \xi^2} - rc\,\frac{\partial v_p}{\partial \tau} + rcu\,\frac{\partial v_p}{\partial \xi} - rg(v_0)v_p = 0. \tag{4.10-7}$$

Equation (4.10-7) is a linear partial differential equation for the development of a small perturbation to the dss waveform. It is nonuniform because $g(v_0)$ is a function of ξ; for example, if

$$j(v) = Bv(v - V_1)(v - V_2) \tag{4.10-8}$$

the dss solution (obtained in Section 4.8) is

$$v_0(\xi) = \frac{V_2}{2}\left\{1 + \tanh\left[\frac{V_2}{2}\left(\frac{Br}{2}\right)^{1/2}\xi\right]\right\}. \tag{4.10-9}$$

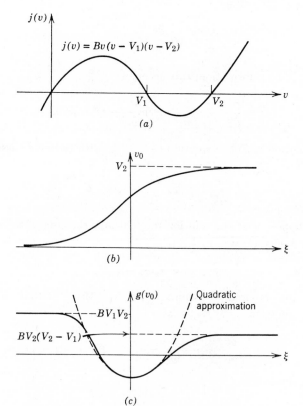

Fig. 4-19 Wave forms for stability calculations.

Equations 4.10-8 and 4.10-9 are sketched in Figs. 4-19*a* and 4-19*b*, respectively. The corresponding $g(v_0(\xi))$ is sketched in Fig. 4-19*c*. Our main concern is to determine whether a solution to (4.10-7) will grow with time.

In general we can write a solution to (4.10-7) as the infinite sum

$$v_p = \sum_{i=1}^{\infty} e^{-\sigma_i \tau} v_i(\xi), \qquad (4.10\text{-}10)$$

where the v_i are eigenfunctions of (4.10-7) and solutions of the ordinary differential equation

$$\frac{d^2 v_i}{d\xi^2} + rcu \frac{dv_i}{d\xi} + rc \left[\sigma_i - \frac{g(v_0)}{c} \right] v_i = 0, \qquad (4.10\text{-}11)$$

with corresponding eigenvalues σ_i. Defining new eigenfunctions ϕ_i as

$$v_i \equiv \phi_i(\xi) \exp \left(- \frac{rcu}{2} \xi \right) \qquad (4.10\text{-}12)$$

Equation 4.10-11 becomes

$$\frac{d^2 \phi_i}{d\xi^2} + \left[rc\sigma_i - \left(\frac{rcu}{2} \right)^2 - rg(v_0) \right] \phi_i = 0. \qquad (4.10\text{-}13)$$

It is interesting to notice that (4.10-13) has the form of a one dimensional Schrödinger's equation with an "energy" equal to $rc\sigma$ and a "potential" equal to $[(rcu/2)^2 + rg(v_0)]$. The shape of this potential function, as is evident from Fig. 4-19*c*, is a "well." The analytic properties of Schrödinger's equation have been studied in great detail [Co 1, Chap. 8]. It is known, for example, that the eigenvalues (the σ_i) are real and that they form a sequence bounded from below. The minimum eigenvalue is called the "ground state eigenvalue."

For stability of the dss waveform, a perturbation must not grow with time. A necessary condition for stability is therefore that none of the σ_i in (4.10-10), which are determined from investigation of (4.10-11) or (4.10-13), can be negative. A sufficient condition for stability is that all the σ_i be positive. Since the σ_i form a sequence bounded from below it is necessary only to evaluate the ground state eigenvalue, σ_1.

Lindgren and Buratti have shown that if v_0 is a "change of state waveform," as in (4.10-9), the ground state eigenvalue is equal to zero. To see this note from (4.10-11) that if $\sigma_1 = 0$, v_1 must satisfy

$$\frac{d^2 v_1}{d\xi^2} + rcu \frac{dv_1}{d\xi} - rg(v_0) v_1 = 0. \qquad (4.10\text{-}14)$$

But if we differentiate (4.10-3) with respect to ξ, we obtain

$$\frac{d^2}{d\xi^2} \left(\frac{dv_0}{d\xi} \right) + rcu \frac{d}{d\xi} \left(\frac{dv_0}{d\xi} \right) - rg(v_0) \frac{dv_0}{d\xi} = 0. \qquad (4.10\text{-}15)$$

Thus $dv_0/d\xi$ is an eigenfunction of (4.10-7) with a zero eigenvalue. If v_0 is a change of state waveform, as in Fig. 4-19b, $dv_0/d\xi$ has no zero crossings. It is, from well known properties of Schrödinger's equation, the ground state eigenfunction. Thus

$$v_1 = \frac{dv_0}{d\xi} \quad \text{and} \quad \sigma_1 = 0. \qquad (4.10\text{-}16)$$

Since $\sigma_1 = 0$, a necessary but not a sufficient condition for stability has been established. Note, however, that if the dss waveform is shifted along the ξ axis by an infinitesimal amount $d\xi$

$$v_0(\xi + d\xi) = v_0(\xi) + \frac{dv_0}{d\xi}\, d\xi$$
$$= v_0(\xi) + v_1(\xi)\, d\xi. \qquad (4.10\text{-}17)$$

Thus the nondecaying perturbation $v_1(\xi)$ represents merely a shift in the dss waveform along the ξ axis. We can say therefore that a change of state waveform on the line of Fig. 4-11a is stable for all perturbations except a translation along the ξ axis, and there is no exponential growth or decay of a translational perturbation.

For an introduction to a nonlinear stability theory in which the interaction between growing eigenfunctions is considered see [Ec 2].

4.11. STEADY PROPAGATION ON A LUMPED LINE
[Ku 3, Ri 1, Ri 2]

We now consider the infinite lumped transmission line shown in Fig. 4-20a. The line has a series resistance of R ohms per section, a shunt capacitance of C farads per section and a nonlinear shunting current element $I(v)$ which is indicated in Fig. 4-20b. Above a threshold voltage V_T zero current flows through the nonlinear element. Below V_T it looks like a linear shunt conductance of G mhos per section. A fully distributed version of this system was investigated in Section 4.8. In the present case the line is described not by partial differential equations but by the *difference differential equations*

$$v_{i-1} - v_i = i_i R, \qquad \text{where} \quad I(v_i) = G v_i \quad \text{for} \quad v_i < V_T$$
$$i_i - i_{i+1} = C\frac{dv_i}{dt} + I(v_i), \qquad = 0 \quad \text{for} \quad v_i > V_T. \qquad (4.11\text{-}1)$$

The system supports a steady waveform if the voltage on the ith section is the same as the voltage on the $(i-1)$th section except for a constant *section delay* τ:

$$v_i(t + \tau) = v_{i-1}(t).$$

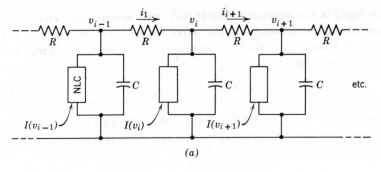

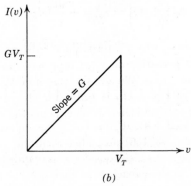

Fig. 4-20 A lumped nonlinear line.

Equation 4.8-12 for dss velocity on the fully distributed system indicates

$$u = \left[\frac{g}{rc^2} \frac{V_T^2}{V_0(V_0 - V_T)} \right]^{\frac{1}{2}}.$$

One might therefore expect the section delay on the lumped system to go to zero as G approaches infinity. Indeed an early but *approximate* analysis of (4.11-1) supported this idea [Sc 9]. However, Richer has carried through an *exact* analysis for the case $G = \infty$ which he calls "switch line" [Ri 2]. The main result of this analysis is an implicit relation between normalized section delay τ/RC and the ratio of threshold to resting voltage V_T/V_0 as

$$\frac{V_T}{V_0} = \exp \left[-\int_0^{\pi/2} F\left(\alpha, \frac{\tau}{RC}\right) \operatorname{ctn} \alpha \, d\alpha \right], \qquad (4.11\text{-}2)$$

where

$$F\left(\alpha, \frac{\tau}{RC}\right) = \frac{2}{\pi} \tan^{-1} \left[(\operatorname{ctn} \alpha) \tanh \left(\frac{2\tau}{RC} \sin^2 \alpha \right) \right]. \qquad (4.11\text{-}3)$$

Equation 4.11-2 appears a bit unwieldy but fortunately it can be closely approximated by the much simpler expression

$$\frac{V_T}{V_0} \approx \frac{1}{1 + \tau/RC}.$$ (4.11-4)

This is found to be asymptotically correct for both large and small τ and has a maximum error of about 20% at τ/RC equal to unity.

As the product RG approaches zero, the section delay must approach that indicated by (4.8-12) or

$$\frac{\tau}{RC} = \left[\frac{V_0(V_0 - V_T)}{RGV_T^2} \right]^{\frac{1}{2}}.$$ (4.11-5)

A simple algebraic relation which interpolates between (4.11-4) and (4.11-5) is

$$\frac{\tau}{RC} \approx \frac{V_0}{V_T} \left[\left(1 - \frac{V_T}{V_0} \right) \left[\frac{1}{RG} + \left(1 - \frac{V_T}{V_0} \right) \right] \right]^{\frac{1}{2}}.$$ (4.11-6)

This equation agrees well with digital computer solutions for a long but finite system [Ku 3, pp. 83–116] and also with the results of an analog simulation [Ku 2]. Richer has also considered the addition of a bias battery and series resistor across the capacitor in each section and has shown that only a positive or negative level change can propagate (not a pulse) just as in the distributed case [Ri 1]. It is interesting to note that in addition there is an intermediate range of bias for which no pulse can propagate.

Predonzani and Roveri [Pr 1a] have recently considered the equilibrium stability of a transmission line consisting of lumped nonlinear active networks separated by lossless transmission lines. They have obtained necessary and sufficient conditions for stability of the linearized network and sufficient conditions for stability of the nonlinear network.

4.12. PULSE INTERACTION [Ha 12, Il 2, Ni 1]

Consider now the interaction between two oppositely directed pulses as they collide. This phenomena has been studied experimentally in some detail by Nishizawa, Hayasaka and Sasaki for the transmission line of Fig. 4-13a [Ha 12, Ni 1]. They found that under certain conditions of bias the two pulses would undergo a "destructive" collision. When the bias voltage exceeded a certain value, on the other hand, one of the signals was not destroyed and a "nondestructive" collision took place. A phenomenological explanation was developed by supposing that the line following each pulse

is insensitive for the duration of a recovery (or refractory) time τ_R and therefore each pulse attenuates the other as $\exp(-\alpha x)$. The recovery length λ_R
equals $u\tau_R$ so the amplitude of one pulse as it emerges from the refractory
range of the other pulse is

$$V_0 = V_i \exp(-\alpha\lambda_R), \tag{4.12-1}$$

where V_i is the initial pulse amplitude. If V_0 is less than the threshold value
for the initiation of pulse propagation on the line, a destructive collision
occurs.

A more sophisticated analysis of the problem has been carried out by
Il'inova [Il 2]. She begins with the pde for the voltage on the line of Fig.
4-13a

$$\frac{\partial^2 v}{\partial x^2} = lc\frac{\partial^2 v}{\partial t^2} + l\frac{\partial j(v)}{\partial t}, \tag{4.12-2}$$

and notes that for $j(v) = gv$ (where g is a small conductance per unit length)
an approximate solution of (4.12-2) is

$$v(x, t) = e^{-(g/2c)t}[F_1(x - ut) + F_2(x + ut)], \tag{4.12-3}$$

where $u = 1/\sqrt{lc}$. Thus for a pulse interaction time τ which is small compared
with

$$\tau \ll \frac{2c}{g} \tag{4.12-4}$$

it is natural to assume a solution for (4.12-2) as a function of the independent
variables

$$\xi = x - ut \quad \text{and} \quad \eta = x + ut. \tag{4.12-5}$$

In the spirit of the discussion of Section 4.9d this will be called a (ξ, η)
transformation. The partial derivatives with respect to x and t transform as

$$\frac{\partial}{\partial x} \rightarrow \frac{\partial}{\partial \xi} + \frac{\partial}{\partial \eta},$$

$$\frac{\partial}{\partial t} \rightarrow u\left(\frac{\partial}{\partial \eta} - \frac{\partial}{\partial \xi}\right). \tag{4.12-6a,b}$$

Equation 4.12-2 therefore transforms to

$$\frac{\partial^2 v}{\partial \xi\, \partial \eta} + \frac{1}{4}\left(\frac{l}{c}\right)^{1/2}\left(\frac{\partial v}{\partial \xi} - \frac{\partial v}{\partial \eta}\right)\frac{dj}{dv} = 0. \tag{4.12-7}$$

For $j(v) = 0$ (4.12-7) becomes $\partial^2 v/\partial \xi\, \partial \eta = 0$ for which a general solution is
simply $F_1(\xi) + F_2(\eta)$. Thus it is the second term on the left-hand side of
(4.12-7) from which we must calculate the interaction between two pulses.

Upon integration of (4.12-7) we obtain

$$v(\xi, \eta) + \frac{1}{4}\left(\frac{l}{c}\right)^{1/2} \int_{-\infty}^{\eta} j[v(\xi, \phi)]\, d\phi$$

$$+ \frac{1}{4}\left(\frac{l}{c}\right)^{1/2} \int_{+\infty}^{\xi} j[v(\phi, \eta)]\, d\phi = F_1(\xi) + F_2(\eta). \tag{4.12-8}$$

For a relatively small interaction (4.12-8) can be written in the approximate form

$$v(\xi, \eta) \approx \frac{1}{4}\left(\frac{l}{c}\right)^{1/2}\left\{ -\int_{+\infty}^{\xi} j[F_1(\phi) + F_2(\eta)]\, d\phi - \int_{-\infty}^{\eta} j[F_1(\xi) + F_2(\phi)]\, d\phi\right\}$$

$$+ F_1(\xi) + F_2(\eta). \tag{4.12-9}$$

The geometrical interpretation of the (ξ, η) transformation is illustrated in Fig. 4-21. The *rectangular* coordinates x and t are exchanged for the

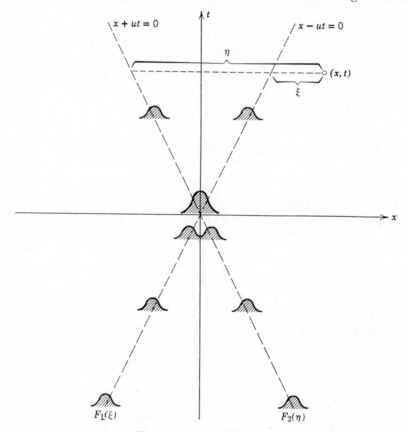

Fig. 4-21 Pulse interaction.

horizontal coordinates ξ and η. The functions of integration $[F_1(\xi)$ and $F_2(\eta)]$ which appear in (4.12-8) can be construed as initial conditions which have been excited at some negative value of time. The integration in (4.12-9) determines the approximate change in these waveforms as the interaction occurs in the vicinity of $t = 0$.

If we suppose $j(v)$ to be as indicated in Fig. 4-16b and consider the interaction of two identical, rectangular pulses of amplitude V, then it is evident that the interaction will cause a *gain* in pulse amplitude for

$$V_1 < 2V < V_2. \qquad (4.12\text{-}10)$$

This conclusion also holds for the reflection of a pulse from an open circuit end of a line. Reflection gain is an important factor in explaining the stable oscillations which are observed on finite lengths of active transmission lines [Sc 6, Vo 3]. The propagation argument from Section 4.9 taken by itself would imply that the oscillator pulse must either shrink to zero length or grow to include the entire length of the line; in either case the oscillation would be extinguished. It is important to emphasize that (4.12-8) and (4.12-9) are valid only for interaction times which are short enough to satisfy (4.12-4). Otherwise the more approximate considerations must be employed [Ha 12, Ni 1].

4.13. TUNNEL JUNCTION TRANSMISSION LINES

In addition to the experiments which have been performed upon lumped ladder circuit analogs of active transmission lines [Ha 12, Ku 2, Ku 3, Ku 4, Na 1, Na 2, Ni 1, No 1, Sc 7, Vo 3, Vo 5] there have been several attempts to fabricate truly distributed active lines. One of the first of these consisted of a distributed semiconductor (Esaki) tunnel diode reported by Cote [Co 9, Co 11]. Propagation velocities of the order of 10^5 m/sec were observed for diode peak current densities of 250 and 2500 A/cm^2. Similar results were obtained by Logunov et al. [Lo 1]. The equivalent circuit for these devices was discussed in considerable detail in [Sc 5], in which it was shown that the equivalent circuit of Fig. 4-15d becomes approximately correct over the frequency range for which the transverse dimension of the diode is small compared with the electromagnetic penetration depth into the semiconductor material.

Truly distributed active transmission lines can also be obtained by application of the nonlinear tunneling of normal electrons through a thin oxide layer separating two superconducting metals. The equivalent circuit for such a structure should be approximately that shown in Fig. 4-13c [Sw 1,

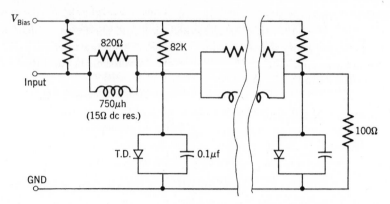

Fig. 4-22 Schematic diagram of 21-section lumped-circuit analog. Tunnel diode parameters: $I_p = 0.95$–1.0 ma., $I_v = 0.1$–0.2 ma., $V_p = 75$–90 mv., $V_v = 350$–400 mv., $V_f = 500$–550 mv.

Sc 10], which was analyzed in detail in Section 4.8d. A 21-section lumped-circuit analog of this equivalent circuit investigated by Parmentier, is shown in Fig. 4-22 [Pa 2, Pa 6]. The "pulse shaping" effects on this line are shown in Fig. 4-23 and the threshold effect in Fig. 4-24. Preliminary attempts to observe dss propagation on a fully distributed superconductor-oxide-superconductor transmission line have been reported by Yuan [Yu 1] and by Parmentier. The device is shown in Fig. 4-25a. It is fabricated by evaporating a base layer of tin, oxidizing, and then evaporating a thin top strip of lead. The completed structure has the active *v-i* characteristic shown in Fig. 4-25b. The device was tested in the experimental set up of Fig. 4-25c; dc current bias is applied to terminal I and a short pulse input to terminal IV. Pulse transmission is observed on terminals III and II. The threshold effect for this transmission is illustrated in Figs. 4-25d and 4-25e.

4.14. THE NERVE AXON

The study of electrical processes in animals has been of interest to physiologists ever since the initial research by Galvani in 1790. Of particular concern over the past fifty years has been the process by which a nerve impulse or "action potential" travels along a *nerve axon*. As early as 1940 Offner, Weinberg and Young considered the nonlinear transmission line model of Section 4.8a and derived an expression for the propagation velocity of a dss wave [Of 1]. In 1952 Hodgkin and Huxley published a remarkable series of papers in which they demonstrated how detailed measurements of the axon properties can be used to calculate the shape and velocity of the nerve impulse, and for which they received the Nobel prize [Ho 2, Ho 3, Ho 4, Ho 5]. The main purpose of this section is to give a brief introduction to the Hodgkin-Huxley theory. Those who wish to study the propagation of the nerve impulse in greater detail are referred to the interesting books which have recently been published by Katz [Ka 2] and by Cole [Co 3].

a. Structure of a Neuron. The basic building block of the central nervous system is the nerve cell or neuron [Co 2]. A typical neuron is shown schematically in Fig. 4-26a. It consists of *dendrites* which receive impulses from other neurons or from the sensory cells, a *cell body* containing the complex chemical engineering apparatus which keeps the cell alive, and an *axon* which carries impulses away to other neurons or to muscle cells. Figure 4-26a is only a schematic representation; the shape and density of the dendrites depends greatly upon the specific function of the neuron. In the nerves of animals the axon is essentially a uniform cylinder covered with a *membrane* as indicated in Fig. 4-26b. It is this membrane which embodies the active character of the axon.

b. Properties of the Nerve Membrane. The membrane which covers a nerve axon is very thin (50–100 Å as indicated in Fig. 4-26c) and has the following peculiar properties. The details are for the giant motor axon of the squid [Ho 5, Ka 2, Co 3].

1. In the undisturbed state the membrane supports a *resting potential* of 60–90 millivolts. The inside of the neuron is negative with respect to the outside.

2. The ratios of ion concentrations inside the axon to outside the axon for sodium, potassium and chlorine ions are approximately

$$\frac{(\text{Na})_i}{(\text{Na})_0} = 1:9, \qquad \frac{(\text{K})_i}{(\text{K})_0} = 40:1, \qquad \frac{(\text{Cl})_i}{(\text{Cl})_0} \approx 1:10.$$

These ratios are about what one would expect from the polarity of the resting potential for the potassium and chlorine ions but not for the sodium ions. There is a high concentration of sodium ions outside the axon and the resting potential is directed to force them in. Thus in the resting state there must be some mechanism to pump sodium ions out of the axon and the inward permeability must be very small.

3. If the membrane resting potential is reduced in magnitude by about 25 mv, the membrane conductance per unit area increases from about 10^{-3} $\mho/\text{cm}^2$ by a factor of about 50 for a period of the order of a millisecond. Throughout this activity the membrane capacity remains constant at about one microfarad per square cm.

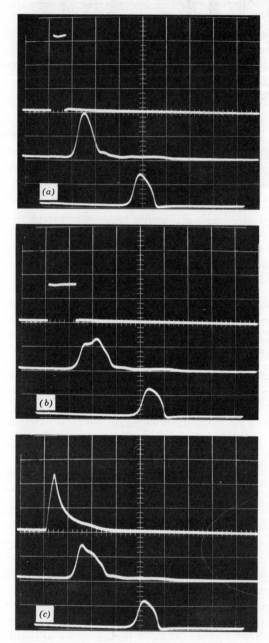

Fig. 4-23 (a), (b), (c). Pulse shaping effect on the lumped circuit analog for three different input pulses. Vertical scale: 0.1 volt/major div.; horizontal scale: 50 μsec/major div. Bias = 50 volts. Top trace: input; center trace; section #7; bottom trace: section #21.

214

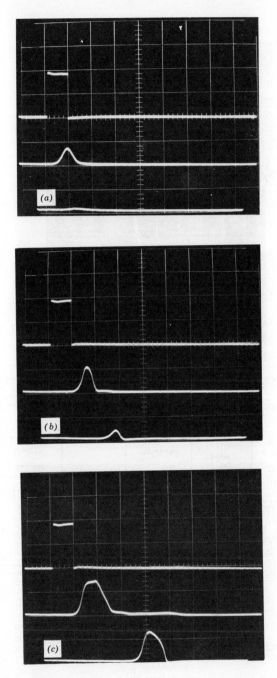

Fig. 4-24 Bias theshold effect on the lumped circuit analog. Vertical scale: 0.1 volt/ major div.; horizontal scale: 50 μsec./major div. (a) Bias = 0. Top trace: input; center trace: section #3; bottom trace: section #5. (b) Bias = 42 volts. Top trace: input; center trace: section #7; bottom trace: section #14. (c) Bias = 50 volts. Top trace: input; center trace: section #7; bottom trace: section #21.

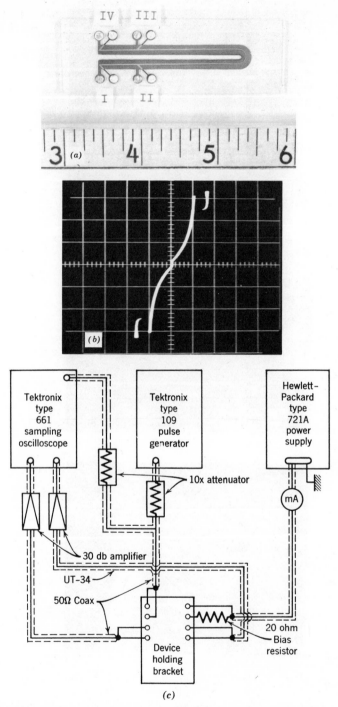

Fig. 4-25 Superconductive tunnel junction neuristor. (*a*) Device structure; (*b*) current-voltage characteristic at **3.3°K**. Vertical—80 ma/div; horizontal—1.0 mv/div; (*c*) pulse measurement circuit.

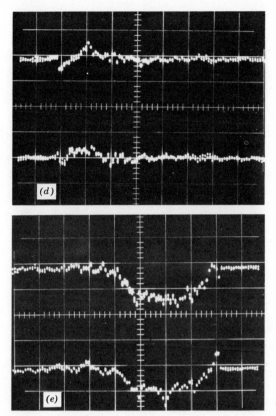

Fig. 4-25   (d) Pulse propagation with zero bias. (e) Pulse propagation with active bias.
Vertical—0.25 mv/div;   horizontal—20 nsec/div;   top trace—terminal III;   bottom
trace—terminal II; bias on terminal I and pulse input on terminal IV.

Hodgkin and Huxley have made extensive measurements of the dynamics
of ion flow across the membrane of the giant squid. They applied "voltage
clamped" pulses (i.e., pulses with the voltage waveform fixed by a feedback
control circuit) and measured the resulting components of ionic current which
flowed across an extended section of the membrane. The membrane current
was experimentally separated into four components: displacement current
through the membrane capacitance, sodium ion current, potassium ion
current, and a "leakage" current due to the other ions. These current
components could be described as follows:

Membrane displacement current,

$$i_D = c \frac{dv}{dt} \; ; \qquad\qquad (4.14\text{-}1)$$

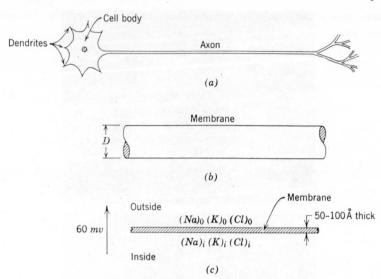

Fig. 4-26   Views of a nerve axon.

Potassium ion current,

$$i_K = g_K n^4 (v - v_K); \qquad (4.14\text{-}2)$$

Sodium ion current,

$$i_{Na} = g_{Na} m^3 h (v + v_N); \qquad (4.14\text{-}3)$$

Leakage ion current,

$$i_L = g_L (v - v_L). \qquad (4.14\text{-}4)$$

The current is taken to be positive when it flows into the axon. The voltage, v, is measured with respect to the resting potential and is positive when the outside of the axon becomes more positive with respect to the inside. The fixed potentials v_K, v_{Na} and v_L are equilibrium potentials calculated from the concentration ratios across the membrane and measured with respect to the resting potential. The experimental values are approximately

$$v_K = 12 \, \text{mv}, \qquad v_{Na} = 115 \, \text{mv}, \qquad v_L = 11 \, \text{mv}.$$

The corresponding maximum ionic conductances are

$$g_K = 36 \times 10^{-3} \frac{\text{mho}}{\text{cm}^2} \, ; \qquad g_{Na} = 120 \times 10^{-3} \frac{\text{mho}}{\text{cm}^2} \, ; \qquad g_L = 0.3 \times 10^{-3} \frac{\text{mho}}{\text{cm}^2} .$$

The time dependence of potassium and sodium ion currents is expressed through the unitless variables n, m and h which vary between a minimum of zero and a maximum of unity. These variables obey the differential equations

$$\frac{dn}{dt} = \alpha_n(1 - n) - \beta_n n, \tag{4.14-5}$$

$$\frac{dm}{dt} = \alpha_m(1 - m) - \beta_m m, \tag{4.14-6}$$

$$\frac{dh}{dt} = \alpha_h(1 - h) - \beta_h h, \tag{4.14-7}$$

where the α's and β's are the following experimentally determined functions of the voltage v.

$$\alpha_n = \frac{0.01(v + 10)}{\exp\left[(v + 10)/10\right] - 1} \; ; \tag{4.14-8}$$

$$\beta_n = 0.125 \exp\left(\frac{v}{80}\right); \tag{4.14-9}$$

$$\alpha_m = \frac{0.1(v + 25)}{\exp\left[(v + 25)/10\right] - 1} \; ; \tag{4.14-10}$$

$$\beta_m = 4 \exp\left(\frac{v}{18}\right); \tag{4.14-11}$$

$$\alpha_h = 0.07 \exp\left(\frac{v}{20}\right); \tag{4.14-12}$$

$$\beta_h = \frac{1}{\exp\left[(v + 30/)10\right] + 1} \; . \tag{4.14-13}$$

Equations 4.14-8 through 4.14-13 have units of (milliseconds)$^{-1}$ and all voltages are in millivolts. These equations "work" in the following way: if v is decreased to -25 mv or more α_m [from (4.14-10)] becomes large and m [from (4.14-6)] increases rapidly. Thus the sodium conductance [given by (4.14-3)] rapidly increases and the *inward* directed sodium battery v_{Na} in Fig. 4-27a (which represents the tendency of sodium ions to diffuse inward due to their concentration gradient) causes a surge of sodium ion current into the axon. As the voltage is negative and greater than 20 mv, α_h is essentially zero. This requires a steady state value of zero for h which, through (4.14-3) forces the sodium conductivity back to zero. The conductivity of the membrane is then due mainly to potassium which relaxes more slowly back to zero.

c. Propagation of the Action Potential. A transmission line equivalent circuit for a smooth nerve axon of diameter D is indicated in Fig. 4-27a. There is series resistance to longitudinal current flow outside the axon, r_0,

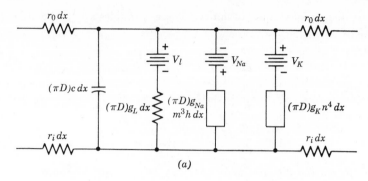

(a)

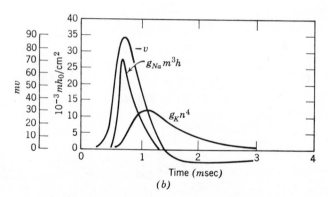

Time (*msec*)

(b)

Fig. 4-27 The Hodgkin-Huxley model (reprinted from [Ho 5]).

and inside the axon, r_i. The current across the membrane per unit length is
determined by (4.14-1) through (4.14-4) and represented by a fairly complex
shunt element in Fig. 4-27a. There are five dependent variables so the
corresponding ξ-space has five dimensions. Numerical solutions for dss
waveforms have been computed, and an example is shown in Fig. 4-27b.
The voltage spike goes negative and the sodium conductance rises to a large

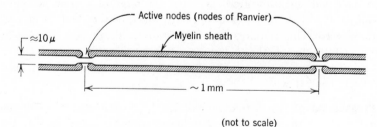

(not to scale)

Fig. 4-28 A myelinated nerve axon.

value then both fall back toward zero in about a millisecond. The potassium conductance rises and falls more slowly. Lieberstein has recently demonstrated the stability of this solution by direct integration of the partial differential equations [Li 1a].

The propagation of the leading edge is very much like the threshold propagation problem discussed in Section 4.8a and illustrated in Fig. 4-11. From (4.8-12) we can therefore assume

$$u \propto \left[\frac{g_{\max} D}{(r_0 + r_i) c^2 D^2} \right]^{1/2}, \tag{4.14-14}$$

where g and c are per unit area rather than per unit length and D is the axon diameter. If the inside resistance dominates (as is usually the case)

$$r_0 + r_i \approx r_i \propto 1/D^2, \tag{4.14-15}$$

so that we expect

$$u \propto \sqrt{D}. \tag{4.14-16}$$

The pulse velocity should be approximately proportional to the square root of the axon diameter [Bu 2]. Equations 4.14-14 and 4.14-16 have an interesting evolutionary implication. For the squid giant axons studied by Hodgkin and Huxley the diameters were about $\frac{1}{2}$ mm and the pulse velocity was about 20 m/sec. In order to double the propagation velocity the axon diameter would have to increase by a factor of four. But since (g/c^2) is inversely proportional to active area, a faster velocity can be obtained at fixed diameter simply by reducing the active area. Just such a reduction in active area is observed in the motor nerve axons of the vertebrate animals. Almost all of the axon is covered with an insulating sheath of *myelin* leaving isolated *active nodes* (or nodes of Ranvier) as is shown in Fig. 4-28. Pulse velocities of the order of 20 m/sec are achieved with much smaller fiber diameters ($\sim 15 \mu$) so it is practical for the motor nerves to be constructed as bundles of axons with an associated increase in reliability and information carrying capacity. Such myelinated nerve axons can be approximately analyzed using the equations for steady propagation on lumped lines described in Section 4-11.

d. Nerve Models. In 1936 the "passive iron wire" model of a nerve axon was described in detail by Lillie [Li 6]. This model takes advantage of the fact that iron will not dissolve in concentrated nitric acid; instead a thin oxide film immediately forms which renders the surface passive. However if the passive surface of such a wire is stimulated by a small negative potential a local energetic reaction develops and propagates along the wire at constant speed. If the stimulation is removed, the surface again becomes passive. The analysis and possible applications of these models have recently been discussed by Suzuki [Su 3].

In 1962 Nagumo, Arimoto and Yoshizawa demonstrated that the transmission line model of Fig. 4-15a (with $l = 0$) could serve as a useful model for a simplification of the Hodgkin-Huxley equation developed by Fitzhugh. Also in 1962 Crane discussed in detail the concept of the *neuristor* or the electronic analog of a nerve axon [Cr 2]. He showed how such lines can be interconnected to achieve complete logic capability and suggested that they could be useful in the construction of highly miniaturized electronic systems.

PROBLEMS

1. Sketch the limit cycle for the circuit of Fig. 4-1a with $I(v) = -G(v - \frac{4}{3}v^3/v_0{}^2)$ for the three cases $G[L/C]^{1/2} = 0.1$, 1 and 10. Assume, for convenience, $\sqrt{L/C} = 10$ ohm.

2. What are the requirements on the parameters a, b, c and d in (4.3-1) for the singular point to be a node, a saddle point, a focus?

3. Derive an equation analogous to (4.3-1) for the behavior of trajectories near a singular point in a three dimensional phase space.

4. Sketch trajectories in the vicinity of a singular point in a three dimensional phase space for a node, a saddle point, a focus, a saddle focus, a center.

5. Show that the index of a curve C is (a) zero if C contains no singular points, (b) $+1$ if C contains a node, focus or center, (c) -1 if C contains a saddle point.

6. Prove (4.4-1).

7. Using Green's theorem, show that (4.4-3) is correct.

8. Consider a ring shaped region in the phase plane. Using the Poincaré-Bendixson theorem state conditions which are sufficient for the existence of a closed trajectory within the region.

9. What is the ξ-space dimension for a lossless, linear telegraph line?

10. Show that any two of the following conditions imply the third.
    (a) Energy is conserved,
    (b) Charge is conserved,
    (c) Kirchhoff's laws are satisfied.

11. Consider an infinite linear lecher wire with a series inductance per unit length, l, a shunt conductance per unit length g, and a shunt capacitance per unit length, c. A small boy is pushing a voltage source along this line at constant velocity u (Fig. P4-1). Find the shunt voltage and series current on the line as a function of x.

12. Verify (4.8-12).

13. Choose some approximately equivalent parameters for $j(v)$ in Figs. 4-11b and 4-11c and compare $v(\xi)$ from (4.8-6), (4.8-8) and (4.8-17). Compare also the value of u calculated from (4.8-12) and (4.8-16).

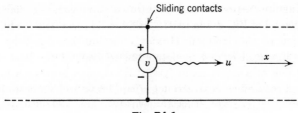

Fig. P4-1

14. In the system of Fig. 4-11*a* suppose that $j(v)$ has the piecewise linear representation

$$j(v) = g_1 v \quad \text{for} \quad v < V_T,$$
$$j(v) = g_2(v - V_0) \quad \text{for} \quad v > V_T.$$

Show that the dss velocity is

$$u = \frac{\pm \left[\left(\dfrac{V_0 - V_T}{V_T} \right)^2 g_2 - g_1 \right]}{\left\{ rc^2 \dfrac{(V_0 - V_t)V_0}{V_T^2} \left[\dfrac{V_0 - V_t}{V_T} g_2 + g_1 \right] \right\}^{\frac{1}{2}}}.$$

15. Show that the result of Problem 14 implies that a discharge wave from V_0 to 0 will propagate only if the ratio $S_1/S_2 > 0$ where $S_1 = \int_0^{V_T} j(v)\, dv$ and $S_2 = -\int_{V_T}^{V_0} j(v)\, dv$.

16. Discuss the application of dss analysis to an n-segment piecewise linearization of an arbitrary $j(v)$ in the system of Fig. 4-11*a*.

17. Derive (4.8-24) and (4.8-25) and, from them, (4.8-26).

18. Can you determine the dss velocity for a discharge pulse on the line of Fig. 4-13*b* for $j(v)$ as in Problem 14?

19. What is the dimension of ξ-space for each of the lines in Fig. 4-15?

20. Write the partial differential equations and the corresponding dss equations for each of the lines in Fig. 4-15.

21. What is a simple approximate expression for the pulse width of the line in Fig. 4-15*a*.

22. Discuss the character of the singular points for the line in Fig. 4-15*a*.

23. Consider the line of Fig. 4-11*a* with $j(v)$ as in Fig. 4-11*b* and $v(\xi)$ and $i(\xi)$ as in Fig. 4-12. Show by direct integration of the loss per unit length connected with $v(\xi)$ and with $i(\xi)$ that the dissipation in the dss waveform is equal to $cuV_0^2/2$ and therefore that the dss wave "digests" energy at the same rate it is "eaten."

24. Derive (4.8-36).

25. Show that the solution of (4.9-6) with $\partial/\partial x = 0$ is a dss waveform.

26. Discuss the effects of both the (ζ, τ) and the (ξ, τ) transformation on the dispersion relation $s = S(\gamma)$ or $\gamma = \Gamma(s)$.

27. Use the quadratic approximation to the "potential well" indicated in Fig. 4-19c to show that the ground state eigenvalue of (4.10-13) is approximately zero.

28. What is the trigger level of voltage required to initiate a pulse on the line shown in Fig. 4-16?

29. Using the measured value of about 1 $\mu f/\text{cm}^2$ for nerve membrane capacitance and an assumed relative dielectric constant of 5, calculate the membrane thickness.

30. Use the model associated with (4.8-12) to estimate the velocity of pulse propagation on a squid axon. Assume a resistivity inside the axon of 100 Ω-cm, membrane capacity of 1 $\mu F/\text{cm}^2$, axon diameter of 0.5 mm, initial conductivity of 10^{-3} $\mho/\text{cm}^2$, conductivity just after the pulse discharge of 25×10^{-3} $\mho/\text{cm}^2$.

31. Can an arbitrarily large propagation velocity on a myelinated fiber be obtained by increasing the node spacing? If not, why not?

32. Can you derive an approximate formula for the maximum node spacing of a myelinated nerve?

CONSERVATIVE NONLINEAR PROPAGATION

In the previous chapter we consider propagation on transmission lines for which the nonlinearity appears mainly in the active elements. This leads to a mode of steady propagation which is critically influenced by the requirement that a balance must obtain between power released and power absorbed by the wave. We now turn our attention to lines for which the nonlinearity appears mainly in the conservative or energy storage elements. Systems of this sort have been studied for many years in connection with wave propagation in liquids and gases and are found to have the interesting property that a continuous excitation can lead eventually to a discontinuous response called a *shock wave*. Shock waves are familiar phenomena to many people from the soldier (or hunter) who hears the "crack" of a bullet going past his ear and the suburbanite whose midafternoon reverie is disturbed by a "sonic boom" to the traveler on a modern super highway who becomes suddenly involved in a rear end collision.

It is interesting (and indeed somewhat disturbing) to note that problems of this sort have been almost totally ignored by electrical engineers until about the year 1960. Presently such problems are of great interest because of the availability of high frequency nonlinear magnetic and dielectric materials and *p-n* diodes from which nonlinear lossless transmission lines can be constructed and also because the high power laser oscillator has opened the new field of *nonlinear optics*.

5.1. SIMPLE TRANSIENT EFFECTS

In order to appreciate the shock wave phenomena let us consider the simple nonlinear transmission line shown in Fig. 5-1a [Kh 1, La 4, Ri 9]. The nonlinear partial differential equations are

$$\frac{\partial v}{\partial x} = -l\frac{\partial i}{\partial t},$$

$$\frac{\partial i}{\partial x} = -c(v)\frac{\partial v}{\partial t}.$$

$$(5.1\text{-}1a,b)$$

It is a simple matter to verify that solutions to (5.1-1) are of the form

$$v = v(x - t/\sqrt{lc(v)})$$

$$i = \int_0^v \left[\frac{c(\alpha)}{l}\right]^{1/2} d\alpha,$$

$$(5.1\text{-}2a,b)$$

where α is a dummy variable of integration.

Suppose that $c(v)$ is such that the capacitance decreases with increasing voltage. Equation 5.1-2a then implies that the higher voltage parts of the wave will travel faster. If the initial excitation is a sinusoid, as indicated in Fig. 5-1b, the crests will overtake the troughs and eventually discontinuities in voltage or shock waves will develop. The position on the line at which the shocks begin and their subsequent motion can be simply determined from a graphical construction in the *x-t* plane. Equation 5.1-2a indicates that a definite velocity of propagation can be assigned to each value of initial voltage. We can therefore draw straight lines in the *x-t* plane with slopes which are equal to the inverse of this velocity. These lines emanate from the *t*-axis where $v(0, t) = F(t)$ and slope = (velocity)$^{-1}$ = $\sqrt{c(F)l}$. Evidently if there is a range on the *t*-axis for which the slope decreases (velocity increases) with increasing time, the lines will eventually intersect. These intersections imply that several values of voltage are at the same position or that the

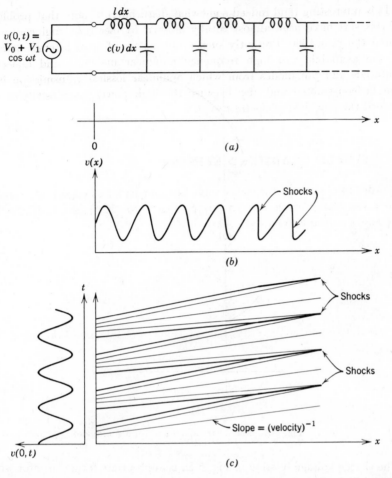

Fig. 5-1 Shock waves on a simple transmission line. Note that the scale of x is not the same in (b) and (c).

voltage is discontinuous. Since the construction of Fig. 5-1c gives the locus of the discontinuities in the x-t plane, the velocity of the shocks is also determined.

Two simple forms of nonlinear capacitance are indicated in Figs. 5-2 and 5-3. The charge voltage relation in Fig. 5-2a is appropriate for the capacitance of a reverse biased p-n diode. For small enough voltage we can write approximately

$$q(v) = c_0 \left(v - \frac{a}{2} v^2 \right), \tag{5.1-3}$$

so that

$$c(v) = c_0 (1 - av). \tag{5.1-4}$$

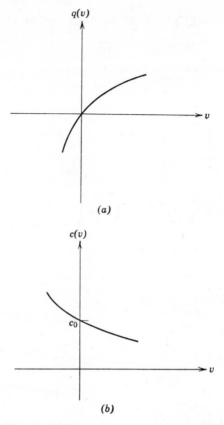

Fig. 5-2 Nonlinear capacitance of a *p-n* diode.

The charge voltage relation in Fig. 5-3*a* is appropriate for a capacitor with a ferroelectric dielectric at a temperature just above the Curie point. For small enough voltage we can write approximately

$$q(v) = c_0\left(v - \frac{b}{3}v^3\right), \tag{5.1-5}$$

so that

$$c(v) = c_0(1 - bv^2). \tag{5.1-6}$$

The charge-voltage relation in Fig. 5-2 corresponds to the polarization-field relation in a piezoelectric crystal while the charge-voltage relation in Fig. 5-3 corresponds to the polarization-field relation in a centrosymmetric crystal. Thus many of the results of this chapter can be applied directly in the field of nonlinear optics.

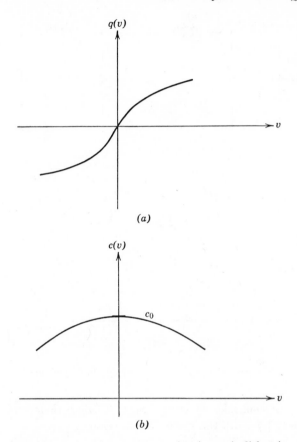

Fig. 5-3   Nonlinear capacitance of an isotropic dielectric.

No energy storage element is completely free from losses and even small losses can greatly affect the formation of shock waves. This can be rather clearly seen by analyzing the line shown in Fig. 5-4a which includes some shunt conductance in the nonlinear capacitance. For the analysis it is convenient to use the transient analysis technique developed by Khokhlov which was introduced in Section 4.9 [Kh 1]. The nonlinear partial differential equation for the shunt voltage is

$$\frac{\partial^2 v}{\partial x^2} - l\frac{\partial^2 q}{\partial t^2} - lg\frac{\partial v}{\partial t} = 0. \tag{5.1-7}$$

We shall suppose that the line is initially uncharged and that it is driven at $x = 0$ by a source such that

$$v(0, t) = F(t). \tag{5.1-8}$$

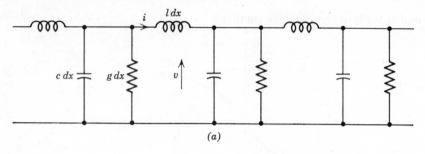

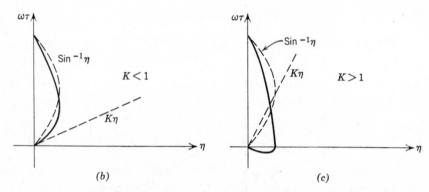

Fi₃ 5-4   Shock wave development on a lossy line.

Furthermore we shall take the charge per unit length to depend upon shunt voltage as in (5.1-3) with the specific assumption

$$av \ll 1, \tag{5.1-9}$$

and also we shall suppose that the losses are small or that

$$g \ll \omega c, \tag{5.1-10}$$

where ω is the lowest frequency of importance on the line.

In the case of no nonlinearity or attenuation (5.1-7) together with the boundary value of (5.1-8) has the solution

$$v = F(t - x\sqrt{lc_0}). \tag{5.1-11}$$

Thus it is reasonable to assume in the case of small attenuation and non-linearity that the solution is basically the same as (5.1-11) except that it could be expected to change slowly with increasing distance from the input. In this situation it is natural to employ the (ζ, τ) transformation of (4.9-22) and (4.9-23) in the previous chapter.

$$x \to \zeta = x,$$

$$t \to \tau = t - x\sqrt{lc_0},$$

so that

$$\frac{\partial}{\partial x} \to \frac{\partial}{\partial \zeta} - \sqrt{lc_0}\,\frac{\partial}{\partial \tau},$$

$$\frac{\partial}{\partial t} \to \frac{\partial}{\partial \tau}.$$

With this transformation (5.1-7) becomes

$$\frac{\partial^2 v}{\partial \zeta^2} - 2\sqrt{lc_0}\,\frac{\partial^2 v}{\partial \zeta\,\partial \tau} + lac_0\,\frac{\partial}{\partial \tau}\left(v\,\frac{\partial v}{\partial \tau}\right) - lg\,\frac{\partial v}{\partial \tau} = 0. \tag{5.1-12}$$

Since variation with respect to the variable ζ is assumed to be small, the first term on the left hand side of this equation can be neglected leaving

$$\frac{\partial}{\partial \tau}\left[2\sqrt{lc_0}\,\frac{\partial v}{\partial \zeta} - lac_0 v\,\frac{\partial v}{\partial \tau} + lgv\right] = 0. \tag{5.1-13}$$

This equation can be integrated with respect to τ yielding, in general, an arbitrary function of ζ on the right hand side. If we assume the system to be initially uncharged, however, this function will be zero. Then

$$2\sqrt{lc_0}\,\frac{\partial v}{\partial \zeta} - lac_0 v\,\frac{\partial v}{\partial \tau} + lgv = 0, \tag{5.1-14}$$

or if we write

$$\gamma \equiv \frac{a}{2}\sqrt{lc_0} \quad \text{and} \quad \alpha \equiv \frac{g}{2}\left(\frac{l}{c_0}\right)^{1/2},$$

Equation 5.1-14 becomes

$$\frac{\partial v}{\partial \zeta} - \gamma v\,\frac{\partial v}{\partial \tau} + \alpha v = 0. \tag{5.1-15}$$

We seek the solution $v(\zeta, \tau)$ of this equation subject to the initial condition of (5.1-11) that

$$v(0, \tau) = F(\tau). \tag{5.1-16}$$

Equation 5.1-15 has the form of Lagrange's equation with the implicit solution

$$\tau \equiv F^{-1}(ve^{\alpha\zeta}) - \frac{\gamma}{\alpha}(e^{\alpha\zeta} - 1)v. \tag{5.1-17}$$

That (5.1-17) is a solution of (5.1-15) may be easily verified by directly calculating $\partial\tau/\partial v$ and $\partial\tau/\partial\xi$ and then calculating $\partial v/\partial\zeta$ from the condition $(\partial v/\partial\zeta)(\partial\zeta/\partial\tau)(\partial\tau/\partial v) = -1$.

Let us now suppose that the line is sinusoidally excited at $\zeta = 0$ so

$$F(\tau) = V_0 \sin \omega\tau. \tag{5.1-18}$$

We can then write (5.1-17) in the dimensionless form

$$\omega\tau = \sin^{-1}\left(\frac{ve^{\alpha\zeta}}{V_0}\right) - \frac{\omega\gamma V_0}{\alpha}(1 - e^{-\alpha\zeta})\left(\frac{ve^{\alpha\zeta}}{V_0}\right), \tag{5.1-19}$$

which can conveniently be graphically analyzed in the following manner. We define

$$\eta \equiv \frac{ve^{\alpha\zeta}}{V_0}, \tag{5.1-20}$$

and write (5.1-20) as

$$\omega\tau = \sin^{-1}(\eta) - K\eta, \tag{5.1-21}$$

where

$$K \equiv \frac{\omega\gamma V_0}{\alpha}(1 - e^{-\alpha\zeta}). \tag{5.1-22}$$

It is evident from the graphical constructions of Figs. 5-4b and 5-4c that η is a multiple valued function of $\omega\tau$ if ζ is large enough so that $K > 1$. From (5.1-20) we see that v will be multiple valued if η is multiple valued. Thus $K = 1$ gives the value of ζ at which a shock wave will develop. Note that if $(\omega\gamma V_0/\alpha) < 1$ a shock wave will never develop. Thus the critical input voltage V_c amplitude below which a shock wave cannot form is

$$V_c = \frac{\alpha}{\omega\gamma}$$

$$= \frac{g}{\omega a c_0}. \tag{5.1-23}$$

When $K > 1$ the construction in Fig. 5-4c no longer represents the wave form. The voltage is not *multivalued* but rather *discontinuous* across the shock front. The velocity of the shock can be approximated by writing the dss equations corresponding to (5.1-1) as

$$\frac{dv}{d\xi} = lu\frac{di}{d\xi}, \quad \text{and} \quad \frac{di}{d\xi} = u\frac{dq}{d\xi}.$$

Integrating these across the shock front gives

$$(v_1 - v_2) = lu(i_1 - i_2) \quad \text{and} \quad (i_1 - i_2) = u(q_1 - q_2),$$

or

$$u = \left(\frac{1}{l}\frac{v_1 - v_2}{q_1 - q_2}\right)^{\!1/2}. \tag{5.1-24}$$

Thus the shock travels at a velocity $u = 1/\sqrt{l\langle c \rangle}$ where $\langle c \rangle$ is the average capacitance across the shock front. This result is evident in a qualitative way from Fig. 4-1c.

5.2. KINEMATIC WAVES [Li 3, Li 4]

The simple graphical techniques described in the previous section can be applied to a wide variety of problems. Consider a general situation for which we can define a *flow* of some conserved quantity past a point per unit time and the *concentration* of that quantity per unit distance. Then with the notation

> flow—q (quantity/time),
> concentration—k (quantity/distance),

assume further that there is a known functional relation between flow and concentration,

$$q = q(k). \tag{5.2-1}$$

If the quantity is conserved, q and k must obey the continuity equation

$$\frac{\partial k}{\partial t} + \frac{\partial q}{\partial x} = 0. \tag{5.2-2}$$

Solutions to (5.2-2) with the assumption of (5.2-1) have been called *kinematic waves* by Lighthill and Whitham [Li 3, Li 4]. Such solutions are easily obtained if we multiply both sides of (5.2-2) by the derivative

$$u = \frac{dq}{dk}. \tag{5.2-3}$$

The result is a single first order partial differential equation for the flow

$$\frac{\partial q}{\partial t} + u\frac{\partial q}{\partial x} = 0. \tag{5.2-4}$$

This solution has a solution of the form

$$q = q(x - ut), \tag{5.2-5}$$

where u can be calculated as an explicit function of q by inverting (5.2-1) to obtain

$$k = k(q), \tag{5.2-6}$$

and then writing (5.2-3) in the form

$$u = \left(\frac{dk}{dq}\right)^{-1}. \tag{5.2-7}$$

Suppose q is specified as a function of time at $x = 0$. A certain value of q will then travel at fixed velocity $u(q)$ or along a straight line with slope $[u(q)]^{-1}$ in the x-t plane just as in Fig. 5-1c. Intersection of these straight lines (or *characteristics*) indicate the onset of shock waves across which q changes abruptly.

Lighthill and Whitham have shown that this simple theory can be applied to at least three very different physical situations.

a. Linear Dispersive Wave Propagation.   In this case the quantity being conserved by (5.2-2) is the *number of cycles* of a periodic waveform. The *flow* is then the number of cycles passing a point per unit time or the *frequency*, f. The *concentration* is the number of cycles per unit distance or the *wave number*, $1/\lambda$. Equation 5.2-7 then indicates that a pulse of waves with a fixed number of wave peaks at frequency, f will propagate with the *group velocity*

$$u_g(f) = \left[\frac{d(1/\lambda)}{df}\right]^{-1},$$

as we noted in (1.4-10).

b. Flood Waves [Li 2].   The quantity being conserved is the water itself. The flow is the mass of water passing a point per unit time, and the height of the water is the concentration. In this case the curve of flow as a function of concentration (5.2-1) is concave *upward* so the velocity is an *increasing* function of the concentration. It is not difficult to show that shocks tend to form on the *front* of a flow pulse.

c. Traffic Flow Waves [Ga 4, Li 4].   The quantity being conserved is the number of vehicles. The flow is the number of vehicles passing a point per unit time, and the number of vehicles per unit distance is the concentration. The curve of flow as a function of concentration is concave *downward;* indeed it appears to reach a maximum value and eventually to return to zero for a sufficiently high concentration of vehicles. The characteristic velocity is a *decreasing* function of concentration. It is not difficult to show in this case that shocks tend to form on the *rear* of a pulse of vehicles.

5.3. QUASILINEAR HYPERBOLIC SYSTEMS [Co 13, Je 1]

The analytic techniques suggested in the previous sections can be generalized for systems with an arbitrary number of dependent variables. Consider, for example, the general nonlinear ladder line. We can define a column vector

$$
V = \begin{bmatrix} v \\ i \\ v_i \\ \cdot \\ \cdot \\ \cdot \\ v_n \\ i_1 \\ \cdot \\ \cdot \\ \cdot \\ i_m \end{bmatrix}, \tag{5.3-1}
$$

where $v_1, \ldots v_n, i_1, \ldots i_m$ are capacitor voltages and inductor currents; and v and i are the shunt voltage and series current respectively if not already counted among the energy storage variables. Since a great many partial derivatives must be written we shall, where convenient, employ the standard notation

$$
v_{1x} \equiv \frac{\partial v_1}{\partial x}, \quad i_{mt} = \frac{\partial i_m}{\partial t}, \quad \text{etc.}
$$

Thus the partial derivatives of the column vector (5.3-1) can be written

$$
V_x = \begin{bmatrix} v_x \\ i_x \\ v_{1x} \\ \cdot \\ \cdot \\ \cdot \\ v_{1x} \\ i_{1x} \\ \cdot \\ \cdot \\ \cdot \\ i_{mx} \end{bmatrix} \quad \text{and} \quad V_t = \begin{bmatrix} v_t \\ i_t \\ v_{1t} \\ \cdot \\ \cdot \\ \cdot \\ v_{nt} \\ i_{1t} \\ \cdot \\ \cdot \\ \cdot \\ i_{mt} \end{bmatrix},
$$

and the partial differential equations of the general ladder line can be written in the compact matrix notation as

$$A_0 V_t + A_1 V_x + B_1 = 0. \qquad (5.3\text{-}2)$$

The matrices A_0, A_1 and B_1 depend *only* on the components of V and *not* upon the components of V_x or V_t. Such a system is called *quasilinear*. Each equation will include a time derivative of one of the dependent variables. Thus often we should expect A_0 to be nonsingular. We can then write (5.3-2) in the form

$$V_t + A V_x + B = 0, \qquad (5.3\text{-}3)$$

where $A \equiv A_0^{-1} A_1$ and $B \equiv A_0^{-1} B_1$.

There will be some values of the dependent variables, or the column vector V, for which

$$B = 0. \qquad (5.3\text{-}4)$$

These values of V will be solutions of (5.3-2) with no x or t variation and are called *regions of constant state* in the x-t plane. We can also define a *disturbed region* in which the partial derivatives with respect to x and t are not all zero. Furthermore we can define a *wavefront* as a curve

$$\phi(x, t) = 0, \qquad (5.3\text{-}5)$$

which divides a disturbed region and a region of constant state. It is convenient to assume the wavefront to be imbedded in the family

$$\phi(x, t) = \text{const}, \qquad (5.3\text{-}6)$$

where $\phi < 0$ in the disturbed region and $\phi > 0$ in the region of constant state (see Fig. 5-5). If we take $\partial/\partial\phi$ to be a partial derivative with respect to the direction normal to the curve $\phi = 0$, then

$$\frac{\partial}{\partial t} = \phi_t \frac{\partial}{\partial \phi},$$

$$\frac{\partial}{\partial x} = \phi_x \frac{\partial}{\partial \phi}. \qquad (5.3\text{-}7a,b)$$

With reference again to Fig. 5-5 we define the

$$\text{``jump of } f \text{ at } P\text{''} \equiv [f]_P \equiv \lim_{P^+, P^- \to P} [f(P^+) - f(P^-)],$$

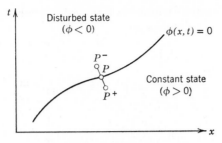

Fig. 5-5 Wavefront.

and suppose that V is continuous across the wavefront. Then (5.3-3) and (5.3-7) yield

$$(I\phi_t + A\phi_x)[V_\phi]_P = 0, \tag{5.3-8}$$

where I is the unity matrix. Thus, if V_ϕ is discontinuous at P, the determinant

$$\det |I\phi_t + A\phi_x| = 0. \tag{5.3-9}$$

Since the direction of the wavefront is given by

$$-\frac{\phi_t}{\phi_x} = u, \tag{5.3-10}$$

Equation 5.3-9 can be written

$$\det |A - uI| = 0. \tag{5.3-11}$$

The direction of a wavefront in the x-t plane as defined in (5.3-10) is the *wavefront velocity* of a disturbance into a region of constant state. Thus we have the important

Statement. *Wavefront velocities for the system (5.3-3) correspond to eigenvalues of the matrix A.*

The number of possible wavefront velocities will be equal to the order of the matrix A which in turn is equal to the number of dependent variables necessary to describe the system. These wavefront velocities correspond to the maximum *signal velocity*, discussed in Section 1.4, for the various modes which can propagate on the system. If all of the wavefront velocities (eigenvalues of A) are real, the system is called *hyperbolic*.

For each of the eigenvalues u_i there is a corresponding *right* eigenvector V_i which satisfies the matrix equation

$$(A - u_iI)V_i = 0. \tag{5.3-12}$$

This eigenvector tells us the ratio of the dependent variables at the wavefront for the ith mode of propagation. It is often convenient to suppose that the index i is chosen so the wavefront velocities are ordered as

$$u_1 \leq u_2 \leq \cdots \leq u_i \leq \cdots \leq u_N, \tag{5.3-13}$$

where N is the total number of dependent variables.

Consider now a problem in which a point source of disturbance is located at a point P on the x-axis (as in Fig. 5-6). A family of N wavefronts or *characteristics* will emanate from P and we can define the *range of influence* of P as that region lying between characteristics C_1 and C_N corresponding to wavefront velocities u_1 and u_N respectively. Conversely a point Q in the x-t plane (Fig. 5-6) can only be influenced by initial conditions on that portion of the x-axis which lies between the intersections with the characteristics C_1 and C_N which pass through Q. This portion of the x-axis (the line segment AB in Fig. 5-6) is called the *domain of dependence* of the point Q.

The matrix A has also N *left* eigenvectors Λ_i, which satisfy the N matrix equations

$$\Lambda_i A = u_i \Lambda_i \tag{5.3-14}$$

corresponding to the N values of u_i. These left eigenvectors are evidently row vectors. If we multiply (5.3-3) on the left by these eigenvectors we obtain

$$\Lambda_i (V_t + u_i V_x + B) = 0. \tag{5.3-15}$$

This equation is convenient for a numerical solution. Suppose, for example, that V is determined as an initial condition along the x-axis at the discrete points $(0, 0)$, $(x_1, 0)$, $(x_2, 0)$, $(x_3, 0)$, etc. as is indicated in Fig. 5-7. The corresponding values of V at the discrete point $(0, t_1)$, (x_1, t_1), (x_2, t_1), (x_3, t_1), etc.

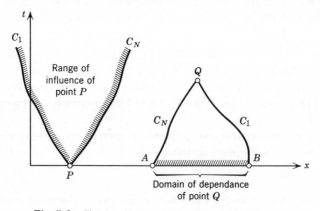

Fig. 5-6   Characteristics and boundary conditions.

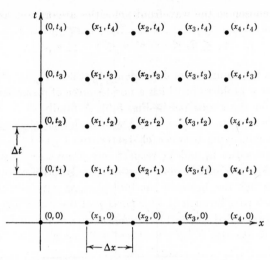

Fig. 5-7   Discrete values of x and t.

can be determined by writing a discrete approximation to (5.3-15) in the form

$$\Lambda_i(x_j, 0)\, \frac{V(x_j, t_1) - V(x_j, 0)}{\Delta t} + u_i(x_j, 0)\, \frac{V(x_j, 0) - V(x_{j-1}, 0)}{\Delta x} + B(x_j, 0) = 0.$$

$$(5.3\text{-}16)$$

This equation has N unknowns, the components of $V(x_j, t_1)$; but there are N equations like (5.3-16) one for each Λ_i and u_i. Thus one can solve directly for the components of $V(x_j, t_1)$. A necessary condition for the convergence of this approximate solution to the true solution in the limit $\Delta x \to 0$ and $\Delta t \to 0$ is that each new point derived from data which lies within its domain of dependence. Thus Δx and Δt must be chosen so that

$$\frac{\Delta x}{\Delta t} > \text{maximum } |u_i|. \qquad (5.3\text{-}17)$$

5.4. NONLINEAR TRANSMISSION LINES WITH DISPERSION

In this section we consider the hitherto neglected effects of dispersion on nonlinear lossless transmission lines. Dispersion implies essentially that different harmonic components of the waveform travel at different velocities; thus we should expect dispersive effects to greatly influence the formation of shocks. It is particularly important to take such effects into account in nonlinear optics since optical media always exhibit dispersion. We shall

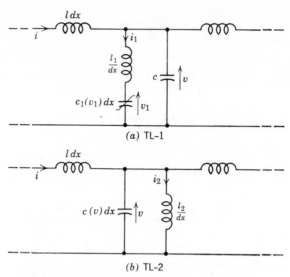

(a) TL-1

(b) TL-2

Fig. 5-8   Dispersive transmission line structures.

concentrate our attention primarily upon the two systems shown in Fig. 5-8 which Prasanna has designated TL-1 and TL-2 [Pr 1]. He has shown that TL-1 serves as a suitable model for propagation in nonlinear optical media while TL-2 can represent propagation of transverse plasma waves in a medium with nonlinear dielectric.

a. Examination of the Characteristics.   The partial differential equations which describe TL-1 are

$$l\frac{\partial i}{\partial t} + \frac{\partial v}{\partial x} = 0,$$

$$c\frac{\partial v}{\partial t} + \frac{\partial i}{\partial x} + i_1 = 0,$$

$$c_1(v_1)\frac{\partial v_1}{\partial t} - i_1 = 0,$$

(5.4-1a,b,c,d)

$$l_1\frac{\partial i_1}{\partial t} - v + v_1 = 0.$$

These can be written in matrix form as

$$
\begin{bmatrix} l & 0 & 0 & 0 \\ 0 & c & 0 & 0 \\ 0 & 0 & c_1(v_1) & 0 \\ 0 & 0 & 0 & l_1 \end{bmatrix}
\begin{bmatrix} i_t \\ v_t \\ v_{1t} \\ i_{1t} \end{bmatrix}
+
\begin{bmatrix} 0 & 1 & 0 & 0 \\ 1 & 0 & 0 & 0 \\ 0 & 0 & 0 & 0 \\ 0 & 0 & 0 & 0 \end{bmatrix}
\begin{bmatrix} i_x \\ v_x \\ v_{1x} \\ i_{1x} \end{bmatrix}
+
\begin{bmatrix} 0 \\ i_1 \\ -i_1 \\ v_1 - v \end{bmatrix}
= 0, \quad (5.4\text{-}2)
$$

which is of the form indicated by (5.3-2)

$$A_0 V_t + A_1 V_x + B_1 = 0.$$

After premultiplication by A_0^{-1} we have

$$\begin{bmatrix} i_t \\ v_t \\ v_{1t} \\ i_{1t} \end{bmatrix} + \begin{bmatrix} 0 & 1/l & 0 & 0 \\ 1/c & 0 & 0 & 0 \\ 0 & 0 & 0 & 0 \\ 0 & 0 & 0 & 0 \end{bmatrix} \begin{bmatrix} i_x \\ v_x \\ v_{1x} \\ i_{1x} \end{bmatrix} + \begin{bmatrix} 0 \\ i_1/c \\ -i_1/c_1(v_1) \\ (v_1 - v)/l_1 \end{bmatrix} = 0, \qquad (5.4\text{-}3)$$

which has the form of (5.3-3)

$$V_t + A V_x + B = 0.$$

The eigenvalues of A are easily found to be

$$u_1 = u_2 = 0, \quad u_3 = +1/\sqrt{lc}, \quad u_4 = -1/\sqrt{lc},$$

with the corresponding left eigenvectors

$$\Lambda_1 = [0 \quad 0 \quad 1 \quad 0]; \quad \Lambda_2 = [0 \quad 0 \quad 0 \quad 1],$$
$$\Lambda_2 = [\sqrt{c/l}, 1, 0 \quad 0]; \quad \Lambda_4 = [\sqrt{c/l}, -1, 0 \quad 0].$$

All of the characteristic velocities are real so the system of equations is hyperbolic. It is important to notice that the nonzero characteristic velocities (u_3 and u_4) are *constants* because of the assumed linear nature of the capacitor c. Thus the characteristics are always straight lines and shock formation cannot occur.

The system $TL\text{-}2$ can also be described by equations in the form of (5.3-3) where

$$A = \begin{bmatrix} 0 & 1/l & 0 \\ 1/c(v) & 0 & 0 \\ 0 & 0 & 0 \end{bmatrix} \quad B = \begin{bmatrix} 0 \\ i_2/c(v) \\ -v/l_2 \end{bmatrix} \quad \text{and} \quad V = \begin{bmatrix} i \\ v \\ i_2 \end{bmatrix}.$$

In this case the eigenvalues of A are

$$u_1 = 0, \quad u_2 = 1/\sqrt{lc(v)}, \quad u_3 = -1/\sqrt{lc(v)},$$

with left eigenvectors

$$\Lambda_1 = [0, 0, 1], \quad \Lambda_2 = [\sqrt{l/c(v)}, 1, 0], \quad \Lambda_3 = [\sqrt{l/c(v)}, -1, 0].$$

In this case the slopes of the characteristics depend upon the voltage so we expect the possibility of shock formation.

b. The Profile Deformation Process [Ko 3, Pr 1]. Using the transient technique which was developed by Khokhlov [Kh 1] (see Section 5.1) approximate expressions can be developed for the deformation of a wave profile as it propagates on TL-1 and TL-2. Assuming small dispersion $(\omega^2 l_1 c_0 \ll 1)$ and weak nonlinearity $(|av| \ll 1$ for $c(v)$ given by (5.1-4) or $bv^2 \ll 1$ for $c(v)$ given by (5.1-6)), the equation for v on TL-1 becomes for $c_1(v_1) = c_0(1 - av_1)$,

$$\left\{ -\frac{\partial^2 v}{\partial x^2} + l(c + c_0)\frac{\partial^2 v}{\partial t^2} - l_1 c_0 \frac{\partial^4 v}{\partial x^2 \partial t^2} + l l_1 c c_0 \frac{\partial^4 v}{\partial t^4} \right\} = \frac{alc_0}{2}\frac{\partial^2(v^2)}{\partial t^2}, \quad (5.4\text{-}4a)$$

and for $c_1(v_1) = c_0(1 - bv_1^2)$,

$$\left\{ -\frac{\partial^2 v}{\partial x^2} + l(c + c_0)\frac{\partial^2 v}{\partial t^2} - l_1 c_0 \frac{\partial^4 v}{\partial x^2 \partial t^2} + l l_1 c c_0 \frac{\partial^4 v}{\partial t^4} \right\} = \frac{blc_0}{3}\frac{\partial^2(v^3)}{\partial t^2}. \quad (5.4\text{-}4b)$$

After performing the (ζ, τ) transformation, neglecting quantities which are second order and integrating with respect to τ, (5.4-4) become

$$\frac{\partial v'}{\partial y} - v'\frac{\partial v'}{\partial \tau} = \mu'\frac{\partial^3 v'}{\partial \tau^3},$$

$$\frac{\partial v''}{\partial y} - (v'')^2\frac{\partial v''}{\partial \tau} = \mu''\frac{\partial^3 v''}{\partial \tau^3}, \qquad (5.4\text{-}5a,b)$$

where $y = \frac{1}{2}\zeta\sqrt{lc_0^2/(c + c_0)}$, $v' = av$, $v'' = b^{1/2}v$, $\mu' = l_1 c_0$ and $\mu'' = 2l_1 c_0/3$. Each of these equations displays a nonlinear term which tends to steepen the wavefront and a higher order term which prevents the formation of discontinuities. Formal solutions to (5.4-5) can be written as Taylor series expansions

$$v'(y, \tau) = v'(0, \tau) + y\frac{\partial v'}{\partial y}\Big|_{(0,\tau)} + \frac{y^2}{2}\frac{\partial^2 v'}{\partial y^2}\Big|_{(0,\tau)} + \text{etc.},$$

in which the $\partial v'/\partial y$ can be replaced by derivatives with respect to τ from (5.4-5a). Neglecting terms in y^2 and returning to the original variables we can approximate the deformations by

$$v(\zeta, \tau) = f(\tau) + \frac{\zeta}{2}\left(\frac{lc_0^2}{c + c_0}\right)^{1/2}\left(+af(\tau)\frac{df}{d\tau} + l_1 c_0 \frac{d^3 f}{d\tau^3}\right) \qquad (5.4\text{-}6a)$$

for $c_1(v_1) = c_0(1 - av_1)$, and

$$v(\zeta, \tau) = f(\tau) + \frac{\zeta}{2}\left(\frac{lc_0^2}{c + c_0}\right)^{1/2}\left(+bf^2(t)\frac{df}{d\tau} + \frac{2}{3}l_1 c_0 \frac{d^3 f}{d\tau^3}\right) \qquad (5.4\text{-}6b)$$

for $c_1(v_1) = c_0(1 - bv_1^2)$. Equations 5.4-6a,b have been found to give reasonably good agreement with measurements on experimental lines for moderate deformation [Pr 1].

For TL-2 we make the same approximations of weak nonlinearity and small dispersion ($\omega^2 l_2 c_0 \gg 1$) and also the change of dependent variable

$$v(x, t) = \exp\left[-x\sqrt{l/l_2}\right]w(x, t).$$

Then after performing the (ζ, τ) transformation, neglecting second order quantities and integrating over τ we obtain for $c(v) = c_0(1 - av)$,

$$\frac{\partial w}{\partial \zeta} - \frac{a}{2}\sqrt{lc_0}\, w\, \frac{\partial w}{\partial \tau} - \sqrt{l/l_2}\, w = 0, \tag{5.4-7a}$$

and for $c(v) = c_0(1 - bv^2)$,

$$\frac{\partial w}{\partial \zeta} - \frac{b}{3}\sqrt{lc_0}\, w^2\, \frac{\partial w}{\partial \tau} - \sqrt{l/l_2}\, w = 0. \tag{5.4-7b}$$

In terms of the original variables (5.4-7) have respectively the implicit solutions

$$\tau = -\frac{a}{2}\sqrt{l_2 c_0}\,(e^{\zeta\sqrt{l/l_2}} - 1)v + F^{-1}(v)$$

and

$$\tau = -\frac{b}{6}\sqrt{l_2 c_0}\,(e^{2\zeta\sqrt{l/l_2}} - 1)v^2 + F^{-1}(v).$$

Graphical analysis of these equations proceeds just as in Section 5.1. For a sine wave input of the form $v(0, \tau) = V_0 \sin \omega t$ a shock will develop at a distance ζ from the input determined by

$$\frac{aV_0}{2}(\omega\sqrt{l_2 c_0})(e^{\zeta\sqrt{l/l_2}} - 1) = 1.$$

Denoting by Z_{ND} and Z_D the critical distances for nondispersive (i.e., $l_2 = \infty$) and dispersive lines ($l_2 < \infty$) respectively we have

$$Z_D = \sqrt{\frac{l_2}{l}}\log\left(1 + \sqrt{\frac{l}{l_2}}\,Z_{ND}\right),$$

which indicates that the shock should form in a *shorter* distance on the *dispersive* line.

c. **Harmonic Generation [Ak 2, Ar 1, Bl 4, Br 9, Os 2, Pr 1].** Another approach to the question of waveform distortion in the case of weak nonlinearity is to suppose that only one harmonic of a sinusoidal driving frequency is generated. Equations for growth of the harmonic and decay of the fundamental can then be obtained. It is important to note that this approach is not necessarily limited to the case of weak dispersion; stronger dispersion will cause the higher harmonics to be even more out of step with the fundamental which then further weakens the interaction. Equations 5.4-4a,b are written with linear partial differential operators on the left hand side and nonlinear terms on the right hand side. These nonlinear members can be considered generators of the harmonic component. For a nonlinear capacitor of the form $c_0(1 - av_1)$ the nonlinear term is proportional to v^2 and therefore generates the *second harmonic*. For a nonlinear capacitor of the form $c_0(1 - bv_1{}^2)$ the nonlinear term is proportional to v^3 and generates the *third harmonic*.

Consider first the problem of second harmonic generation on *TL*-1. Into (5.4-4a) we substitute a harmonic expansion for $v(x, t)$

$$v(x, t) = \text{Re} \sum_i V_i(x)e^{-j(\omega_i t - \beta_i x)}, \tag{5.4-8}$$

where we are prepared to assume that the complex amplitudes, V_i, are slowly varying functions of x. Note that $\omega_i = i\omega_1$ in (5.4-8) but $\beta_i \neq i\beta_1$. Substitution of (5.4-8) into (5.4-4a) neglecting harmonics higher than the second, and equating the coefficients of both $e^{-j\omega t}$ and $e^{-2j\omega t}$ yields two equations

$$(1 - \omega^2 l_1 c_0)\frac{d^2 V_1}{dx^2} + 2j\beta_1(1 - \omega^2 l_1 c_0)\frac{dV_1}{dx}$$
$$- [\beta_1{}^2(1 - \omega^2 l_1 c_0) + \omega^4 ll_1 cc_0 - \omega^2 l(c + c_0)]V_1 = \omega^2 \frac{alc_0}{2} V_1^* V_2 e^{j(\beta_2 - 2\beta_1)x}, \tag{5.4-9a}$$

$$(1 - 4\omega^2 l_1 c_0)\frac{d^2 V_2}{dx^2} + 2j\beta_2(1 - 4\omega^2 l_1 c_0)\frac{dV_2}{dx}$$
$$- [\beta_2{}^2(1 - 4\omega^2 l_1 c_0) + 16\omega^4 ll_1 cc_0 - 4\omega^2 l(c + c_0)]V_2 = \omega^2 alc_0 V_1{}^2 e^{j(2\beta_1 - \beta_2)x}. \tag{5.4-9b}$$

Now assuming small nonlinearity and substituting the approximate (linear) expressions

and

$$\beta_1 = \omega \left[\frac{l(c + c_0)\left(1 - \omega^2 \dfrac{l_1 cc_0}{c + c_0}\right)}{1 - \omega^2 l_1 c_0}\right]^{1/2}$$

$$\beta_2 = 2\omega \left[\frac{l(c + c_0)\left(1 - 4\omega^2 \dfrac{l_1 cc_0}{c + c_0}\right)}{1 - 4\omega^2 l_1 c_0}\right]^{1/2} \tag{5.4-10a,b}$$

into the left hand sides of (5.4-9) causes the coefficients of V_1 and V_2 to vanish. Furthermore the assumption of small change in a wavelength implies

$$\frac{d^2V_i}{dx^2} \ll \beta_i \frac{dV_i}{dx},$$

and justifies neglecting the second derivatives on the left hand sides of (5.4-9). Finally with the assumption of weak dispersion [which was already employed in the derivation of (5.4-4)]

$$\omega^2 l_1 c_0 \ll 1,$$

and if we define

$$\Delta\beta \equiv \beta_2 - 2\beta_1$$

then

$$\frac{\Delta\beta}{2\beta_1} \approx \left(\frac{c_0}{c + c_0}\right) \frac{\frac{5}{2}\omega^2 l_1 c_0}{1 - 5\omega^2 l_1 c_0}.$$

Equations 5.4-9a,b yield

$$\frac{dV_1}{dx} = -j\,\frac{2\omega^2}{\tilde{\beta}_1}\,\frac{alc_0}{8}\,V_1^*V_2 e^{j\Delta\beta x},$$

$$\frac{dV_2}{dx} = -j\,\frac{4\omega^2}{\tilde{\beta}_2}\,\frac{alc_0}{8}\,V_1^{\,2}e^{-j\Delta\beta x}, \qquad (5.4\text{-}11a,b)$$

where $\tilde{\beta}_1 \equiv \beta_1(1 - \omega^2 l_1 c_0)$ and $\tilde{\beta}_2 \equiv \beta_2(1 - 4\omega^2 l_1 c_0)$. Equations 5.4-11a,b describe slow variation of the amplitudes of the first and second harmonic for weak dispersion and nonlinearity.

It is convenient at this point to introduce the polar notation

$$V_1 = |V_1|\,e^{j\phi_1}, \qquad V_2 = |V_2|\,e^{j\phi_2},$$

whereupon (5.4-11) becomes

$$\frac{d\,|V_1|}{dx} = +\,\frac{2\omega^2}{\tilde{\beta}_1}\,\frac{alc_0}{8}\,|V_1|\,|V_2|\sin\theta,$$

$$\frac{d\,|V_2|}{dx} = -\,\frac{4\omega^2}{\tilde{\beta}_2}\,\frac{alc_0}{8}\,|V_1|^2\sin\theta,$$

$$\frac{d\theta}{dx} = \Delta\beta - \frac{alc_0}{8}\left(\frac{4\omega^2}{\tilde{\beta}_2}\frac{|V_1|^2}{|V_2|} - \frac{4\omega^2}{\tilde{\beta}_1}|V_2|\right)\cos\theta, \qquad (5.4\text{-}12a,b,c,d)$$

$$\theta = \phi_2 - 2\phi_1 + \Delta\beta x.$$

Equation 5.4-12c can be written in more compact form as

$$\frac{d\theta}{dx} = \Delta\beta - (\cot\theta)\frac{d}{dx}\left[\log\left(|V_1|^2\,|V_2|\right)\right]. \qquad (5.4\text{-}13)$$

An approximate solution to (5.4-12) can be obtained by assuming that $|V_1|$ remains a constant or, equivalently, that almost all the energy remains in the first harmonic. Equations 5.4-12b and 5.4-12c then become

$$\frac{d\,|V_2|}{dx} = K \sin \theta,$$

$$\frac{d\theta}{dx} = \Delta\beta + \frac{K}{|V_2|} \cos \theta,$$

(5.4-14a,b)

where

$$K \equiv -\frac{\omega^2 a l c_0\,|V_1|^2}{2\tilde{\beta}_2}.$$

(5.4-15)

These equations have the solutions

$$|V_2| = \frac{2K}{\Delta\beta} \sin \left(\frac{\Delta\beta x}{2}\right),$$

(5.4-16a)

$$\theta = \frac{\Delta\beta x}{2} + \frac{\pi}{2}.$$

(5.4-16b)

Equation 5.4-16a is sketched in Fig. 5-9. Note that the phase of the second harmonic advances with respect to the fundamental only as $\Delta\beta x/2$ which is half the corresponding value for the wave without interaction. From (5.4-12c) this result holds only for

$$|V_2|^2 \ll \frac{\tilde{\beta}_1\,|V_1|^2}{\tilde{\beta}_2},$$

(5.4-17)

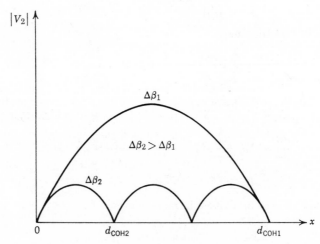

Fig. 5-9   Variation of second harmonic amplitude for two amounts of mismatch.

or when the second harmonic power is much less than half the first harmonic power.

The separation between successive minima of (5.4-16a) is called the *coherence length*, d_{COH}. It is given by

$$d_{COH} = \frac{2\pi}{\Delta\beta}.$$ (5.4-18)

In a physical sense we can say that the second harmonic which is generated at one point is *out of phase* with the second harmonic which is generated at a point a coherence length away. To maximize the second harmonic generation it is necessary to make the coherence length as large as possible.

5.5. STEADY PROPAGATION ON LOSSLESS TRANSMISSION LINES

In the previous chapter our attention was concentrated upon modes of steady propagation for which waves move at constant speed without attenuation or distortion down the transmission line. It is evident from the consideration of Section 5.1 that steady propagation is not possible for the nonlinear dispersionless line of Fig. 5-1a. This is because each voltage level travels at its own characteristic velocity so the wave shape must always be changing. Eventually shocks can form after which the wave amplitude is attenuated. In this section we shall see that steady propagation does occur on *dispersive*, lossless, nonlinear lines. This situation is an interesting contrast to that for propagation on linear lines since a linear, nondispersive line can support steady propagation with arbitrary wave shape but a linear dispersive line cannot. This effect is not new; the solitary shallow water wave was observed as early as 1844 by Scott-Russell and discussed in detail in 1895 by Korteweg and deVries [Ko 3]. For a recent review of the theory of water waves of permanent profile see [St 1, pp. 461–469].

a. The Mechanical Transmission Line [Sc 18]. We shall begin by considering the possibility of dss propagation on the mechanical transmission which was described in Section 2.7. The angle of rotation of the pendula, ϕ, obeys the normalized partial differential equation (2.7-3)

$$\frac{\partial^2\phi}{\partial x^2} - \frac{\partial^2\phi}{\partial t^2} = \sin\phi,$$ (5.5-1)

where distance is measured in units of $\lambda_0 = 5$ cm and time in units of $\tau_0 = 0.1$ seconds. Velocity is therefore normalized to a value of λ_0/τ_0 or 50 cm/sec.

If we ask for solutions of the form $\phi = \phi(\xi)$ where $\xi = x - ut$, (5.5-1) becomes

$$\frac{d^2\phi}{d\xi^2} = \frac{\sin\phi}{1 - u^2}.$$ (5.5-2)

This is analogous to a simple pendulum equation. It can be integrated, after multiplying both sides by $d\phi/d\xi$, to obtain

$$\frac{d\phi}{d\xi} = \left[\frac{2(E - \cos\phi)}{1 - u^2}\right]^{\frac{1}{2}},$$ (5.5-3)

where E is a constant of integration. Two distinct pulse solutions can be obtained from (5.5-3)

$\underline{E = +1 \quad\text{and}\quad u < 1}$

$$\phi = 4\tan^{-1}\left[\exp \pm\left(\frac{x - ut}{\sqrt{1 - u^2}}\right)\right],$$ (5.5-4)

and

$\underline{E = -1 \quad\text{and}\quad u > 1}$

$$\phi = 4\tan^{-1}\left[\exp \pm\left(\frac{x - ut}{\sqrt{u^2 - 1}}\right)\right] + \pi.$$ (5.5-5)

The pulse solution of (5.5-4) is easily demonstrated on the mechanical transmission line. It consists of a single rotation of through an angle of 2π as shown in Fig. 5-10. It is interesting to notice that such a pulse can travel at *any* normalized velocity less than unity. As the pulse normalized velocity approaches unity, the pulse gets narrower due to the factor $\sqrt{1 - u^2}$ in the denominator of the exponent. The reason for this "Lorentz contraction" is discussed in detail in the next section.

The pulse solution of (5.5-5) is essentially that of (5.5-4) rotated through an angle of π. This means that the pendula must be balanced in their upward (unstable) positions as $x \to \pm \infty$. This solution is obviously unstable.

If the magnitude of the integration constant, E, in (5.5-3) is not equal to unity, ϕ can still be written as an implicit function of ξ defined by the integral relation

$$\sqrt{1 - u^2}\int_0^\phi \frac{d\phi}{\sqrt{2(E - \cos\phi)}} = \xi.$$ (5.5-6)

Two solutions to (5.5-6) are of particular interest. The first is that for which

$$\underline{E > 1 \quad\text{and}\quad u < 1.}$$

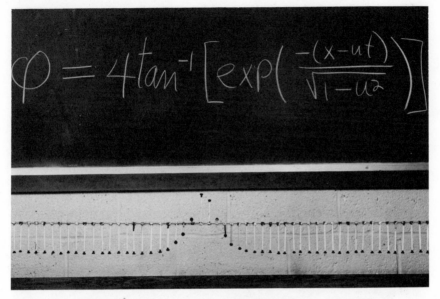

$$\varphi = 4 \tan^{-1}\left[\exp\left(\frac{-(x - ut)}{\sqrt{1 - u^2}} \right) \right]$$

Fig. 5-10 Pulse waveform on mechanical transmission line.

In this case ϕ is monotonically increasing function of ξ which can be written

$$\phi = \cos^{-1}\left[2\, \mathrm{cd}^2 \left(\frac{\xi}{\gamma\sqrt{1 - u^2}} \right) - 1 \right], \tag{5.5-7}$$

where cd is an elliptic function of modulus [By 1]

$$\gamma = \frac{2}{E + 1}. \tag{5.5-8}$$

The wave which corresponds to (5.5-7) is demonstrated in Fig. 5-11. For $E \gg 1$ (5.5-7) reduces to

$$\phi \approx \left[\frac{2E}{1 - u^2} \right]^{1/2} \xi, \tag{5.5-9}$$

as is evident from (5.5-6). The second case of interest is that for which

$$-1 < E < +1 \quad \text{and} \quad u > 1.$$

In this case ϕ is a *periodic* function of ξ which can be written

$$\phi = 2 \sin^{-1}\left[\gamma\, \mathrm{sn} \left(\frac{\xi}{\sqrt{u^2 - 1}} \right) \right], \tag{5.5-10}$$

Fig. 5-11 Equation 5.5-7 on the mechanical transmission line.

where sn is an elliptic function of modulus

$$\gamma = \left[\frac{1 - E}{2}\right]^{1/2}. \tag{5.5-11}$$

The wave which corresponds to (5.5-10) is demonstrated in Fig. 5-12. Since the magnitude of sn is always less than or equal to unity, the magnitude of ϕ is restricted by

$$\phi \leq 2 \sin^{-1}(\gamma), \tag{5.5-12}$$

and is approximately zero for $E \approx + 1$. This corresponds to the small amplitude propagation illustrated in Fig. 2-18.

The mechanical transmission line can serve as an analog for several interesting physical effects. These include: the Josephson junction transmission line (which is discussed in detail in the following two sections), the motion of a Bloch wall between ferromagnetic domains [Be 0, Do 1, En 2, Fe 3a], the motion of a dislocation in a crystal [Ko 1], and a one dimensional model for elementary particles [En 1, Pe 3, Sk 2]. A similar nonlinear pde ($\phi_{tx} + \phi_{tt} = \sin \phi$) has recently been studied in connection with the observation of "self induced transparency" in a laser medium which is excited by pulsed coherent light [La 1a, La 1b, Ma 1].

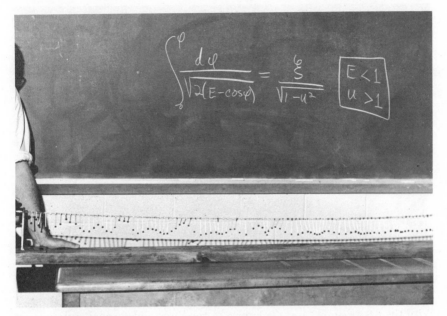

Fig. 5-12   Equation 5.5-10 on the mechanical transmission line.

Elementary particle interactions are vividly demonstrated on the mechanical line. "Particle-antiparticle creation" is accomplished simply by folding a section of the pendula over to form two pulses of the sort illustrated in Fig. 5-10 but with opposite screw senses. If two pulses with the opposite screw senses collide, they often annihilate each other and radiate their energy onto the line. If a moving pulse collides with a standing pulse of the same screw sense, the moving pulse will stop and the standing pulse will move just as if they were billiard balls.

Perring and Skyrme [Pe 3] have studied such interactions in detail on a digital computer and have discovered simple analytic expressions which describe the collision processes. These are

pulse-pulse collision,

$$\tan \frac{\phi}{4} = \frac{u \sinh (x/\sqrt{1 - u^2})}{\cosh (ut/\sqrt{1 - u^2})} ; \tag{5.5-13}$$

pulse-antipulse collision,

$$\tan \frac{\phi}{4} = \frac{\sinh (ut/\sqrt{1 - u^2})}{u \cosh (x/\sqrt{1 - u^2})} ; \tag{5.5-14}$$

These equations are exact solutions for (5.5-1). Equation 5.5-14 indicates that a pulse and an antipulse can collide without mutual destruction. This is sometimes but not always observed on the mechanical transmission line.

b. Steady Propagation on *TL*-1. We now consider the transmission line *TL*-1 shown in Fig. 5-8a. The modes of steady propagation on this system have been investigated in [Sc 13] and in great detail in Chapter 5 of [Pr 1]. The partial differential equations are repeated for convenience.

$$\frac{\partial v}{\partial x} = -l\frac{\partial i}{\partial t},$$

$$\frac{\partial i}{\partial x} = -c\frac{\partial v}{\partial t} - i_1,$$

$$l_1\frac{\partial i_1}{\partial t} = v - v_1, \qquad\qquad (5.4\text{-}1)$$

$$c_1(v_1)\frac{\partial v_1}{\partial t} = i_1.$$

With the dss assumption these reduce to the three dimensional, autonomous set

$$\frac{dv}{d\xi} = -l'ui_1,$$

$$\frac{di_1}{d\xi} = \frac{v_1 - v}{ul_1}, \qquad\qquad (5.5\text{-}15a,b,c)$$

$$\frac{dv_1}{d\xi} = -\frac{i_1}{uc_1(v_1)},$$

where $l' = l/(1 - lcu^2)$. Each point of the set

$$v - v_1 = 0, \qquad i_1 = 0 \qquad\qquad (5.5\text{-}16)$$

is a possible equilibrium point for (5.5-15). This is a straight line through the origin in the ξ-space lying entirely in the $v - v_1$ coordinate plane. From (5.5-15a) and (5.5-15c) we can write

$$q(v_1) = \frac{v}{l'u^2} + \text{constant.} \qquad\qquad (5.5\text{-}17)$$

Solutions must lie on the surface defined by (5.5-17). The interaction of this surface with the straight line defined by (5.5-16) gives the equilibrium points for (5.5-15). These ideas are sketched in Fig. 5-13.

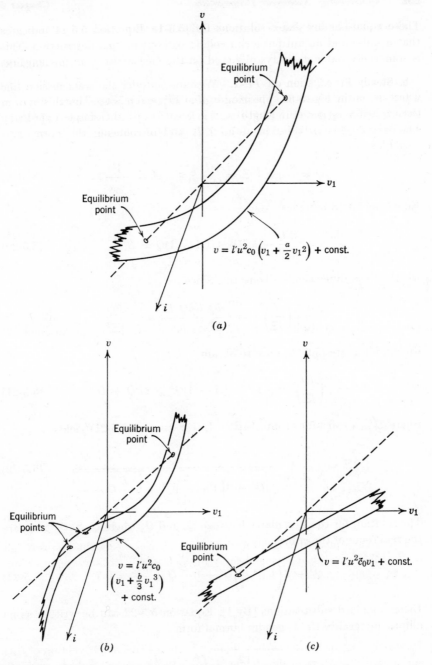

Fig. 5-13 Configuration of nonlinear ξ-space trajectories. (a) $c_1(v_1) = c_0(1 + av_1)$; (b) $c_1(v_1) = c_0(1 + bv_1^2)$; (c) corresponding linearized line.

From (5.5-15) and (5.5-17) it is not difficult to show that

$$\frac{d^2q}{d\xi^2} + \frac{v_1}{l_1 u^2} - \frac{l'}{l}q = -\frac{l'B_1}{l_1},$$ (5.5-18)

where B_1 is the constant appearing in (5.5-17), and q is the charge stored in the capacitor c_1 per unit length of the line. Taking the simple expression $c_1(v_1) = c_0(1 + av_1)$, assuming $|av_1| \ll 1$, and introducing the normalized variables

$$Q = \frac{a}{c_0}q, \qquad \Xi = \sqrt{\frac{l'}{l_1}}\,\xi, \qquad A = \frac{1}{l'c_0u^2},$$ (5.5-19)

Equation 5.5-18 becomes

$$\frac{d^2Q}{d\Xi^2} - \tfrac{1}{2}AQ^2 + (A - 1)Q = B,$$ (5.5-20)

where B is a dimensionless constant. Since

$$\frac{d}{dQ}\left[\left(\frac{dQ}{d\Xi}\right)^2\right] = 2\frac{dQ}{d\Xi}\frac{d(dQ/d\Xi)}{dQ} = 2\frac{d^2Q}{d\Xi^2},$$

we can integrate (5.5-20) once to obtain

$$\left(\frac{dQ}{d\Xi}\right)^2 = \frac{A}{3}Q^3 - (A - 1)Q^2 + 2BQ + D,$$ (5.5-21)

where D is a constant of integration. Integration of (5.5-21) yields

$$\Xi = \sqrt{\frac{3}{A}}\int_{Q_3}^{Q}\frac{dQ}{\sqrt{Q^3 - 3\left(1 - \dfrac{1}{A}\right)Q^2 + 6\dfrac{B}{A}Q + \dfrac{3D}{A}}}$$ (5.5-22)

The solution for $Q(\Xi)$ oscillates between Q_2 and Q_3 where $Q_1 > Q_2 > Q_3$ are the real roots of the cubic

$$Q^3 - 3\left(1 - \frac{1}{A}\right)Q^2 + 6\frac{B}{A}Q + \frac{3D}{A} = 0.$$ (5.5-23)

Using standard substitutions [By 1], Equation 5.5-22 can be written as an elliptic integral in the Legendre normal form

$$\Xi = \sqrt{\frac{12}{A(Q_1 - Q_3)}}\int_0^{\phi}\frac{d\phi}{\sqrt{1 - k^2\sin^2\phi}},$$ (5.5-24)

where $k^2 = (Q_2 - Q_3)/(Q_1 - Q_3) < 1$ is the modulus of the elliptic integral. The wavelength is obtained by letting $\phi = \pi/2$ whereby

$$\lambda = \sqrt{\frac{48}{A(Q_1 - Q_3)}} K(k), \tag{5.5-25}$$

where $K(k)$ is the complete elliptic integral of the first kind. The solution for $Q(\Xi)$ can then be expressed as

$$Q(\Xi) = Q_2 - (Q_2 - Q_3) \operatorname{cn}^2 \left(\frac{2K}{\lambda} \Xi, k \right), \tag{5.5-26}$$

where cn is a Jacobian elliptic function. Equation 5.5-26 is sketched in Fig. 5-14a. When $Q_1 = Q_2$ the elliptic function degenerates to the hyperbolic function

$$Q(\Xi) = Q_1 - (Q_1 - Q_3) \operatorname{sech}^2 \left(\sqrt{\frac{A}{12}(Q_1 - Q_3)} \, \Xi \right). \tag{5.5-27}$$

Equation 5.5-27 represents a solitary wave or *pulse of charge* and is sketched in Fig. 5-14b.

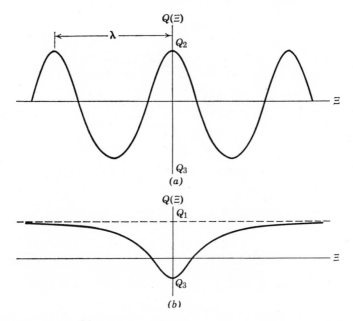

Fig. 5-14   DSS waves on TL-1. (a) Periodic solution, (b) solitary wave solution.

5.6. THE LORENTZ TRANSFORMATION ON A JOSEPHSON JUNCTION TRANSMISSION LINE [Ku 1, Le 1, Sc 16, Sc 18]

a. The Josephson Junction Transmission Line.   Consider the Josephson junction transmission line shown in Fig. 5-15a which consists of two superconductor strips separated by an insulating layer which permits coupling of the superconducting wave functions or (equivalently) tunneling of superconducting electrons [Jo 3]. The transmission line will have a series inductance per unit length which is due to the storage of magnetic field energy within a London penetration depth, λ_L, of the superconductor surfaces and within the insulating region. Then (in MKS units) the series inductance per unit length is [Sw 1]

$$l = \frac{2\lambda_L + d}{a} \mu_0 \text{ henrys/meter,} \tag{5.6-1}$$

where $\mu_0 = 4\pi \times 10^{-7}$ henrys/meter. The shunt capacitance per unit length

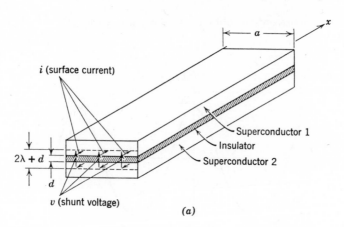

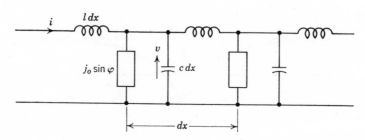

Fig. 5-15   Josephson junction transmission line.

is connected with the storage of electric energy within the insulating layer. Thus

$$c = \frac{a\kappa\varepsilon_0}{d} \text{ farads/meter,} \tag{5.6-2}$$

where $\varepsilon_0 = (1/36\pi) \times 10^{-9}$ farads/meter and κ is the relative dielectric constant of the insulator.

The two superconductors can be described by electronic wave functions for the superconducting state of the form [Fe 4]

$$\psi_1 = \sqrt{\rho_1}\, e^{j\phi_1}, \qquad \psi_2 = \sqrt{\rho_2}\, e^{j\phi_2},$$

where ρ_1 and ρ_2 are the electronic charge densities. The Josephson tunneling current between these two superconducting regions is related to the angle

$$\phi = \phi_1 - \phi_2, \tag{5.6-3}$$

which is the difference between the phases of the wave functions on the two sides of the insulating layer. In particular the Josephson current per unit area is

$$I = I_0 \sin \phi, \tag{5.6-4}$$

where ϕ is related to the applied voltage by

$$\frac{d\phi}{dt} = \frac{4\pi e}{h} v. \tag{5.6-5}$$

In (5.6-5) e is the electronic charge and h is Planck's constant. Equations 5.6-4 and 5.6-5 indicate that a Josephson junction has the electrical character of a nonlinear *inductor* as indicated in Fig. 5-16. If we take the inductor flux to be

$$\Phi = \int v\, dt,$$

then (5.6-4) can be written

$$I = I_0 \sin \frac{2\pi\Phi}{\Phi_0}, \tag{5.6-6}$$

where $\Phi_0 = h/2e$ is the flux *quantum* (equal to 2×10^{-7} gauss-cm^2). This relation between flux and current is plotted in the usual manner for a nonlinear inductor in Fig. 5-16b.

From (5.6-1), (5.6-2), (5.6-5) and (5.6-6) the partial differential equations for the shunt voltage v, the series current i, and the Josephson shunt flux

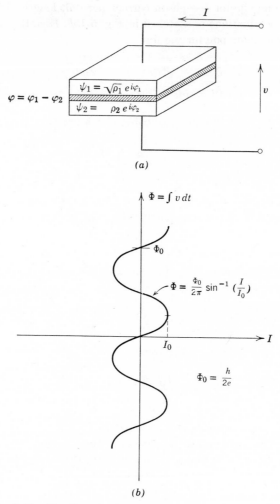

(a)

(b)

Fig. 5-16   The Josephson junction as a nonlinear inductor.

can be written

$$\frac{\partial v}{\partial x} = -l\,\frac{\partial i}{\partial t},$$

$$\frac{\partial i}{\partial x} = -c\,\frac{\partial v}{\partial t} - j_0 \sin\frac{2\pi\Phi}{\Phi_0}, \qquad (5.6\text{-}7a,b,c)$$

$$\frac{\partial \Phi}{\partial t} = v,$$

where j_0 is the maximum Josephson current per unit length. An equivalent circuit for these equations is sketched in Fig. 5-15*b*. Equation 5.6-7 can be combined into a single pde for the flux

$$\frac{\partial^2 \Phi}{\partial x^2} - lc \frac{\partial^2 \Phi}{\partial t^2} = lj_0 \sin \frac{2\pi\Phi}{\Phi_0}. \tag{5.6-8}$$

If we measure distance in units of the Josephson length

$$\lambda_J = \left[\frac{\Phi_0}{2\pi j_0 l} \right]^{\frac{1}{2}}, \tag{5.6-9}$$

time in units of

$$\tau_J = \left[\frac{\Phi_0 c}{2\pi j_0} \right]^{\frac{1}{2}}, \tag{5.6-10}$$

and flux in units of $\Phi_0/2\pi$ so

$$\phi = 2\pi\Phi/\Phi_0, \tag{5.6-11}$$

Equation 5.6-8 reduces to the normalized form

$$\frac{\partial^2 \phi}{\partial x^2} - \frac{\partial^2 \phi}{\partial t^2} = \sin \phi. \tag{5.6-12}$$

Note that (5.6-12) is exactly the same as the normalized pde on the mechanical transmission line (5.5-1). The variable ϕ in (5.6-12) is, of course, just the change in angle of the superconducting wavefunction across the junction which was defined in (5.6-3). All of the solutions obtained in the previous section for the mechanical line can be interpreted directly on the Josephson junction transmission line. In particular the pulse solution of (5.5-4) and Fig. 5-10 implies the motion of a single flux quantum along the junction. The monotonic solution of (5.5-7) and Fig. 5-11 implies the motion of a series of flux quanta along the junction.

b. The Lorentz Transformation.   The form of (5.6-12) is invariant to the Lorentz transformation of the independent variables from (x, t) to (x', t').

$$x \to x' = \frac{x - ut}{\sqrt{1 - u^2}},$$

$$t \to t' = \frac{t - ux}{\sqrt{1 - u^2}}. \tag{5.6-13a,b}$$

To see this we need only to note that (5.6-13) imply that the partial derivatives transform as

$$\frac{\partial}{\partial x} \rightarrow \frac{(\partial/\partial x') - u(\partial/\partial t')}{\sqrt{1 - u^2}},$$

$$\frac{\partial}{\partial t} \rightarrow \frac{(\partial/\partial t') - u(\partial/\partial x')}{\sqrt{1 - u^2}}. \tag{5.6-14a,b}$$

Substitution of (5.6-14) into (5.6-12) leaves the form unchanged.

This invariance to a Lorentz transformation leads to a contraction of both space and time by the factor $\sqrt{1 - u^2}$ just as in the special theory of relativity. The effect is clearly evident in the pulse solution of (5.5-4) and is easily demonstrated on the mechanical line. In Fig. 5-17 we have a stroboscopic photograph of a pulse wave initiated at a fairly high velocity and which gradually slowed to a stop because of dissipative effects. The pulse is traveling from left to right and $\Delta t = 0.6$ seconds.

On the Josephson junction the unnormalized limiting velocity is

$$u_0 = \frac{1}{\sqrt{lc}}. \tag{5.6-15}$$

From (5.6-1) and (5.6-2) this velocity can be written in the form

$$u_0 = \left(\frac{d/u_0\varepsilon_0}{\kappa(2\lambda_L + d)}\right)^{1/2} \tag{5.6-16}$$

which is about $\frac{1}{20}$ the velocity of light in free space for typical junction geometry.

Although the form of (5.6-12) remains invariant to the Lorentz transformation, (5.6-7) change. Voltage and current get "mixed up" just as the electric and magnetic fields get mixed up when a Lorentz transformation is performed on Maxwell's equations [Sc 18]. If we define transformed

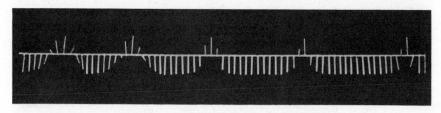

Fig. 5-17 Pulse traveling from right to left (and slowing down) on mechanical line. ($\Delta t = 0.6$ seconds).

voltages and currents under the transformation such that

$$v \rightarrow v' = \frac{v - lui}{\sqrt{1 - u^2/u_0{}^2}},$$

$$i \rightarrow i' = \frac{i - cuv}{\sqrt{1 - u^2/u_0{}^2}},$$

Equations 5.6-7a,b,c also remain invariant.

5.7. THE ACTIVE JOSEPHSON JUNCTION LINE [Jo 2]

In this section we shall again briefly consider propagation on a Josephson junction transmission line but include the effects of loss elements and introduce a distributed bias current source which can supply energy to the pulse waveform. This problem has recently been studied in great detail by Johnson [Jo 2]. In addition to its intrinsic interest, it serves as a good illustration of the utility of a modern *hybrid* (analog-digital) computer in the solution of complex dynamic steady state equations.

An equivalent circuit for the system under investigation is shown in Fig. 5-18a. Included is a series resistor, r, which accounts for losses due to normal (i.e., not superconducting) electron current parallel to the junction and a shunt conductor, g, which accounts for losses due to tunneling of normal electrons across the junction. There are four dynamical variables (v, i_1, i_2, ϕ) which are related by the four partial differential equations

$$\frac{\partial v}{\partial x} = -ri_2,$$

$$l\frac{\partial i_1}{\partial t} = ri_2,$$

$$\frac{\partial i_1}{\partial x} + \frac{\partial i_2}{\partial x} = -c\frac{\partial v}{\partial t} - gv - j_0 \sin \phi + j_B,$$

$$\frac{\partial \phi}{\partial t} = \frac{2e}{\hbar} v$$

(5.7-1a,b,c,d)

where $\hbar \equiv h/2\pi$. We will be concerned only with dss solutions of (5.7-1). According to the rule developed in Section 4.7 the number of independent

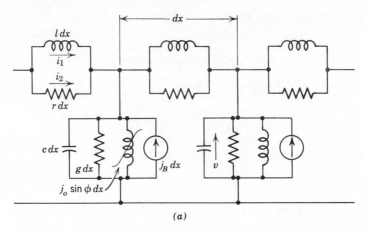

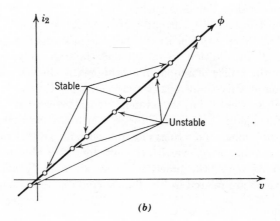

Fig. 5-18 (*a*) Josephson line with bias and losses; (*b*) singular points in ξ-space.

dss equations is three. These can be written for the three dependent variables (v, i_2, ϕ) as

$$\frac{dv}{d\xi} = -ri_2,$$

$$\frac{di_2}{d\xi} = \left(\frac{1 - lcu^2}{lu}\right)ri_2 - gv - j_0 \sin \phi + j_B, \qquad (5.7\text{-}2a,b,c)$$

$$\frac{d\phi}{d\xi} = -\frac{2e}{\hbar u}v,$$

or we can write a single third order pde as

$$\frac{d^3\phi}{d\xi^3} - r\left(\frac{1 - lcu^2}{lu}\right)\frac{d^2\phi}{d\xi^2} - rg\frac{d\phi}{d\xi} + \frac{2ej_0r}{\hbar u}\left(\sin\phi - \frac{j_B}{j_0}\right) = 0. \quad (5.7\text{-}3)$$

Singular points in the (v, i_2, ϕ) ξ-space occur where

$$v = 0, \quad i_2 = 0, \quad \text{and} \quad \phi = \sin^{-1}\frac{j_B}{j_0}. \quad (5.7\text{-}4a,b,c)$$

These are illustrated in Fig. 5-18b. Note that (5.7-4c) is satisfied at

$$\phi = 2\pi n + \phi_0 \quad (n = 0, \pm 1, \pm 2, \ldots), \quad (5.7\text{-}5a)$$

and at

$$\phi = (2n + 1)\pi + \phi_0 \quad (n = 0, \pm 1, \pm 2, \ldots), \quad (5.7\text{-}5b)$$

where ϕ_0 is the principal value of $\sin^{-1}(j_B/j_0)$. Taking a linear expansion about the singular points and using Routh's criterion [Ga 2] it is not difficult to show that the characteristic equation near the singular points of (5.7-5a) has one real negative root and two roots with positive real parts. Near the singular points of (5.7-5b) there is one real positive root and two with negative real parts. Thus all of the singular points are either foci or saddle foci (as discussed in Section 4.3) and can serve as initial or terminal points for pulse waveforms. However, the singular points of (5.7-5b) are *absolutely unstable* in the sense of Chapter II since they correspond to a negative differential shunt inductance of the Josephson current. Thus we shall be concerned only with trajectories which connect the singular points of (5.7-5a). For transitions between these singular points ϕ must change by an integer times 2π. Thus the total flux in any dss waveform must be an integer times the flux quantum $\Phi_0 = h/2e$ or

$$\int_{-\infty}^{+\infty} v \, dt = n\Phi_0. \quad (5.7\text{-}6)$$

Assuming values for the line parameters which were appropriate for lead-oxide-lead Josephson junction transmission lines, Johnson has used the University of Wisconsin's AD 256/SDS 930 hybrid (analog digital) computer to determine dss waveforms. In Fig. 5-19 is shown the corresponding values of

$$normalized\ bias = \frac{j_B}{j_0}$$

and

$$normalized\ pulse\ velocity = u\sqrt{lc},$$

at which dss pulse propagation can occur. The various curves ($n = 1, 2, 3,$ etc.) correspond to the number of flux quanta in the pulse as defined in

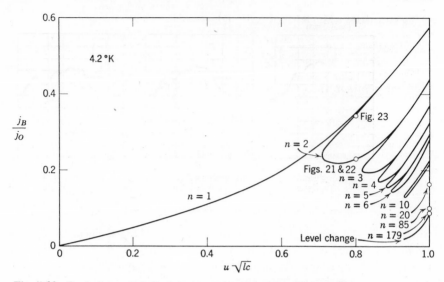

Fig. 5-19   Loci of $n = 1, 2, 3, 4, 5, 6$ and 10 pulse solutions at 4.2°K. Solution points at $u\sqrt{lc} = 1$ and various j_B/j_0 for $n = 20, 85$ and 179.   Lead junction.

(5.7-6). Note that for one flux quantum the dss pulse velocity is a single valued function of the bias current, but for two or more flux quanta the pulse velocity is a double valued function of bias.

The voltage waveforms at various points on the curve for $n = 4$ (four flux quanta) are illustrated in Fig. 5-20. On the lower branch of the curve in the velocity-bias plane the dss pulse is traveling faster and the four flux quanta are bunched rather closely together. On the upper branch the pulse travels more slowly for a given value of bias current and one of the flux quanta is becoming *detached* from the *trailing edge*. Thus we should expect a mode of instability in which pulse waveforms "scatter their flux quanta behind them."

The existence of a dynamic steady state waveform is evidence of a power balance between dissipation in the elements r and g and input from the bias current source. The power balance equation is

$$g \int_{-\infty}^{\infty} v^2(\xi)\, d\xi + r \int_{-\infty}^{\infty} i_2{}^2(\xi)\, d\xi = j_B \int_{-\infty}^{\infty} v(\xi)\, d\xi. \tag{5.7-7}$$

The power input on the right hand side of (5.7-7) can be written as

$$\text{Power input} = j_B u \int_{-\infty}^{\infty} v(t)\, dt, \tag{5.7-8}$$

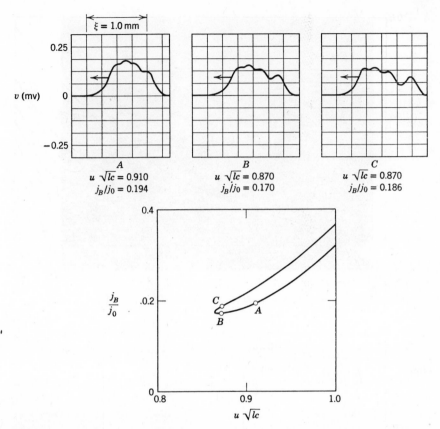

Fig. 5-20 Change in $n = 4$ voltage pulse for different points in the $u\sqrt{lc} - j_B/j_0$ plane. The pulses propagate to the left.

and from (5.7-6) this becomes

$$\text{Power input} = j_B n \Phi_0 u$$
$$= \text{force} \times \text{velocity}. \qquad (5.7\text{-}9)$$

Thus the bias current appears to exert a Lorentz *force* equal to $j_B\Phi_0$ on each flux quantum.

To utilize the versatility of the hybrid computer for problems of this sort a digital algorithm was developed which allowed the computation of an entire curve as in Fig. 5-20 without manual intervention. Furthermore, the digital half was used to compute right and left eye stereoprojections of the trajectories in the (v, i_2, ϕ) phase space which were visually displayed during operation. Three of these are shown in Figs. 5-21, 5-22 and 5-23 for $n = 2$.

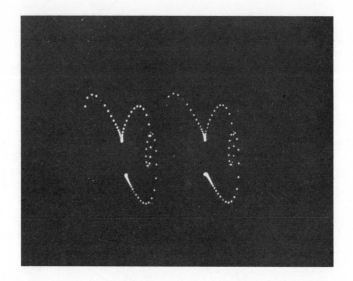

$$u \sqrt{lc} = 0.800 \qquad \frac{j_B}{j_0} = 0.228$$

(a)

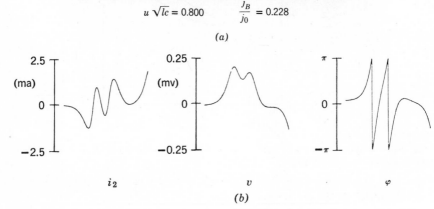

(b)

Fig. 5-21   (a) Stereographic view of a $n = 2$ trajectory in the (v, i_2, ϕ) phase space. (b) i_2, v and φ as a function of ξ.

Observe that there is no change in the third digit of $u\sqrt{lc}$ and j_B/j_0 between the trajectories of Fig. 5-21 and 5-22. Note again how the flux quanta are spread on the low velocity branch in Fig. 5-23.

5.8.   THE MANLEY-ROWE RELATIONS [Ma 3, Pe 2]

The lossless character of a linear circuit element can be specified by requiring that the average power flow into the element must be zero at each frequency.

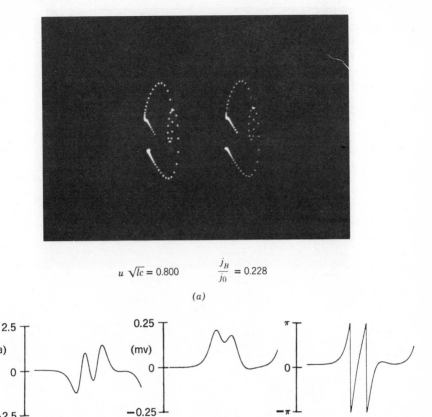

$$u\ \sqrt{lc} = 0.800 \qquad \frac{j_B}{j_0} = 0.228$$

(a)

(b)

Fig. 5-22   (a) Stereographic view of a $n = 2$ trajectory in the (v, i_2, ϕ) phase space. (b) i_2, v and φ as a function of ξ.

For a nonlinear lossless element this is not the case since energy at one frequency can be converted to another frequency via the nonlinearity. There is however a restriction upon the powers that can flow at various frequencies which was initially derived by Manley and Rowe in 1956 [Ma 3]. A very thorough review of the theoretical background related to these Manley-Rowe equations has been provided by Penfield [Pe 2].

In order to appreciate these restrictions consider a nonlinear capacitor for which the charge is specified as a single valued function of the voltage by

$$q = q(v). \tag{5.8-1}$$

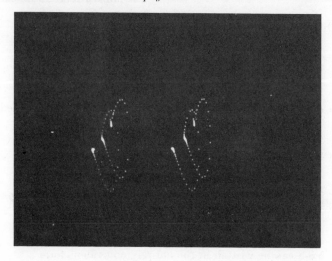

$$u \sqrt{lc} = 0.800 \qquad \frac{j_B}{j_0} = 0.342$$

(a)

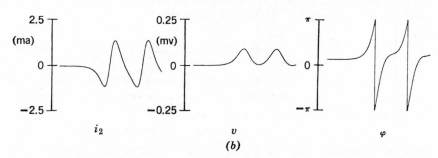

(b)

Fig. 5-23 (*a*) Stereographic view of a $n = 2$ trajectory in the (v, i_2, ϕ) phase space. (*b*) i_2, v and ϕ as a function of ξ.

We suppose that the applied voltage waveform has frequency components at

$$\omega_{mn} = m\omega_1 + n\omega_2, \qquad (5.8\text{-}2)$$

where ω_1 and ω_2 can be specified independently. Thus

$$v(t) = V_0 + \operatorname{Re} \sum_{m,n} V_{mn} \exp j(m\omega_1 + n\omega_2)t. \qquad (5.8\text{-}3)$$

The charge and current will have frequency components at sums and differences of those specified in (5.8-2), but these are included in the set specified by (5.8-2). Thus we can also write the charge and current as

$$q(t) = Q_0 + \mathrm{Re} \sum_{m,n} Q_{mn} \exp j(m\omega_1 + n\omega_2)t, \tag{5.8-4}$$

$$i(t) = I_0 + \mathrm{Re} \sum_{m,n} I_{mn} \exp j(m\omega_1 + n\omega_2)t. \tag{5.8-5}$$

Since $i = dq/dt$, the coefficients in (5.8-4) and (5.8-5) must be related by

$$I_{mn} = j(m\omega_1 + n\omega_2)Q_{mn}. \tag{5.8-6}$$

The power flowing into the capacitor at ω_{mn} will be

$$P_{mn} = \tfrac{1}{2} \, \mathrm{Re} \, V_{mn}^* I_{mn}, \tag{5.8-7}$$

and a statement of energy conservation is

$$\sum_{mn} P_{mn} = 0. \tag{5.8-8}$$

Equation 5.8-8 can be written in the entirely equivalent form

$$\omega_1 \sum_{m,n} \frac{m P_{mn}}{m\omega_1 + n\omega_2} + \omega_2 \sum_{m,n} \frac{n P_{mn}}{m\omega_1 + n\omega_2} = 0, \tag{5.8-9}$$

where we have assumed that the frequencies ω_1 and ω_2 can be independently specified. Now from (5.8-6) and (5.8-7) the factor

$$\frac{P_{mn}}{m\omega_1 + n\omega_2} = \tfrac{1}{2} \, \mathrm{Re} \, j V_{mn}^* Q_{mn}, \tag{5.8-10}$$

and we observe from (5.8-1) that the Q_{mn} depends upon the shape of the curve $q(v)$ and on the voltage amplitudes but not upon ω_1 or ω_2. Therefore the individual sums in (5.8-9) must be zero.

$$\sum_{m,n} \frac{m P_{mn}}{m\omega_1 + n\omega_2} = 0,$$

$$\sum_{m,n} \frac{n P_{mn}}{m\omega_1 + n\omega_2} = 0. \tag{5.8-11a,b}$$

Equations 5.8-11a,b are the Manley-Rowe relations. Since we wish to assign a unique power to each magnitude of frequency it is convenient to take the sum from $m = 1$ to $m = \infty$ and from $n = -\infty$ to $n = +\infty$.

As a simple example of the application of (5.8-11) consider the problem of down conversion from a carrier frequency ω_c by lossless mixing with a local oscillator frequency ω_0 to an intermediate frequency ω_i. Evidently we must have

$$\omega_0 + \omega_i = \omega_c, \tag{5.8-12}$$

so we can consider the two independent frequencies to be ω_i and ω_0. Equation

5.8-11a then says

$$\frac{P_0}{\omega_0} + \frac{P_c}{\omega_c} = 0, \qquad (5.8\text{-}13a)$$

and (5.8-11b) says

$$\frac{P_i}{\omega_i} + \frac{P_c}{\omega_c} = 0. \qquad (5.8\text{-}13b)$$

Thus the power available at the i.f. terminals is only (ω_i/ω_c) times the input to the mixer at the carrier frequency. There is always a conversion loss upon down conversion with a lossless mixer. For up conversion, on the other hand, there is always a conversion gain.

It has been pointed out in a very interesting note by Weiss [We 2] that (5.8-13) follow from the simple quantum mechanical idea that as one photon is absorbed with energy $\hbar\omega_c$, simultaneously two photons are emitted with energies $\hbar\omega_i$ and $\hbar\omega_0$. Since the powers are simply equal to photon energies times the photon rate (which must be the same for all three channels), we are led directly to (5.8-13). An attempt to generalize this idea in order to obtain the complete Manley-Rowe equations has been described by Brown [Br 13].

It is important to remember that a vital assumption in deriving the Manley-Rowe equations was (5.8-1) which implies a condensor charge (voltage) as a single valued function of the voltage (charge). This assumption is necessary in order to establish that the ratio $P_{mn}/(m\omega_1 + n\omega_2)$ which appears in (5.8-9) is independent of ω_1 and ω_2. Thus it is not sufficient for a device to be lossless in order that the Manley-Rowe relations apply. For example an "ideal diode" which has zero voltage for positive current and zero current for negative voltage is certainly lossless, but it does not connect the Q_{mn} and the V_{mn} and it is not restricted by (5.8-11). It is evident that a similar argument could be carried through for a nonlinear inductor with the flux (current) specified as a single valued function of the current (flux). We expect therefore that (5.8-11) should represent a basic limitation upon frequency conversion at the terminals of any lumped circuit composed of such inductors and capacitors. Another way of saying this is that the system should be describable by an energy which is a constant of the motion. For a distributed system these ideas can be directly extended. The Manley-Rowe equations apply at the input ports of a lossless nonlinear medium if that medium can be described by an energy density (see [Pe 2], Chap. 6).

5.9. THE DISTRIBUTED PARAMETRIC AMPLIFIER

In Section 5.4 we considered techniques for estimating the growth of harmonics when a nonlinear transmission line is excited by a single sinusoid.

We shall now investigate the interaction between three harmonics which remain synchronized both in space and in time. We shall find that under certain conditions exponential growth of a wave occurs which can be applied as a traveling wave parametric amplifier [Bl 1, Ch 2, Lo 4].

The system under consideration is sketched in Fig. 5-24a. We suppose that three waves are propagated: a "pump" wave with argument $(\omega_P t - \beta_P x)$, a "signal" wave with argument $(\omega_1 t - \beta_1 x)$, and an "idler" wave with argument $(\omega_2 t - \beta_2 x)$. Furthermore we suppose that the frequencies and propagation constants are related by

$$\omega_1 + \omega_2 = \omega_P,$$
$$\beta_1 + \beta_2 = \beta_P. \qquad (5.9\text{-}1a,b)$$

The purpose of the pump wave is to supply energy and to permit amplification at frequencies ω_1 and ω_2. A suitable approximation to the original system (Fig. 5-24a) for the case of a large pump signal is shown in Fig. 5-24b. Here it is assumed that the action of the pump wave is only to cause the shunt capacitance to vary with space and time as

$$c(x, t) = c_0 + \Delta c \cos (\omega_P t - \beta_P x)$$

or

$$c(x, t) = c_0 + \frac{\Delta c}{2} \left[e^{j(\omega_P t - \beta_P x)} + e^{-j(\omega_P t - \beta_P x)} \right]. \qquad (5.9\text{-}2)$$

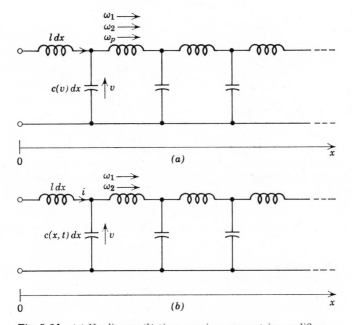

Fig. 5-24   (a) Nonlinear, (b) time varying parametric amplifiers.

The signal and idler waves can be represented by the real sinusoids

$$v_1 = V_1(x)e^{j(\omega_1 t - \beta_1 x)} + V_1^*(x)e^{-j(\omega_1 t - \beta_1 x)},$$

$$i_1 = I_1(x)e^{j(\omega_1 t - \beta_1 x)} + I_1^*(x)e^{-j(\omega_1 t - \beta_1 x)},$$

$$v_2 = V_2(x)e^{j(\omega_2 t - \beta_2 x)} + V_2^*(x)e^{-j(\omega_2 t - \beta_2 x)},$$

$$(5.9\text{-}3a,b,c,d)$$

$$i_2 = I_2(x)e^{j(\omega_2 t - \beta_2 x)} + I_2^*(x)e^{-j(\omega_2 t - \beta_2 x)}.$$

The partial differential equations for the line of Fig. 5-15*b* are

$$\frac{\partial v}{\partial x} = -l\frac{\partial i}{\partial t},$$

$$\frac{\partial i}{\partial x} = -\frac{\partial [c(x,t)v]}{\partial t}, \qquad (5.9\text{-}4a,b)$$

where neglecting other harmonics we can write $v = v_1 + v_2$ and $i = i_1 + i_2$. To simplify the notation let us write $\phi_1 = (\omega_1 t - \beta_1 x)$, $\phi_2 = (\omega_2 t - \beta_2 x)$ and $\phi_P = (\omega_P t - \beta_P x)$. Thus (5.9-1) becomes

$$\phi_1 + \phi_2 = \phi_P. \qquad (5.9\text{-}5)$$

Now we can write (5.9-4) in the form

$$\frac{\partial^2 v}{\partial x^2} = \frac{l\partial^2(c \cdot v)}{\partial t^2}, \qquad (5.9\text{-}6)$$

We assume that (5.9-6) is satisfied for each harmonic. In particular this condition requires

$$\frac{\partial^2}{\partial x^2}(V_1 e^{j\phi_1}) = l\frac{\partial^2}{\partial t^2}\left(c_0 V_1 e^{j\phi_1} + \frac{\Delta c}{2} V_2^* e^{j(\phi_P - \phi_2)}\right). \qquad (5.9\text{-}7)$$

Carrying out the differentiation in (5.9-7) we have

$$\frac{dV_1}{dx^2} - 2j\beta_1\frac{dV_1}{dx} - \beta_1^2 V_1 = -\omega_1^2 l c_0 V_1 - \omega_1^2 \frac{l\,\Delta c}{2} V_2^*. \qquad (5.9\text{-}8)$$

If we assume V_1 to be a slowly varying function of x, the first term $\partial^2 V_1/\partial x^2$ on the left hand side of (5.9-8) can be dropped. Furthermore $\beta_1^2 = \omega_1^2 l c_0$. Thus (5.9-8) becomes

$$\frac{dV_1}{dx} \approx -\frac{j}{4}\beta_1\frac{\Delta c}{c_0}V_2^*. \qquad (5.9\text{-}9a)$$

In a similar manner one can show that

$$\frac{dV_2^*}{dx} \approx +\frac{j}{4}\beta_2\frac{\Delta c}{c_0}V_1. \qquad (5.9\text{-}9b)$$

From (5.9-9) we can write

$$\frac{d^2V_1}{dx^2} = \frac{\beta_1\beta_2}{16}\left(\frac{\Delta c}{c_0}\right)^2 V_1. \tag{5.9-10}$$

So V_1 must vary with x as $\exp(\pm\alpha x)$ where

$$\alpha = \frac{\sqrt{\beta_1\beta_2}}{4}\left(\frac{\Delta c}{c_0}\right). \tag{5.9-11}$$

It is not difficult to show in a similar manner that V_2, I_1 and I_2 must have the same spatial variation.

If we specify at the input end ($x = 0$) that $V_1(0) = V_0$ and $V_2(0) = 0$, then the amplitudes must depend upon x as

$$V_1(x) = V_0 \cosh \alpha x,$$
$$V_2(x) = jV_0\left(\frac{\beta_2}{\beta_1}\right)^{1/2} \sinh \alpha x, \tag{5.9-12a,b}$$

where the factor j in (5.9-12b) indicates that the idler wave is $90°$ out of phase with the signal wave.

This analysis supposes that only the pump, signal and idler waves are present on the line. A detailed and elegant analysis of the case when all harmonics of the pump wave are present has been carried through by Cassidy [Ca 5, Ca 6]. He shows that the line becomes absolutely unstable at the signal frequency when the phase velocity for the pump exceeds that for the signal.

5.10. SATURATION ON A DISTRIBUTED PARAMETRIC AMPLIFIER

In the previous section we consider the question of propagation on the line of Fig. 5-24b for which the capacitance per unit length varies as $c(x, t) = c_0 + \Delta c \cos(\omega_P t - \beta_P x)$. The result is an exponential gain function indicated by (5.9-12a) without saturation. In practice, of course, when the amplitude of the signal wave becomes approximately equal to the amplitude of the pump wave, saturation effects occur and the gain per unit length diminishes. To estimate this effect we must return to the system of Fig. 5-24a for which the partial differential equation for the shunt voltage is

$$\frac{\partial^2 v}{\partial x^2} = l\frac{\partial^2 q(v)}{\partial t^2}, \tag{5.10-1}$$

and suppose that the shunt voltage includes a pump wave voltage. Thus

$$v = V_1 e^{j\phi_1} + V_2 e^{j\phi_2} + V_P e^{j\phi_P} + \text{complex conjugate,} \qquad (5.10\text{-}2)$$

where as before $\phi_1 = (\omega_1 t - \beta_1 x)$, $\phi_2 = (\omega_2 t - \beta_2 x)$ and $\phi_P = (\omega_P t - \beta_P x)$. If we assume that

$$q(v) = c_0\left(v - \frac{a}{2} v^2\right), \qquad (5.10\text{-}3)$$

and also that $\phi_1 + \phi_2 = \phi_P$, we obtain (just as in the previous section)

$$\frac{dV_1}{dx} = -\frac{j\beta_1 a}{4} V_P V_2^*,$$

$$\frac{dV_2}{dx} = -\frac{j\beta_2 a}{4} V_P V_1^*, \qquad (5.10\text{-}4a,b,c)$$

$$\frac{dV_P}{dx} = +\frac{j\beta_P a}{4} V_1 V_2.$$

Now if we further assume that the phase angles of V_1 and V_2 with respect to V_P remain independent of x, (5.10-4) can be interpreted as applying only to the magnitudes of pump, idler and signal wave amplitudes. Thus

$$\frac{d|V_1|}{dx} = -\frac{\beta_1 a}{4} |V_P| |V_2|,$$

$$\frac{d|V_2|}{dx} = -\frac{\beta_2 a}{4} |V_P| |V_1|, \qquad (5.10\text{-}5a,b,c)$$

$$\frac{d|V_P|}{dx} = +\frac{\beta_P a}{4} |V_1| |V_2|.$$

Equations 5.10-5a,b,c were first derived by Cullen [Cu 1] and have been investigated in detail by Jurkus and Robson [Ju 1, Ju 2, Kr 2]. Their approach was to divide (5.10-5a) by (5.10-5b) to obtain

$$\frac{d|V_1|}{d|V_2|} = \frac{\beta_1}{\beta_2} \frac{|V_2|}{|V_1|}. \qquad (5.10\text{-}6)$$

Upon integration with the assumption that $|V_1| = V_{10}$ and $|V_2| = 0$ at $x = 0$ we have

$$|V_1|^2 = \frac{\beta_1}{\beta_2} |V_2|^2 + V_{10}^2. \qquad (5.10\text{-}7)$$

In a similar way

$$|V_P|^2 = -\frac{\beta_P}{\beta_2}|V_2|^2 + V_{P0}{}^2, \tag{5.10-8}$$

$$|V_1|^2 = -\frac{\beta_1}{\beta_P}(|V_P|^2 - V_{P0}{}^2) + V_{10}{}^2. \tag{5.10-9}$$

Substitution of (5.10-7) and (5.10-8) into (5.10-5b) yields

$$\frac{d\,|V_2|}{dx} = -\frac{\beta_2 a}{4}\left[\frac{\beta_1}{\beta_2}|V_2|^2 + V_{10}{}^2\right]^{\frac{1}{2}}\left[V_{P0}{}^2 - \frac{\beta_P}{\beta_2}|V_2|^2\right]^{\frac{1}{2}},$$

or

$$\int_0^{|V_2|}\frac{d\,|V_2|}{\left[|V_2|^2 + \frac{\beta_2}{\beta_1}V_{10}{}^2\right]^{\frac{1}{2}}\left[\frac{\beta_2}{\beta_P}V_{P0}{}^2 - |V_2|^2\right]^{\frac{1}{2}}} = \frac{\sqrt{\beta_1\beta_P}\,a}{4}\int_0^x dx, \tag{5.10-10}$$

which has as a solution the elliptic function [By 1]

$$|V_2| = \left(\frac{\beta_2}{\beta_1}\right)^{\frac{1}{2}}kV_{10}\,\mathrm{sd}\,(\alpha_0 x, k), \tag{5.10-11}$$

where

$$k = \left[1 + \frac{\beta_P}{\beta_1}\frac{V_{10}{}^2}{V_{P0}{}^2}\right]^{-\frac{1}{2}} \tag{5.10-12}$$

is the modulus and

$$\alpha_0 = \frac{V_{P0}a}{4}\sqrt{\beta_1\beta_2}. \tag{5.10-13}$$

Substitution of (5.10-11) into (5.10-7) and (5.10-8) yields

$$|V_1| = V_{10}\,\mathrm{nd}\,(\alpha_0 x, k), \tag{5.10-14}$$
$$|V_P| = V_{P0}\,\mathrm{cd}\,(\alpha_0 x, k). \tag{5.10-15}$$

Since the power levels in the three waves are proportional to the squares of the voltage amplitudes, (5.10-11), (5.10-14) and (5.10-15) can also be written

$$P_1 = P_{10}\,\mathrm{nd}^2(\alpha_0 x, k),$$

$$P_2 = P_{20}\frac{\beta_2}{\beta_1}k^2\,\mathrm{sd}^2(\alpha_0 x, k), \tag{5.10-16a,b,c}$$

$$P_P = P_{P0}\,\mathrm{cd}^2(\alpha_0 x, k),$$

where

$$k = \left[1 + \frac{\beta_P}{\beta_1}\frac{P_{10}}{P_{P0}}\right]^{-\frac{1}{2}}. \tag{5.10-17}$$

For a small input signal $k \approx 1$ and (5.10-16) reduce to

$$P_1 = P_{10} \cosh^2 (\alpha_0 x),$$

$$P_2 = \frac{\beta_2}{\beta_1} P_{10} \sinh^2 (\alpha_0 x), \qquad\qquad (5.10\text{-}18a,b,c)$$

$$P_P = P_{PO},$$

which follow directly from (5.9-12) of the previous section. For $k^2 = 0.8$ the power levels in the three modes are plotted as a normalized function of $\alpha_0 x / k$ in Fig. 5-25a.

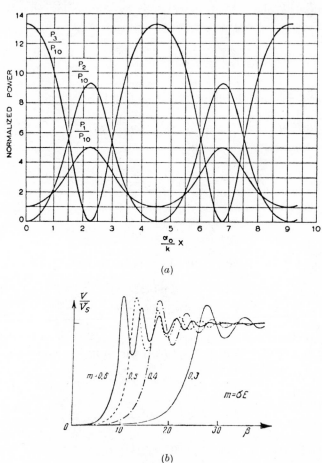

(a)

(b)

Fig. 5-25 (a) Variation of signal, idling and pump power along the line for $k^2 = 0.8$ [Ju 1]. (b) Curve for change in amplitude with distance, illustrating oscillatory nature of the approximation to saturation operation [Ak 1].

In going from (5.10-4) and (5.10-5) we specifically assumed that the phase of the signal and idler waves with respect to the pump wave did not depend upon x. This calculation therefore yields a saturation effect which is due only to the loss of power by the pump wave. Saturation effects resulting from phase changes have been ignored. The results are in good agreement with experimental observations when both signal and pump are applied at the input end [Ju 2]. However it is quite possible to apply the pump signal with an external distributed voltage source which is applied in series with the nonlinear capacitor. The pump amplitude will then remain independent of x and phase variations will play the major role in saturation phenomena. This situation has been studied in detail by Akhmanov and Dmitriyev [Ak 1] who assumed a charge voltage relation

$$q(v) = c_0(v + av^2 + bv^3) \tag{5.10-19}$$

and a shunt conductance of g mhos per unit length along the line. The voltage on the line was

$$v = V_1(x) \cos [\omega_1 t - \beta_1 x + \theta_1(x)] + V_2(x) \cos [\omega_2 t - \beta_2 x + \theta_2(x)]$$
$$+ E \cos (\omega_P t - \beta_P x), \tag{5.10-20}$$

where V_1, V_2, θ_1 and θ_2 are assumed to be slowly varying functions of x and E is a constant pump wave amplitude. The differential equations for the slowly varying amplitudes and phases are then

$$\frac{dV_1}{dx} + \sigma_1 E V_2 \sin \Phi + \delta_1 V_1 = 0,$$

$$\frac{dV_2}{dx} + \sigma_2 E V_1 \sin \Phi + \delta_2 V_2 = 0,$$

$$\tag{5.10-21a,b,c}$$

$$\frac{d\Phi}{dx} - (\Delta_1 + \Delta_2) + \left(\sigma_1 \frac{V_2}{V_1} + \sigma_2 \frac{V_1}{V_2}\right) E \cos \Phi + \tfrac{3}{2}(\gamma_1 + \gamma_2)E^2$$
$$+ \frac{3}{2}\left(\frac{\gamma_1}{2} + \gamma_2\right) V_1{}^2 + \frac{3}{2}\left(\gamma_1 + \frac{\gamma_2}{2}\right) V_2{}^2 = 0,$$

where $\Phi = \theta_1 + \theta_2$, $\sigma_{1,2} = a\beta_{1,2}/2$, $\gamma_{1,2} = b\beta_{1,2}/2$, $\delta_{1,2} = lg\omega_{1,2}/2\beta_{1,2}$, $\Delta_{1,2} = (\omega_{1,2}/2)[(\beta_{1,2}/\omega_{1,2}) - (\beta_P/\omega_P)]$. Equations 5.10-21a,b,c have steady solutions when the derivatives are set equal to zero. From (5.10-21a) and (5.10-21b) we find for the saturation levels

$$\frac{V_{1s}{}^2}{V_{2s}{}^2} = \frac{\sigma_1 \delta_2}{\sigma_2 \delta_1} \quad \text{and} \quad E \sin \Phi_s = -\left[\frac{\delta_1 \delta_2}{\sigma_1 \sigma_2}\right]^{1/2},$$

which upon substitution into (5.10-21c) (with $d\Phi/dx = 0$) yield

$$V_{1s} = \left[\frac{2[\Delta_1 + \Delta_2 - \frac{3}{2}(\gamma_1 + \gamma_2)E^2 \mp (\delta_1 + \delta_2)\left(\dfrac{\sigma_1\sigma_2 E^2}{\delta_1\delta_2} - 1\right)^{1/2}]}{3\left[\gamma_1\left(\dfrac{1}{2} + \dfrac{\sigma_2\delta_1}{\sigma_1\delta_2}\right) + \gamma_2\left(1 + \dfrac{1}{2}\dfrac{\sigma_2\delta_1}{\sigma_1\delta_2}\right)\right]} \right]^{1/2} . \quad (5.10\text{-}22)$$

Equations 5.10-21*a,b,c* have been numerically integrated in reference [Ak 1] to exhibit the oscillatory manner in which this stationary amplitude is approached for varying amounts of capacitive nonlinearity. These results are reproduced in Fig. 5-25*b*.

5.11. LAGRANGIAN FORMULATION FOR A DISTRIBUTED SYSTEM [Go 2]

We now introduce an alternative description for a conservative wave system which is sometimes convenient. It is supposed that the state of the system can be described by a *Lagrangian density*, $\mathcal{L}$, which is a function of the dynamical variables ϕ_i and their time and space derivatives. Thus

$$\mathcal{L} = \mathcal{L}(\phi_{ix}, \phi_{it}, \phi_i). \qquad (5.11\text{-}1)$$

The solution can be specified by giving the ϕ_{ix}, ϕ_{it} and ϕ_i as functions of x and t. The Lagrangian density is assumed to have the property that for a *solution* the integral

$$\iint \mathcal{L}\, dx\, dt$$

is *stationary* with respect to a variation in the ϕ_i which vanishes on the spatial boundaries and at the initial and final instants of time. Such a variation of the ϕ_i is indicated by the symbol δ and the stationary requirement can be written

$$\delta \iint \mathcal{L}\, dx\, dt = 0. \qquad (5.11\text{-}2)$$

This is known as *Hamilton's principle*. Any variation in $\mathcal{L}$ can be written to the first order as

$$\delta\mathcal{L} = \frac{\partial\mathcal{L}}{\partial\phi_x}\,\delta\phi_x + \frac{\partial\mathcal{L}}{\partial\phi_t}\,\delta\phi_t + \frac{\partial\mathcal{L}}{\partial\phi}\,\delta\phi, \qquad (5.11\text{-}3)$$

where the subscript i which denotes the different dependent variables has been neglected.

It is now convenient to introduce the symbol $\doteq$ [Pe 2, pp. 79–81] which implies that the difference between the quantities it separates integrates over the given boundaries to zero. Thus for any scalar function S

$$S \, \delta\phi_t \doteq -S_t \, \delta\phi, \tag{5.11-4}$$

since

$$\int_{t_1}^{t_2} (S \, \delta\phi_t + S_t \, \delta\phi) \, dt = \int_{t_1}^{t_2} \frac{\partial}{\partial t} (S \, \delta\phi) \, dt = S \, \delta\phi \Big|_{t_1}^{t_2} = 0,$$

which is zero because $\delta\phi$ vanishes at the initial and final instants (t_1 and t_2). Likewise

$$S \, \delta\phi_x \doteq -S_x \, \delta\phi. \tag{5.11-5}$$

Using this notation we can write Hamilton's principle as $\delta\mathcal{L} \doteq 0$ or

$$0 \doteq \delta\mathcal{L} = \frac{\partial\mathcal{L}}{\partial\phi_x} \delta\phi_x + \frac{\partial\mathcal{L}}{\partial\phi_t} \delta\phi_t + \frac{\partial\mathcal{L}}{\partial\phi} \delta\phi,$$

and making use of (5.11-4) and (5.11-5)

$$0 \doteq -\frac{\partial}{\partial x} \left(\frac{\partial\mathcal{L}}{\partial\phi_x} \right) \delta\phi - \frac{\partial}{\partial t} \left(\frac{\partial\mathcal{L}}{\partial\phi_t} \right) \delta\phi + \frac{\partial\mathcal{L}}{\partial\phi} \delta\phi.$$

Thus we can write

$$\left[\frac{\partial}{\partial x} \left(\frac{\partial\mathcal{L}}{\partial\phi_x} \right) + \frac{\partial}{\partial t} \left(\frac{\partial\mathcal{L}}{\partial\phi_t} \right) - \frac{\partial\mathcal{L}}{\partial\phi} \right] \delta\phi \doteq 0. \tag{5.11-6}$$

Since $\delta\phi$ is arbitrary except at the temporal and spatial boundaries, the left-hand side of (5.11-6) will integrate to zero only if

$$\frac{\partial}{\partial x} \left(\frac{\partial\mathcal{L}}{\partial\phi_x} \right) + \frac{\partial}{\partial t} \left(\frac{\partial\mathcal{L}}{\partial\phi_t} \right) - \frac{\partial\mathcal{L}}{\partial\phi} = 0 \tag{5.11-7}$$

for all space and time. Equation 5.11-7 is called the Lagrange-Euler equation. For several dependent variables (the ϕ_i) there are several Lagrange-Euler equations.

The "trick" in developing a Lagrangian formulation for a wave system is to choose a Lagrangian density such that the Lagrange-Euler equations are in fact the true dynamical equations describing the system. One way of executing this choice is simply to guess. A more systematic approach is to consider a Lagrangian formulation for a *lumped* system of energy storage elements. Partial derivatives with respect to x do not appear. The Lagrangian is then written

$$L = L(\phi_{it}, \phi_i), \tag{5.11-8}$$

Hamilton's principle becomes

$$\delta \int L \, dt = 0, \tag{5.11-9}$$

and the corresponding Lagrange-Euler equations are

$$\frac{d}{dt}\left(\frac{\partial L}{\partial \phi_{it}}\right) - \frac{\partial L}{\partial \phi_i} = 0. \tag{5.11-10}$$

A suitable Lagrangian is then the difference of electric coenergy $\int Q(v)\, dv$ and magnetic energy $\int i(\Phi)\, d\Phi$ evaluated for each node [Ch 3]. Thus

$$L(v_i, \Phi_i) = \int Q(v_i)\, dv_i - \int i(\Phi_i)\, d\Phi_i. \tag{5.11-11}$$

Since the flux at the ith node is related to the voltage at the ith node by

$$v_i = \frac{d\Phi_i}{dt}, \tag{5.11-12}$$

substitution of this Lagrangian into (5.11-10) yields

$$\frac{dQ}{dt} + i_1 = 0. \tag{5.11-13}$$

Equation 5.11-13 is simply a statement of Kirchhoff's current law in the form that the total current flowing away the ith node through magnetic energy storage elements is equal to the rate of change of the total charge stored in capacitors at the ith node.

An equally suitable Lagrangian function for a lumped system is the difference between magnetic coenergy $\int \Phi(i)\, di$ and electric energy $\int v(Q)\, dQ$ evaluated for each loop. Thus

$$L(i_i, Q_i) = \int \Phi(i_i)\, di_i - \int v(Q_i)\, dQ_i. \tag{5.11-14}$$

Since loop current is related to loop charge by

$$i_1 = \frac{dQ_i}{dt}, \tag{5.11-15}$$

substitution of this Lagrangian into (5.11-10) yields

$$\frac{d\Phi_i}{dt} + v_i = 0. \tag{5.11-16}$$

Equation 5.11-16 is simply a statement of Kirchhoff's voltage law in the form that the sum of capacitor voltages and inductor voltages around a closed loop must be zero.

In order to obtain a Lagrangian density function for a distributed system one can construct a Lagrangian in the lumped approximation and then proceed to the distributed limit. This technique is best explained with an example [Sc 13]. Consider the dispersive nonlinear transmission line TL-1 in Fig. 5-8a. Suppose that the line is lumped with the section length a so that

$$I_1 = i_1 a,$$
$$L = la,$$
$$C_1(v_1) = c_1(v_1)a, \qquad \text{(5.11-17)}$$
$$L_1(I_1) = l_1(i_1)/a,$$
$$C = ca,$$

have the units of amperes, henrys and farads per section. The Lagrangian per section can then be written on a node basis as the difference between electric coenergy and magnetic energy per section. Thus

$$L_n = \sum_j \int Q_j \, dv_j - \sum_j \int i_j \, d\Phi_j, \qquad \text{(5.11-18)}$$

where j is an index which catalogs the independent node fluxes or their time derivatives the node voltages for each section. The independent fluxes necessary to describe the nth section are

$$\Phi_{1n} = \int v_1 \, dt \quad \text{at the } n\text{th section,}$$

$$\Phi_n = \int v \, dt \quad \text{at the } n\text{th section,}$$

and

$$\Phi_{n+1} = \int v \, dt \quad \text{at the } (n+1)\text{st section.}$$

In terms of these the Lagrangian becomes the sum of the Lagrangians evaluated for each section

$$L = \sum_n L_n$$

$$= \sum_n \left[\int_0^{v_{1n}} Q_1(v) \, dv + \tfrac{1}{2} C v_n{}^2 - \int_0^{\Phi_n - \Phi_{1n}} I_1(\Phi) \, d\Phi - \frac{(\Phi_{n+1} - \Phi_n)^2}{2L} \right],$$

$$\text{(5.11-19)}$$

where $Q_1(v)$ describes the capacitor $C_1(v)$ and $I_1(\Phi)$ describes the inductor $L_1(\Phi)$. Equation 5.11-19 is evidently the same as

$$L = \sum_n a \left[\int_0^{v_{1n}} \frac{Q_1(v) \, dv}{a} + \frac{1}{2} \frac{C}{a} v_n{}^2 - \int_0^{\Phi_n - \Phi_{1n}} \frac{I_1}{a} \, d\Phi - \frac{1}{2L/a} \left(\frac{\Phi_{n+1} - \Phi_n}{a^2} \right) \right],$$

which in the limit as a approaches zero becomes

$$L = \int \mathcal{L}\, dx, \tag{5.11-20}$$

where $\mathcal{L}$ is the Lagrangian density

$$\mathcal{L} = \int_0^{v_1} q_1(v)\, dv + \frac{cv^2}{2} - \int_0^{\Phi - \Phi_1} i_1(\Phi)\, d\Phi - \frac{1}{2l}\left(\frac{\partial \Phi}{\partial x}\right)^2. \tag{5.11-21}$$

That (5.11-21) is in fact an acceptable Lagrangian density function is easily checked by substituting into the Lagrange-Euler equations (5.11-7). These give

$$c\,\frac{\partial^2 \Phi}{\partial t^2} - \frac{1}{l}\frac{\partial^2 \Phi}{\partial x^2} + i_1(\Phi - \Phi_1) = 0,$$

$$\tag{5.11-22a,b}$$

$$c_1(v_1)\,\frac{\partial^2 \Phi_1}{\partial t^2} - i_1(\Phi - \Phi_1) = 0,$$

or

$$c\,\frac{\partial^2 v}{\partial t^2} - \frac{1}{l}\frac{\partial^2 v}{\partial x^2} + \frac{\partial i_1}{\partial t} = 0,$$

$$\tag{5.11-23a,b}$$

$$c_1(v_1)\,\frac{\partial v_1}{\partial t} - i_1 = 0,$$

which are evidently correct dynamical equations.

5.12. STABILITY ANALYSIS

a. Stability of a Periodic Wave Train.   An interesting technique for the stability analysis of lossless transmission systems, which has recently been developed by Whitham [Wh 2, Wh 3, Wh 4, Wh 5], is described in this section. Attention is directed toward dss solutions which are periodic functions of the angle variable

$$\theta = \beta x - \omega t. \tag{5.12-1}$$

The basic idea is to determine the stability of a dss solution $\phi(\theta)$ by supposing that both β and ω are *slowly varying* functions of x and t. The Lagrangian approach can then very conveniently be used to develop quasilinear equations with β and ω as dependent variables. If these quasilinear equations are hyperbolic, small changes in β and ω will propagate with a characteristic velocity. If the equations are not hyperbolic, the characteristic velocities are complex or imaginary. In this case, as we shall see, small disturbances will grow exponentially and the wave is unstable.

As an example of the technique let us examine the nonlinear wave equation

$$\phi_{xx} - \phi_{tt} = f'(\phi). \tag{5.12-2}$$

With the dss variable of (5.12-1) we can write

$$(\beta^2 - \omega^2)\phi_{\theta\theta} = f'(\phi). \tag{5.12-3}$$

Notice that we have neglected the slow variation of β and ω with x and t in (5.12-3). We can then integrate to obtain

$$\tfrac{1}{2}(\beta^2 - \omega^2)(\phi_\theta)^2 = E + f(\phi), \tag{5.12-4}$$

where E is a constant of integration which may also be a slowly varying function of x and t. Equation 5.12-4 can be solved for ϕ_θ as

$$\phi_\theta = \left(\frac{2[E + f(\phi)]}{(\beta^2 - \omega^2)}\right)^{\!\!\tfrac{1}{2}}, \tag{5.12-5}$$

which can be integrated to give

$$\theta = \sqrt{(\beta^2 - \omega^2)} \int \frac{d\phi}{\sqrt{2(E + f)}}. \tag{5.12-6}$$

Equation 5.12-6 gives ϕ as an implicit function of θ in the form of an elliptic integral. In general $\phi(\theta)$ will oscillate periodically between zeros of $[E + f(\phi)]$. If there are no such zeros, φ will increase monotonically with increasing θ.

The Lagrangian density function from which (5.12-2) can be derived via the Lagrange-Euler equation is

$$\mathcal{L} = \tfrac{1}{2}[(\phi_x)^2 - (\phi_t)^2] + f(\phi). \tag{5.12-7}$$

With the dss variable of (5.12-1) this becomes

$$\mathcal{L} = \tfrac{1}{2}(\beta^2 - \omega^2)(\phi_\theta)^2 + f(\phi), \tag{5.12-8}$$

which upon substituting from (5.12-4) becomes

$$\mathcal{L} = 2[E + f(\phi)] - E. \tag{5.12-9}$$

The corresponding Hamilton's principle is

$$\delta \int_{\theta_1}^{\theta_2} \mathcal{L}\, d\theta = 0. \tag{5.12-10}$$

Now we suppose that in addition to the *fast* variation of the wave with θ, there is a *slow* variation with β, ω and E. That is to say β, ω and E are supposed to be slowly varying functions of x and t rather than constants. The fast variation can be removed from $\mathcal{L}$ by averaging over a cycle in θ.

Thus

$$\tilde{\mathcal{L}} \equiv \frac{1}{2\pi} \int_0^{2\pi} \mathcal{L} \, d\theta \tag{5.12-11}$$

$$= \frac{1}{2\pi} \oint \frac{\mathcal{L}}{\phi_\theta} \, d\phi, \tag{5.12-12}$$

and from substitution of (5.12-5) and (5.12-9)

$$\tilde{\mathcal{L}} = \sqrt{\beta^2 - \omega^2} \, I(E) - E, \tag{5.12-13}$$

where

$$I(E) \equiv \frac{1}{2\pi} \oint \sqrt{2[E + f(\phi)]} \, d\phi \tag{5.12-14}$$

and $\oint$ indicates integration over one cycle in ϕ.

The averaged Lagrangian is a function of E and

$$\theta_x = \beta \quad \text{and} \quad \theta_t = -\omega. \tag{5.12-15a,b}$$

Hamilton's principle (5.12-10) becomes

$$\delta \int_0^{2\pi m} \tilde{\mathcal{L}}(\beta, \omega, E) \, d\theta = 0, \tag{5.12-16}$$

where m is a large integer. The corresponding Lagrange-Euler equations are

$$\frac{\partial}{\partial x}\left(\frac{\partial \tilde{\mathcal{L}}}{\partial \beta}\right) - \frac{\partial}{\partial t}\left(\frac{\partial \tilde{\mathcal{L}}}{\partial \omega}\right) = 0, \tag{5.12-17}$$

$$\frac{\partial \tilde{\mathcal{L}}}{\partial E} = 0. \tag{5.12-18}$$

Also from (5.12-15)

$$\frac{\partial \beta}{\partial t} + \frac{\partial \omega}{\partial x} = 0. \tag{5.12-19}$$

Substitution of (5.12-13) into (5.12-18) yields

$$\sqrt{\beta^2 - \omega^2} \, I'(E) = 1, \tag{5.12-20}$$

where

$$I'(E) = \frac{1}{2\pi} \oint \frac{d\phi}{\sqrt{2(E + f(\phi))}}. \tag{5.12-21}$$

Equation 5.12-20 can be considered a nonlinear generalization of the dispersion equation. In the linear case $f'(\phi) = \phi$ and $f(\phi) = \phi^2/2$ so $I'(E) = 1$

and (5.12-20) becomes

$$\beta^2 = \omega^2 + 1. \tag{5.12-22}$$

If we square both sides of (5.12-20) and then differentiate with respect to x, we find

$$\beta(I')^2 \frac{\partial \beta}{\partial x} - \omega(I')^2 \frac{\partial \omega}{\partial x} + (\beta^2 - \omega^2) I' I'' \frac{\partial E}{\partial x} = 0. \tag{5.12-23}$$

Equation 5.12-23 together with (5.12-17) and (5.12-19) is a set of three quasilinear equations for the three slowly varying parameters, β, ω and E. For $\tilde{\mathcal{L}}$ as in (5.12-13), (5.12-17) becomes

$$-\omega^2 I \frac{\partial \beta}{\partial x} - \omega\beta I \frac{\partial \beta}{\partial t} + \omega\beta I \frac{\partial \omega}{\partial x} + \beta^2 I \frac{\partial \omega}{\partial t}$$

$$+ (\beta^2 - \omega^2)\beta I' \frac{\partial E}{\partial x} + (\beta^2 - \omega^2)\omega I' \frac{\partial E}{\partial t} = 0, \tag{5.12-24}$$

and in matrix notation (5.12-19), (5.12-23) and (5.12-24) are

$$\begin{bmatrix} -\omega\beta I & \beta^2 I & (\beta^2 - \omega^2)\omega I' \\ 0 & 0 & 0 \\ 1 & 0 & 0 \end{bmatrix} \frac{\partial}{\partial t} \begin{bmatrix} \beta \\ \omega \\ E \end{bmatrix}$$

$$+ \begin{bmatrix} -\omega^2 I & \omega\beta I & (\beta^2 - \omega^2)\beta I' \\ (I')^2\beta & -(I')^2\omega & (\beta^2 - \omega^2)I'I'' \\ 0 & 1 & 0 \end{bmatrix} \frac{\partial}{\partial x} \begin{bmatrix} \beta \\ \omega \\ E \end{bmatrix} = 0, \tag{5.12-25}$$

so the characteristic velocities are those for which

$$\det \begin{bmatrix} -I(\omega^2 - \omega\beta u) & I(\omega\beta - \beta^2 u) & I'(\beta - \omega u) \\ \beta(I')^2 & -\omega(I')^2 & I'I'' \\ -u & 1 & 0 \end{bmatrix} = 0$$

or

$$u = \frac{\omega\beta(1 - k) \pm \sqrt{k}\,(\omega^2 - \beta^2)}{\omega^2 - k\beta^2}, \tag{5.12-26}$$

where

$$k = -\frac{II''}{(I')^2}. \tag{5.12-27}$$

Equation 5.12-26 can also be written in the more symmetric form

$$u = \frac{\beta \pm \sqrt{k}\,\omega}{\omega \pm \sqrt{k}\,\beta}. \tag{5.12-28}$$

If the value of k from (5.12-27) is *negative*, the characteristic velocities given by (5.12-26) are *complex*. Since small perturbations in the amplitude variable must vary as

$$E \sim \exp j\beta_e(x - ut) \qquad (5.12\text{-}29)$$

where β_e is determined by the spatial form of the envelope, a complex value of u indicates an exponential growth with time and therefore *instability*.

As an example of the application of this technique consider the mechanical transmission line which was discussed in Section 5.5a. The partial differential equation is

$$\phi_{xx} - \phi_{tt} = \sin \phi. \qquad (5.12\text{-}30)$$

Thus $f'(\phi) = \sin \phi$ and $f(\phi) = -\cos \phi$. From (5.12-6) the dss solutions can be obtained from the elliptic integral

$$\theta = \sqrt{\beta^2 - \omega^2} \int \frac{d\phi}{\sqrt{2(E - \cos \phi)}}. \qquad (5.12\text{-}31)$$

From inspection of (5.12-31) there are four possible types of solutions.

1. $\beta > \omega$, $E > 1$. $\phi(\theta)$ is a monotonically increasing function of θ.
2. $\beta > \omega$, $-1 < E < 1$. $\phi(\theta)$ is a periodic function about $\phi = \pi$.
3. $\beta < \omega$, $-1 < E < 1$. $\phi(\theta)$ is a periodic function about $\phi = 0$.
4. $\beta < \omega$, $E < -1$. $\phi(\theta)$ is a monotonically increasing function of θ.

For $E \gg +1$ (Case 1) the integral $I(E)$ can be directly evaluated from (5.12-14) as $\sqrt{2E}$. Thus $I'(E) = 1/\sqrt{2E}$ and $I''(E) = -1/(2E)^{3/2}$. The value of k in (5.12-28) is then equal to $+1$, and the dss solution is stable. For $E \ll -1$ (Case 4), on the other hand, k is equal to -1 and the dss solution is unstable.

For Case 2 the problem is approximately linear when $E = -(1 - \varepsilon)$ where ε is a small positive number. The angle ϕ is then restricted to small variations about the angle π. From (5.12-21)

$$I'(E) = \frac{1}{2\pi} \oint \frac{d\phi}{\sqrt{2(E - \cos \phi)}}. \qquad (5.12\text{-}32)$$

With the substitution $\phi' = \phi + \pi$ this becomes approximately

$$I'(E) \approx \frac{1}{2\pi} \oint \frac{d(\phi'/\sqrt{2\varepsilon})}{\sqrt{1 - (\phi')^2/2\varepsilon}}$$

$$\approx 1. \qquad (5.12\text{-}33)$$

For Case 2 when $E = +1$

$$I'(E) = \frac{1}{2\pi} \oint \frac{d\phi}{\sqrt{2(1 - \cos \phi)}}$$

$$= \frac{1}{2\pi} \log \tan \left(\frac{\phi}{4}\right)\bigg|_0^{2\pi} = +\infty. \qquad (5.12\text{-}34)$$

Thus a sketch of $I'(E)$ for $\beta > \omega$ will appear as in Fig. 5-26a for Cases 1 and 2. $I''(E)$ is evidently negative for Case 1 and positive for Case 2. From (5.12-27) we find that k will be positive for Case 1 indicating stable propagation and unstable for Case 2 indicating unstable propagation. A similar sketch in Fig. 5-26b indicates that Case 3 is stable and Case 4 is unstable. These conclusions are easily verified on the mechanical transmission line.

See [Sc 18b] for a more complete analysis using the method discussed in Section 4.10.

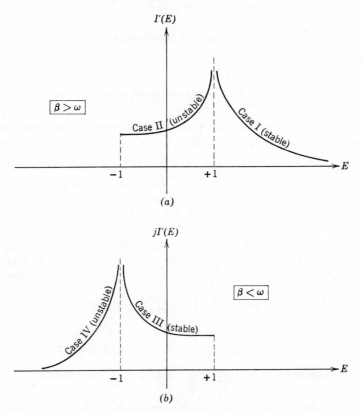

Fig. 5-26   Stability diagrams for periodic DSS waves.

b. Pulse Stability. To demonstrate the stability of the pulse waveform shown in Fig. 5-10,

$$\phi_0 = 4 \tan^{-1} \left[\exp \left(\frac{x - ut}{1 - u^2} \right) \right], \tag{5.12-35}$$

on the mechanical transmission line described by (5.12-30), it is convenient to employ a modification of the technique discussed in Section 4.10. We write

$$\phi = \phi_0 + \phi_p, \tag{5.12-36}$$

where it is assumed that ϕ_p is a small perturbation such that $|\phi_p| \ll |\phi_0|$. Substitution of (5.12-36) into (5.12-30) yields a linear but nonuniform pde for ϕ_p,

$$\frac{\partial^2 \phi_p}{\partial x^2} - \frac{\partial^2 \phi_p}{\partial t^2} = (\cos \phi_0) \phi_p. \tag{5.12-37}$$

A sum of product solutions can be written in the form

$$\phi_p(x, t) = \sum_{i=1}^{\infty} \phi_i(x) e^{j\omega_i t}, \tag{5.12-38}$$

for which the ϕ_i must satisfy

$$\frac{d^2 \phi_i}{dx^2} + (\omega_i^2 - \cos \phi_0) \phi_i = 0. \tag{5.12-39}$$

For $u = 0$ this again is in the form of a "potential well" problem for Schrödinger's equation. The zero frequency eigenfunction ϕ_1 must satisfy

$$\frac{d^2 \phi_1}{dx^2} = (\cos \phi_0) \, \phi_1. \tag{5.12-40}$$

From (5.12-30) this is the same equation which must be satisfied by $\partial \phi_0 / \partial x$ for $u = 0$. Thus for $u = 0$ the zero frequency eigenfunction is $\partial \phi_0 / \partial x$. This has no nodes so the minimum eigenvalue of ω^2 is zero and ω is always real. For $u = 0$ we therefore have no instability of the pulse solution except that arbitrary pulse displacement can occur without growth or decay just as in Section 4.10.

For $u \neq 0$ we can introduce the Lorentz transformation

$$x \to x' = \frac{x - ut}{\sqrt{1 - u^2}}; \qquad t \to t' = \frac{t - ux}{\sqrt{1 - u^2}}, \tag{5.12-41a,b}$$

which were discussed in Section 5.6b. Equation 5.12-30 becomes

$$\frac{\partial^2 \phi}{\partial (x')^2} - \frac{\partial^2 \phi}{\partial (t')^2} = \sin \phi, \tag{5.12-42}$$

with the pulse solution

$$\phi_0 = 4 \tan^{-1} [\exp (x')]. \qquad (5.12\text{-}43)$$

But this is just the problem previously discussed for $u = 0$. Thus the moving pulse solution is also stable.

5.13. PULSE INTERACTION

In this final section we briefly consider the interaction of nonlinear pulse (dss) waveforms on a nonlinear lossless system for which the pde can be derived from a Lagrangian density function. If the pde is symmetric in the independent variables x and t, and if the Lagrangian density is invariant to a Lorentz transformation, then the collision between two pulses can always be studied in a symmetric (i.e., center of energy) frame of reference. An example of such an interaction is either the pulse-pulse or the pulse-antipulse collision on the lossless Josephson line which is mentioned in Section 5.5a. Such collisions are easily demonstrated on the mechanical transmission line.

Another example is the *Born-Infeld equation* which was originally developed in three spatial dimensions as a nonlinear model for the electron [Bo 5]. In one dimensional form it can be derived from the Lagrangian density [Ba 2]

$$\mathcal{L} = \sqrt{1 + \phi_x{}^2 - \phi_t{}^2}, \qquad (5.13\text{-}1)$$

which is evidently symmetric in both x and t and also Lorentz invariant. The corresponding pde is

$$(1 - \phi_t{}^2)\phi_{xx} + 2\phi_x\phi_t\phi_{xt} - (1 + \phi_x{}^2)\phi_{tt} = 0. \qquad (5.13\text{-}2)$$

Barbashov and Chernikov have shown that this equation has dss solutions which interact elastically [Ba 3].

That x and t symmetry and Lorentz invariance are not necessary for elastic interaction of pulses has recently been demonstrated by investigations of the *Korteweg-deVries equation* [Ko 3, La 6, Mi 9, Mi 10]

$$\phi_t + \phi\phi_x + \phi_{xxx} = 0. \qquad (5.13\text{-}3)$$

This equation can be derived from a Lagrangian density if we write

$$\phi = \theta_x, \qquad (5.13\text{-}4)$$

$$\psi = \theta_{xx}, \qquad (5.13\text{-}5)$$

so the pde becomes

$$\theta_{xt} + \theta_x\psi + \psi_{xx} = 0, \qquad (5.13\text{-}6)$$

and

$$\mathcal{L} = \tfrac{1}{2}\theta_x\theta_t + \tfrac{1}{6}\theta_x{}^3 + \theta_x\psi_x + \tfrac{1}{2}\psi^2. \qquad (5.13\text{-}7)$$

The Lagrange-Euler equations derived from (5.13-7) are (5.13-5) and (5.13-6).

Equation 5.13-3 has dss pulse solutions of the form

$$\phi(\xi) = A_0 + A \operatorname{sech}^2\left(\frac{\xi}{\lambda}\right) \tag{5.13-8}$$

where

$$A = 3u, \tag{5.13-9}$$

$$\lambda = 2/\sqrt{u}. \tag{5.13-10}$$

These pulse solutions have been called "Solitons" by Zabusky and Kruskal [Za 1]. Note from (5.13-9) that larger dss velocity implies larger amplitude and, from (5.13-10), smaller pulse width.

Equation 5.13-3 is evidently invariant to a combined reflection of the x and t axes. Thus we expect to find solutions for which

$$\phi(x, t) = \phi(-x, -t). \tag{5.13-11}$$

This symmetry would permit the sort of elastic interaction which is illustrated in Fig. 5-27, and indeed such interactions do occur [La 6, Za 1]. Note that the Lagrangian density (5.13-7) does not have this symmetry, but neither do the transformations, (5.13-4) and (5.13-5), through which it was obtained.

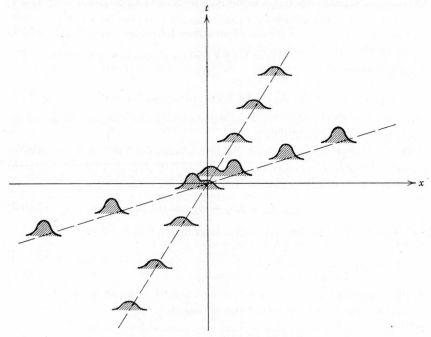

Fig. 5-27   Pulse interaction for the Korteweg-deVries equation.

It is, of course, the symmetry of the original pde which is of primary interest.

Several interesting properties of the Korteweg-deVries equation have recently been discovered. For an introduction see the film "Formation, Propagation and Interaction of Solitons," which is listed in the Bibliography and also [Mi 9, Mi 10].

PROBLEMS

1. Consider a simple nonlinear transmission line with constant shunt capacitance per unit length and a nonlinear series inductance per unit length given by $L(i) = L_0(1 - ai)$. Find a general solution for a simple wave on this system.

2. Suppose that the line described in Problem 1 has a small series resistance per unit length. Derive an amplitude condition for shock wave formation.

3. What is the distance from the input at which a shock wave will form for sinusoidal excitation on the system shown in Fig. 5-4a?

4. Which harmonic of a sinusoidal excitation do you expect primarily to be generated on a transmission line for which the shunt capacitance is (a) a distributed p-n diode, (b) a ferroelectric crystal just above the Curie point?

5. A simple lossless transmission line has a series inductance per unit length equal to $l_0(1 - ai)$ and a shunt capacitance per unit length equal to $c_0(1 - bv)$. Find the ratio of a to b for *minimum* second harmonic generation. See [Ri 5] for results of a simulation of this problem.

6. Which harmonic of a laser light beam do you expect primarily to be generated (a) in glass? (b) in quartz crystal?

7. Consider the problem of second harmonic generation on TL-2 (Fig. 5-8b) assuming that the amplitude of the first harmonic remains constant. How do your results differ from those of Section 5-4c?

8. A simple lossless transmission line has a series inductance per unit length equal to $l_0(1 - ai^2)$ and a shunt capacitance per unit length equal to $C_0(1 - bv^2)$. Find the ratio of a to b for minimum third harmonic generation.

9. Consider the problem of third harmonic generation on TL-1 (Fig. 5-8a) when $C_1(v_1) = C_0(1 - bv_1{}^2)$ assuming that the amplitude of the first harmonic remains constant.

10. Repeat Problem 9 for TL-2 (Fig. 5-8b).

11. Sketch the trajectories in the dss phase plane for the problem of Section 5-5a. Consider the case $u > 1$ as well as $u < 1$.

12. Show that the Manley-Rowe equations permit total conversion from the fundamental to the second or third harmonic.

13. What is the conversion gain (or loss) for up conversion in a lossless. nonlinear mixer?

14. Suppose a nonlinear mixer consists of a periodically time varying capacitor. Discuss how the Manley-Rowe equations, and in particular (5.8-13), can be used to relate power on the carrier and i.f. channels.

15. Describe the operation of a lossless, nonlinear mixer from the quantum theory point of view.

16. Show for the traveling wave parametric amplifier solutions (5.9-12) that at a distance far from the input end the Manley-Rowe equations in the form

$$\frac{dP_1/dx}{\omega_1} = \frac{dP_2/dx}{\omega_2}$$

are satisfied. Derive this result directly from the Manley-Rowe equations (5.8-11).

17. Suppose that the line of Fig. 5-24b has a small shunt conductance per unit length. What is the expression for the gain constant?

18. Show that (5.10-7), (5.10-8) and (5.10-9) follow directly from the Manley-Rowe equations.

19. Derive a Lagrangian density function for the dispersive line TL-2 in Fig. 5-8b.

20. Derive a Lagrangian density function for the line TL-1 in Fig. 5-8a by taking the difference between magnetic co-energy and electric energy and writing equations on the loop basis.

21. Check the details of the stability diagram sketched in Fig. 5-26b. Pay particular attention to the factor $\sqrt{-1}$.

22. Can shock waves form on a linear dispersive wave system? Why not?

23. Show that shocks tend to form on the front of a flow pulse if the flow-concentration relation $q(k)$ is concave upward.

24. Show that shocks tend to form on the rear of a flow pulse if $q(k)$ is concave downward.

25. The Born-Infeld Lagrangian for elementary particles has the one dimensional form

$$\mathcal{L} = 1 - [1 + \phi_x{}^2 - \phi_t{}^2]^{1/2}.$$

   (a) Derive the corresponding wave equation.
   (b) Discuss the dss solutions of this equation.

APPENDIX: THE HILBERT TRANSFORMS

In this appendix we shall outline some general properties of *linear response functions* and their Fourier Transforms. By a linear response function is meant a well defined relation between a linear *effect* which is the result of a *cause*. The electrical engineer is acquainted with several examples of such functions. The relation between voltage and current in a linear passive electric network is perhaps the most familiar. In a driving point immittance either voltage or current can be considered as cause; in a transfer immittance the cause will be specified. The statements which can be made about response functions have applications far beyond circuit theory so it is well for the student to be aware of their full generality. A partial list of linear response relations given in Table A-1 will indicate some of the areas in which these ideas can be applied.

Let us suppose a general linear response relation between a cause $f_A(t)$ and an effect $f_B(t)$. The character of this response can be epitomized by letting $f_A(t)$ be a unit impulse or "delta function,"

$$f_A(t) = \delta(t), \tag{A-1}$$

TABLE A-1 Linear Response Relations

Cause	Effect	Response Function
Voltage	Current	Admittance
Current	Voltage	Impedance
Velocity	Force	Mechanical admittance
Electric field (E)	Electric flux density (D)	Dielectric constant (ε)
Electric field (E)	Polarization (P)	Electric susceptibility $(\varepsilon_0 X_e)$
Electric field (E)	Current density (J)	Electric conductivity (σ)
Magnetic intensity (H)	Magnetic flux density (B)	Magnetic permeability (μ)
Magnetic intensity (H)	Magnetization (M)	Magnetic susceptibility (X_m)

where

$$\delta(t) = 0 \quad \text{for} \quad t \neq 0$$

and

$$\int_{-a}^{a} \delta(t)\, dt = 1 \quad \text{for} \quad a > 0.$$

f_B will then be the impulse response and will be denoted by f_{Bi}. Since f_{Bi} is a response it must follow the cause in time, therefore

$$f_{Bi} = 0 \quad \text{for} \quad t < 0,$$

as indicated in Fig. A-1a.

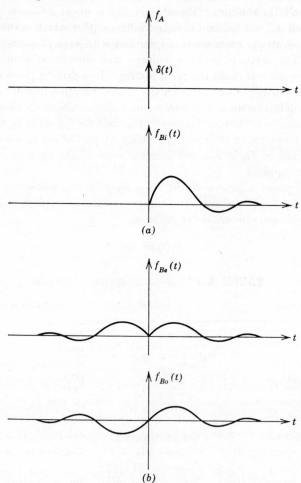

(a)

(b)

Fig. A-1 (a) Response to an impulse of excitation. (b) Even and odd parts of the impulse response.

We can separate *any* function, and in particular f_{Bi}, into unique even and odd parts as follows:

$$f_{Be} = \tfrac{1}{2}[f_{Bi}(t) + f_{Bi}(-t)],$$
$$f_{Bo} = \tfrac{1}{2}[f_{Bi}(t) - f_{Bi}(-t)]. \qquad \text{(A-2a,b)}$$

Evidently these are respectively even and odd and

$$f_{Bi} = f_{Be} + f_{Bo}.$$

We now observe the important fact that since f_{Bi} is zero for t less than zero its even part can be determined from its odd part and vice-versa as is indicated in Fig. A-1*b*.

In general f_A will be an arbitrary function of time. The response to f_A will be given by the *convolution* of f_A with the impulse response, f_{Bi}.

$$f_B(t) = \int_{-\infty}^{\infty} f_A(\tau) f_{Bi}(t-\tau)\, d\tau$$
$$= \int_{-\infty}^{\infty} f_A(t-\tau) f_{Bi}(\tau)\, d\tau. \qquad \text{(A-3a,b)}$$

Convolution is often denoted by the symbol $\otimes$, thus

$$f_B = f_A \otimes f_{Bi} = f_{Bi} \otimes f_A.$$

In particular, if f_A is a sinusoid

$$f_A(t) = Ae^{j\omega t}. \qquad \text{(A-4)}$$

Then from (A-3)

$$f_B(t) = A \int_{-\infty}^{\infty} e^{j\omega(t-\tau)} f_{Bi}(\tau)\, d\tau \qquad \text{(A-5)}$$

or

$$f_B(t) = A F_B(\omega) e^{j\omega t}, \qquad \text{(A-6)}$$

where

$$F_B(\omega) = \int_{-\infty}^{\infty} f_{Bi}(\tau) e^{-j\omega \tau}\, d\tau \qquad \text{(A-7)}$$

is the Fourier Transform of the impulse response. $F_B(\omega)$ is the representation of the response function in the frequency domain and $f_{Bi}(t)$ is the corresponding impulse response in the time domain. If f_{Bi} is considered to be separated into its even and odd parts as indicated in (A-2), (A-7) can be written

$$F_B(\omega) = \int_{-\infty}^{\infty} f_{Be} \cos \omega t\, dt + j \int_{-\infty}^{\infty} f_{Bo} \sin \omega t\, dt.$$
$$= F_{Br}(\omega) + j F_{Bi}(\omega). \qquad \text{(A-8)}$$

Equation A-8 tells us that the real and imaginary parts of the frequency response are not independent. Suppose the real part is determined for all frequency. Then f_{Be} can be determined from an inverse Fourier cosine transformation, f_{Bo} can be determined from f_{Be}, and, finally, $F_{Bi}(\omega)$ can be determined from a Fourier sine transformation of f_{Bo}. Equation A-8 also tells us that the real part of F_B will be an even function of ω while the imaginary part will be an odd function of ω.

From another point of view the interdependence of the real and imaginary parts of $F_B(\omega)$ arises because the continuation of F_B into the right half of the complex frequency plane must be free from singularities or analytic. If this were not so, the response function would not be stable and we could not guarantee zero output for zero input.

An analytic function

$$F(s) = F(\sigma + j\omega)$$
$$= F_r(\sigma, \omega) + jF_i(\sigma, \omega)$$

obeys the Cauchy-Riemann equations

$$\frac{\partial F_r}{\partial \sigma} = \frac{\partial F_i}{\partial \omega},$$

$$\frac{\partial F_r}{\partial \omega} = \frac{-\partial F_i}{\partial \sigma},$$

(A-9a,b)

which in turn imply that

$$\frac{\partial^2 F_r}{\partial \sigma^2} + \frac{\partial^2 F_r}{\partial \omega^2} = 0,$$

$$\frac{\partial^2 F_i}{\partial \sigma^2} + \frac{\partial^2 F_i}{\partial \omega^2} = 0.$$

(A-10a,b)

Thus in a region of the s-plane for which $F(s)$ is analytic the real and imaginary parts of F are solutions of Laplace's equation and can be determined from their values on the boundary of the region.

In our case the right half of the s-plane is the region over which $F_B(s)$ is analytic and the boundary is the $j\omega$ axis. Thus if F_{Br} is specified along the entire $j\omega$ axis, it is determined within the entire right half plane. Then from the Cauchy-Riemann equations F_{Bi} can be determined throughout the right half plane and in particular on the boundary.

The equations which express the relations between the real and imaginary parts of the Fourier transform of a response function are called the *Hilbert transforms* by mathematicians and electrical engineers, the *Kramers-Kronig relations* by physicists and sometimes the *dispersion relations* by people working in optics.

Suppose we have an arbitrarily specified real part, $F_{Br}(\omega)$, as indicated in Fig. A-2a. Notice that it is an even function of frequency as required by (A-8). We can determine the corresponding imaginary part in the following manner. F_{Br} is imagined to be sliced into differential vertical pieces one of which is shown shaded in Fig. A-2a. The imaginary part for each of these vertical slices is computed separately. This can be done by examining the function

$$\left. \frac{1}{s+a} \right|_{s=j\omega} = \frac{a}{\omega^2 + a^2} - \frac{j\omega}{\omega^2 + a^2} \, .$$

This function is evidently analytic in the right half s-plane. The real and

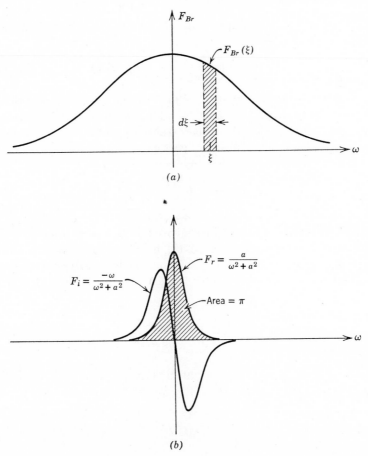

(a)

(b)

Fig. A-2   (a) The real part of the Fourier transform of the impulse response of a response function. (b) Real and imaginary parts of the function $1/(s+a)$ along the $j\omega$ axis.

imaginary parts are plotted in Fig. A-2b. The area under the real part is found by integration to be independent of the value of a and equal to π. In the limit as $a \to 0$ the real part becomes a delta function with argument ω and value π and the imaginary part is just $-1/\omega$. Thus we have the simple Hilbert transform pair

$$F_r = \delta(\omega) \quad \text{and} \quad F_i = -\frac{1}{\pi\omega},$$

or

$$F_r = \delta(\omega - \xi) \quad \text{and} \quad F_i = -\frac{1}{\pi(\omega - \xi)},$$

which gives the imaginary part which corresponds to an impulse in the real part.

The imaginary part which corresponds to the shaded vertical slice in Fig. A-2a is

$$dF_{Bi}(\omega) = \left(-\frac{1}{\pi(\omega - \xi)}\right) F_{Br}(\xi) \, d\xi,$$

since the slice can be considered a delta function in the differential limit. The total value of $F_{Bi}(\omega)$ is found by adding the effects of each of these vertical slices. Thus we have the Hilbert transform which gives the imaginary part corresponding to a specified real part as

$$F_{Bi} = -\frac{1}{\pi} \int_{-\infty}^{\infty} \frac{F_{Br}(\xi) \, d\xi}{\omega - \xi}. \tag{A-11}$$

The other Hilbert transform which gives the real part from a specified imaginary part is obtained from (A-11) by observing from the Cauchy-Riemann equations (A-9a,b) that a function which is analytic remains so if the real and imaginary parts are interchanged and the sign of one is reversed. Thus

$$F_{Br} = \frac{1}{\pi} \int_{-\infty}^{\infty} \frac{F_{Bi}(\xi) \, d\xi}{\omega - \xi}. \tag{A-12}$$

It is interesting to notice that the integrals in (A-11) and (A-12) indicate convolution with the function $1/\omega$. Thus we can write

$$F_{Bi} = -\frac{1}{\pi} F_{Br} \otimes \frac{1}{\omega}, \tag{A-11}$$

$$F_{Br} = \frac{1}{\pi} F_{Bi} \otimes \frac{1}{\omega}, \tag{A-12}$$

and take advantage of many of the important properties of the convolution integral in calculation.

It can be shown that if f and g are arbitrary functions of x

$$f \otimes g = \frac{df}{dx} \otimes \int g \, dx. \tag{A-13}$$

This is a general property of convolution which implies that the Hilbert transforms can be written in the form

$$F_{Bi} = \frac{dF_{Br}}{d\omega} \otimes \left(-\frac{\log \omega}{\pi} \right), \tag{A-14}$$

$$F_{Br} = \frac{dF_{Bi}}{d\omega} \otimes \left(\frac{\log \omega}{\pi} \right), \tag{A-15}$$

and

$$F_{Bi} = \frac{d^2 F_{Br}}{d\omega^2} \otimes \left[-\frac{1}{2\pi} (\omega \log \omega^2 - 2\omega) \right], \tag{A-16}$$

$$F_{Br} = \frac{d^2 F_{Br}}{d\omega^2} \otimes \left[\frac{1}{2\pi} (\omega \log \omega^2 - 2\omega) \right], \tag{A-17}$$

etc. These forms are useful for calculations in which one of the components is approximated by a "staircase" or a "broken linear slope." Then successive differentiation reduces the approximation to a train of impulses which are convolved by inspection. This technique and Hilbert transforms in general have been discussed clearly and in detail by Guillemin [Gu 2]. Many other philosophical and practical aspects of the Hilbert transforms can be found in the classic work on network theory by Bode [Bo 1].

It is important to observe that since a constant is an even function of frequency and since the imaginary part corresponding to a constant, from (A-11), is zero, the real part obtained from (A-12) is only determined to within an arbitrary constant. An example of this is the fact that a resistor may be added to an impedance which changes the resistive part by a constant and leaves the reactance unchanged.

BIBLIOGRAPHY

Books and Journal Articles

Alphabetical Listing

Ad 1 Adler, R. B., L. J. Chu, and R. M. Fano, *Electromagnetic energy transmission and radiation*. Wiley, New York (1960).

Ak 1 Akhmanov, S. A. and V. G. Dmitriyev, "Saturation theory of a traveling-wave amplifier with nonlinear reactance," *REEP* **8** (1963), pp. 1378–1387.

Ak 2 Akhmanov, S. A., V. G. Dmitriyev, and V. P. Modenov, "A theory of frequency multiplication in nonlinear dispersive lines," *REEP* **9** (1964), pp. 661–667.

Ak 3 Akhmanov, S. A., A. P. Sukhorukov, and R. V. Khokhlov, "Self-focusing and diffraction of light in a nonlinear medium," *Sov. Phys.—Usp.* **93** (1968), pp. 609–636.

Al 1 Allis, W. P., S. J. Buchsbaum, and A. Bers, *Waves in anisotropic plasmas.* M.I.T. Press, Cambridge, Massachusetts (1963).

Am 1 Ambartsumyan, R. V., V. S. Zuev, P. G. Kryukov, V. S. Lefokhov, and N. G. Basov, "Nonlinear amplification of light pulses," *Sov. Phys.—JETP* **23** (1966), pp. 16–22.

Am 2 Ambroziak, A., "Semidistributed neuristor line using unijunction transistors," *S.S. Elec.* **7** (1964), pp. 259–265.

Am 3 Ames, W. F., *Nonlinear partial differential equations in engineering.* Academic, New York (1965).

Am 4 Ames, W. F., Ed., *Nonlinear partial differential equations. A symposium on methods of solution.* Academic, New York (1967).

Am 5 Ames, W. F., S. Y. Lee, and J. N. Zaiser, "Non-linear vibration of a traveling threadline," *International Journal of Non-Linear Mechanics* **3** (1968), pp. 449–469.

An 1 Andronov, A. A., A. A. Vitt, and S. E. Khaikin, *Theory of oscillators.* Addison-Wesley, Reading, Massachusetts (1966).

Ar 1 Armstrong, J. A., N. Bloembergen, J. Ducuing, and P. S. Pershan, "Interactions between light waves in a nonlinear dielectric," *Phys. Rev.* **127** (1962), pp. 1918–1939.

Au 1 Auld, B. A., M. Demenico, Jr., and R. H. Pantel, "Traveling-wave harmonic generation along nonlinear transmission lines," *J. Appl. Phys.* **33** (1962), pp. 3537–3545.

Ba 1 Badkevskiy, Yu. N., V. T. Ovcharov, and G. F. Filimonov, "Maximum values of the electronic efficiency of a traveling-wave tube and their dependences on the dimensionless and dimension parameters of the tube," *REEP* **11** (1966), pp. 1370–1377.

Ba 2 Barbashov, B. M. and N. A. Chernikov, "Solution and quantization of a nonlinear two-dimensional model for a Born-Infeld type field," *Sov. Phys.—JETP* **23** (1966), pp. 861–868.

Ba 3 "Solution of the two plane wave scattering problem in a nonlinear scalar field theory of the Born-Infeld type," *Sov. Phys.—JETP* **24** (1967), pp. 437–442.

Be 0 Bean, C. P. and R. W. De Blois, "Ferromagnetic domain wall as a pseudo-relativistic entity," *Bull. Am. Phys. Soc.* **4** (1959) p. 53.

Be 1 Bellman, R., G. Birnbaum, and W. G. Wagner, "Transmission of monochromatic radiation in a two level material," *J. Appl. Phys.* **34** (1963), pp. 780–782.

Be 2 Belyantsev, A. M., A. V. Gaponov, E. Ya. Daume, and G. I. Freidman, "Experimental study of the propagation of electromagnetic waves of finite amplitude in ferrite-filled transmission lines," *Sov. Phys.—JETP* **20** (1965), pp. 1142–1149.

Be 3 Benjamin, T. B. and J. E. Feir, "The disintegration of wave trains on deep water," *J. Fluid Mech.* **27** (1967), pp. 417–430.

Be 4 Benjamin, T. B., "Instability of periodic wavetrains in nonlinear dispersive systems," *Proc. Roy. Soc.* (London) **299A** (1967), pp. 59–75.

Be 5 Benney, D. J., "The asymptotic behavior of nonlinear dispersive waves," *Ann. Phys.* (New York) **46** (1967), pp. 115–132.

Be 6 Benney, D. J. and A. C. Newell, "The propagation of nonlinear wave envelopes," *J. Math. & Phys.* **46** (1967), pp. 133–139.

Be 7 Berezin, Yu. A. and V. I. Karpman, "Nonlinear evolution of disturbances in plasmas and other dispersive media," *Sov. Phys.—JETP* **24** (1967), pp. 1049–1056.

Be 8 Bergel, D. H., "The static elastic properties of the arterial wall," *Journal of Physiology* **156** (1961), pp. 445–457.

Be 9 "The dynamic elastic properties of the arterial wall," *Journal of Physiology* **156** (1961), pp. 458–469.

Be 10 Berkovich, S. Ya., "Superconductor model of nerve impulse behavior," *REEP* **11** (1966), pp. 293–295.

Be 11 Bernstein, I. B. and F. Engelmann, "Quasi-linear theory of plasma waves," *Phys. Fluids* **9** (1966), pp. 937–952.

Be 12 Beurle, R. L., "Properties of a mass of cells capable of regenerating pulses," *Phil. Trans. Roy. Soc. London* **240B** (1956), pp. 55–95.

Be 13 "Storage and manipulation of information in the brain," *Journal IEE* **5** (1959), pp. 75–82.

Be 14 "Functional organization in random networks," in *Principles of self-organization.* H. von Foerster, Ed., Pergamon, New York (1962), pp. 291–314.

Be 15 "Storage and manipulation of information in random networks," in *Artificial intelligence*, C. A. Muses, Ed., Plenum, New York (1962) Chap. 3.

Bi 1 Bickley, D. T., "Wave propagation in nonlinear transmission lines with simple losses," *Elec. Lett.* **2** (1966), pp. 167–169.

Bi 2 Birkhoff, G., *Hydrodynamics.* Princeton University Press, Princeton, New Jersey (1960).

Bl 1 Blackwell, L. A. and K. L. Kotzebue, *Semiconductor diode parametric amplifiers.* Prentice-Hall, New York (1961).

Bl 2 Bloembergen, N. and P. S. Pershan, "Light wave at the boundary of nonlinear media," *Phys. Rev.* **128** (1962), pp. 606–622.

Bl 3 Bloembergen, N., "Wave propagation in nonlinear electromagnetic media," *Proc. IEEE* **51** (1963), pp. 124–131.

Bl 4 *Nonlinear optics.* Benjamin, New York (1965).

Bo 1 Bode, H. W., *Network analysis and feedback amplifier design.* Van Nostrand, Princeton, New Jersey (1949).

Bo 2 Bohm, D. and E. P. Gross, "Plasma oscillations as a cause of acceleration of cosmic-ray particles," *Phys. Rev.* **74** (1948), p. 624.

Bo 3   "Theory of plasma oscillations. A. Origin of medium-like behavior. B. Excitation and damping of oscillations," *Phys. Rev.* **75** (1949), pp. 1851–1876.

Bo 4   "Effects of plasma boundaries in plasma oscillations," *Phys. Rev.* **79** (1950), pp. 992–1001.

Bo 5   Born, M. and L. Infeld, "Foundations of a new field theory," *Proc. Roy. Soc.* (London) **144A** (1934), pp. 425–451.

Br 1   Bradley, J. M., *Shock waves in chemistry and physics.* Wiley, New York (1962).

Br 2   Brayton, R. K., "Stability criteria for large networks," *IBM J. Res. Develop.* **8** (1964), pp. 466–470.

Br 3   Briggs, R. J., *Electron stream interaction with plasmas.* M.I.T. Press, Cambridge, Massachusetts (1964).

Br 4   "Transformation of small-signal energy and momentum of waves," *J. Appl. Phys.* **35** (1964), pp. 3268–3272.

Br 5   Brillouin, L., "Waves and electrons traveling together," *Phys. Rev.* **74** (1948), pp. 90–92.

Br 6   "The traveling wave tube (discussion for waves of large amplitude)," *J. Appl. Phys.* **20** (1949), pp. 1196–1206.

Br 7   *Wave propagation in periodic structures.* Dover, New York (1953).

Br 8   *Wave propagation and group velocity.* Academic, New York (1960).

Br 9   Broer, L. J. F., "Wave propagation in nonlinear media," *Zeit. fur Angew. Math. & Physik.* **16** (1965), pp. 18–26.

Br 10 Broglie, L. de, "Illustration par un exemple de la forme des fonctions d'ondes singulieres de la theorie de la double solution," *Compt. Rend.* **243** (1956), pp. 617–620.

Br 11 *Nonlinear wave mechanics.* Elsevier, New York (1960).

Br 12 *Introduction to the Vigier theory of elementary particles.* Elsevier, New York (1963).

Br 13 Brown, J., "Proof of the Manley-Rowe relations from quantum considerations," *Elec. Lett.* **1** (1965), pp. 23, 129.

Bu 1   Buratti, R. J. and A. G. Lindgren, "Neuristor waveforms and stability analysis by a linear approximation," *Proc. IEEE* **56** (1968), pp. 1392–1393.

Bu 2   Burrows, T., I. Campbell, E. Howe, and J. Z. Young. "Conduction, velocity and diameter of nerve fibres of cephalopods," *J. Physiol.* (London) **179** (1965), pp. 39–40.

By 1   Byrd, P. F. and M. D. Friedman, *Handbook of elliptic integrals.* Springer, New York (1954).

Ca 1   Caianiello, E. R., "Outline of a theory of thought processes and thinking machines," *J. Theoret. Biol.* **2** (1961), pp. 204–235.

Ca 2   Caianiello, E. R. and A. DeLuca, "Decision equations for binary systems. Application to neuronal behavior," *Kybernetik* **3** (1966), pp. 33–40.

Ca 3   Caianiello, E. R., "Decision equations and reverberations," *Kybernetik* **3** (1966), pp. 98–100.

Ca 4   Caianiello, E. R., A. DeLuca, and L. M. Ricciardi, "Reverberations and control of neural networks," *Kybernetik* **4** (1967), pp. 10–18.

Ca 5 Cassedy, E. S. and A. A. Oliner, "Dispersion relations in time-space periodic media: Part I—stable interactions," *Proc. IEEE* **51** (1963), pp. 1342–1359.

Ca 6 Cassedy, E. S., "Dispersion relations in time-space periodic media: Part II—unstable interactions," *Proc. IEEE* **55** (1967), pp. 1154–1168.

Ch 1 Chandrasekhar, S., *Hydrodynamic and hydromagnetic stability*. Oxford, New York (1961).

Ch 2 Chang, K. K. N., *Parametric and tunnel diodes*. Prentice-Hall, New York (1964).

Ch 3 Cherry, C., "Some general theorems for non-linear systems possessing reactance," *Phil. Mag.* **42** (1951), pp. 1161–1177.

Co 1 Coddington, E. A. and N. Levinson, *Theory of ordinary differential equations*, McGraw-Hill, New York (1955).

Co 1a Cohen, H. and S. I. Rubinow, "Some mathematical topics in biology," *System Theory Symposium*, Polytechnic Institute of Brooklyn, April 1965, pp. 321–337.

Co 2 Cole, K. S., "The advance of electrical models for cells and axons," *Biophysical Journal* **2** (1962), pp. 101–119.

Co 3 *Membranes, ions and impulses*. University of California Press (1968).

Co 4 Connell, R. A., "Parametric amplification in thin film superconducting transmission lines," *Proc. IEEE* **51** (1963), pp. 616–617.

Co 5 Cooley, J. W., F. A. Dodge, and H. Cohen, "Digital computer solutions for excitable membrane models," *J. Cellular Comp. Physiol.* **66**, No. 3, Suppl. 2, Part II (1965), pp. 99–108.

Co 6 Cooley, J. W. and F. A. Dodge, "Digital computer solutions for excitation and propagation of the nerve impulse," *Biophysical Journal* **6** (1966), pp. 583–599.

Co 7 Copeland, J. A., "CW operation of LSA oscillator diodes—44–88 GHz," *Bell System Tech. J.* **46** (1967), pp. 284–287.

Co 8 Cote, A. J., Jr., "A neuristor prototype," *Proc. IRE* **49** (1961), pp. 1430–1431.

Co 9 "Neuristor propagation in long tunnel diodes," *Proc. IEEE* **53** (1965), pp. 164–165.

Co 10 "Synthetic nerve networks," NOLTR 65-55, U.S. Naval Ordnance Laboratory, 27 April, 1965.

Co 11 "The tunnel junction neuristor," NOLTR 65-60, U.S. Naval Ordnance Laboratory, 17 May, 1965.

Co 12 Courant, R. and K. O. Friedrichs, *Supersonic flow and shock waves*. Interscience, New York (1948).

Co 13 Courant, R. and D. Hilbert, *Methods of mathematical physics II*. Interscience, New York (1962).

Cr 1 Crane, H. D., "The neuristor," *Trans. IRE* **EC-9** (1960), pp. 370–371.

Cr 2 "Neuristor—a novel device and system concept," *Proc. IRE* **50** (1962), pp. 2048–2060.

Cr 3 Crowley, J. M., "Growth of waves on an accelerated jet," *Phys. of Fluids* **11** (1968), pp. 2172–2178.

Cu 1   Cullen, A. L., "Theory of the travelling-wave parametric amplifier," *Proc. IEE* **107b** (1960), pp. 101–107.

De 1   Denisse, J. F. and J. L. Delcroix, *Plasma waves.* Interscience, New York (1963).

De 2   Derrick, G. H., "Comments on nonlinear wave equations as models for elementary particles," *J. Math. Phys.* **5** (1964), pp. 1252–1254.

Di 1   Dick, D. E., J. E. Kendrick, G. L. Matson, and V. C. Rideout, "Measurement of nonlinearity in the arterial system of the dog using a new method," *Circulation Research* **22** (1968), pp. 101–111.

Di 2   Dietmeyer, D. L., "Bounds on the period of oscillatory activity in randomly interconnected networks of neuron-like elements," *Trans. IEEE* **EC-17** (1968), pp. 578–591.

Di 3   Dirac, P. A. M., "An extensible model of the electron," *Proc. Roy. Soc.* (London) **268A** (1962), pp. 57–67.

Di 4   Disman, M. I. and W. A. Edson, "Simultaneous asynchronous oscillations in class-C oscillators," *Proc. IRE* **46** (1958), pp. 895–903.

Dm 1   Dmitrenko, I. M. and I. K. Yanson, "Investigation of the high frequency Josephson current," *Sov. Phys.—JETP* **22** (1966), pp. 1190–1197.

Do 1   Döring, W., "Über die Trägheit der Wände zwischen weissschen Bezirken," *Z. Naturforsch.* **31** (1948), pp. 373–379.

Dr 1   Drummond, W. E. and D. Pines, "Nonlinear plasma oscillations," *Ann. Phys.* (New York) **28** (1964), pp. 478–499.

Ec 1   Eck, R. E., D. J. Scalapino, and B. N. Taylor, "Self-detection of the ac Josephson current," *Phys. Rev. Letters* **13** (1964), pp. 15–18.

Ec 2   Eckhaus, W., *Studies in nonlinear stability theory.* Springer, New York (1965).

Ed 1   Edson, W. A., "Frequency memory in multi-mode oscillators," *Trans. IRE* **CT-2** (1955), pp. 58–66.

El 1   Eldring, S. and R. A. Johnson, "Impedance transformations of cascaded active or passive identical twoports," *Trans. IRE* **CT-9** (1962), pp. 116–124.

El 2   Eleonskii, V. M., "Stability of simple stationary waves related to the nonlinear diffusion equation," *Sov. Phys. JETP* **26** (1968), pp. 382–384.

En 1   Enz, U., "Discrete mass, elementary length, and a topological invariant as a consequence of a relativistic invariant variational principle," *Phys. Rev.* **131** (1963), pp. 1392–1394.

En 2   Enz, U., "Die Dynamik der blochschen Wand," *Helv. Phys. Acta* **37** (1964), pp. 245–251.

Er 1   Erpenbeck, J. J., "Stability of steady-state equilibrium detonations," *Phys. Fluids* **5** (1962), pp. 604–614.

Er 2   "Stability of step shocks," *Phys. Fluids* **5** (1962), pp. 1181–1187.

Er 3   "Stability of idealized one-reaction detonations," *Phys. Fluids* **7** (1964), pp. 684–696.

Fa 1   Fallside, F. and D. T. Bickley, "Shock waves in a nonlinear delay line," *Elec. Lett.* **2** (1966), pp. 5–7.

Fe 1   Fedorchenko, A. M., "The problem of separating growing waves into amplifying and fading types," *REEP* **7** (1962), pp. 1369–1371, and **11** (1966), pp. 66–71.

Fe 2 Feenberg, E., "On the Born-Infeld theory of the electron," *Phys. Rev.* **47** (1935), pp. 148–157.

Fe 3 Feir, J. E., "Discussion: some results from wave pulse experiments," *Proc. Roy. Soc.* (London) **299A** (1967), pp. 54–58.

Fe 3a Feldkeller, E., "Magnetic domain wall dynamics," *Phys. Stat. Sol.* **27** (1968), p. 161.

Fe 4 Feynman, R. P., *Lectures on Physics III*. Addison-Wesley (1960).

Fi 1 Figueiredo, R. J. P. de and K. S. Chao, "Stability results for classes of distributed parameter networks and systems." *Trans. IEEE CT-16* (1969), pp. 209-214.

Fi 2 Finkelstein, R., R. LeLevier, and M. Ruderman, "Nonlinear spinor fields," *Phys. Rev.* **83** (1951), pp. 326–332.

Fi 3 Finkelstein, R., C. Fronsdal, and P. Kaus, "Nonlinear spinor fields," *Phys. Rev.* **103** (1956), pp. 1571–1579.

Fi 4 Fisher, R. A., "The wave of advance of advantageous genes," *Annals of Eugenics* (now *Annals of Human Genetics*) **7** (1937), pp. 355–369.

Fi 5 Fitzhugh, R., "Impulses and physiological states in theoretical models of nerve membrane," *Biophysical Journal* **1** (1961), pp. 445–466.

Fi 6 "Computation of impulse initiation and saltatory conduction in a myelinated nerve fiber," *Biophysical Journal* **2** (1962), pp. 11–21.

Fo 1 Fontana, R. E., "Internal resonance in circuits containing nonlinear resistance," *Proc. IRE* **39** (1951), pp. 945–951.

Fo 2 Ford, J., "Equipartition of energy for nonlinear systems," *J. Math. Phys.* **2** (1961), pp. 387–393.

Fo 3 Ford, J. and J. Waters, "Computer studies of energy sharing and ergodicity for nonlinear oscillator systems," *J. Math. Phys.* **4** (1963), pp. 1293–1306.

Fr 1 Francis, J. R. D., "Wave motions and the aerodynamic drag on a free oil surface," *Phil. Mag.* **45** (1954), pp. 695–702.

Fr 2 Franck, U. F., "Models for biological excitation processes," *Progress in Biophysics* **6** (1956), pp. 171–206.

Fr 3 Franken, P. A. and J. F. Ward, "Optical harmonics and nonlinear phenomena," *Rev. Mod. Phys.* **35** (1963), pp. 23–39.

Fr 4 Frantz, L. M. and J. S. Nodvik, "Theory of pulse propagation in a laser amplifier," *J. Appl. Phys.* **34** (1963), pp. 2346–2349.

Fr 5 Frenkel, J. and T. Kontorova, "On the theory of plastic deformation and twinning," *Journal of Physics* **1** (1939), pp. 137–149.

Ga 1 Gambardella, G. and G. Trautteur, "Experimental observations on a small active network," *Kybernetik* **3** (1966), pp. 8–13.

Ga 2 Gardner, M. F. and J. L. Barnes, *Transients in linear systems*, Wiley, New York (1942).

Ga 3 Garrett, C. J. R., "Discussion: the adiabatic invariant for wave propagation in a nonuniform moving medium," *Proc. Roy. Soc.* (London) **299A** (1967), pp. 26–27.

Ga 4 Gazis, D. C., "Mathematical theory of automobile traffic," *Science* **157** (1967), pp. 273–281.

Ge 1 Gerwin, R. A., "Hydromagnetic surface waves in a conducting liquid surrounded by a flowing gas," *Phys. Fluids* **11** (1968), pp. 1699–1708.

Ge 2 "Stability of the interface between two fluids in relative motion," *Rev. Mod. Phys.* **40** (1968), pp. 652–658.

Ge 3 Gessner, U., "Wave propagation in arteries with nonlinear distensibility," *Proceedings of Symposium on the Development of Analog Computers in the Study of the Mammalian Circulation System.* Sponsored by the Dutch Biophysical Society, *Zeist*, The Netherlands, April 19–20, 1962, pp. 82–90.

Ge 4 Getty, W. D. and L D. Smullin, "Beam-plasma discharge: buildup of oscillations," *J. Appl. Phys.* **34** (1963), pp. 3421–3429.

Gh 1 M. S. Ghausi and J. J. Kelley, *Introduction to distributed-parameter networks.* Holt, Rinehart and Winston, New York (1968).

Gl 1 Glasko, V. B., F. Leriust, Ia. P. Terletskii, and S. F. Shushurin, "An investigation of particle-like solutions of a nonlinear scalar field equation," *Sov. Phys.—JETP* **16** (1959), pp. 312–315.

Go 1 Goldman, L. and J. S. Albus, "Computation of impulse conduction in myelinated fibers; theoretical basis of velocity-diameter relation," *Biophysical Journal* **8** (1968), pp. 596–607.

Go 2 Goldstein, H., *Classical mechanics.* Addison-Wesley, Reading, Massachusetts (1950).

Go 3 Gould, R. W., "A coupled mode description of the backward-wave wave oscillator and the Kompfner dip conditions," *Trans. IRE* **ED-2** (1955), pp. 37–42.

Go 4 Gould, R. W. and A. W. Trivelpiece, "Electromechanical modes in plasma waveguides," *Proc. IEE* **105B** (1958), pp. 516–519.

Gr 1 Greene, P. H., "On looking for neural networks and 'cell assemblies' that underlie behavior," *Bull. Math. Biophysics* **24** (1962), pp. 247–275 and pp. 395–411.

Gr 2 Griffith, J. S., "A field theory of neural nets," *Bull. Math. Biophysics* **25** (1963), pp. 111–120 and **27** (1965), pp. 187–195.

Gr 3 "On the stability of brain-like structures," *Biophysical Journal* **3** (1963), pp. 299–308.

Gr 4 Gross, B. and E. P. Braga, *Singularities of linear system functions*, Elsevier, New York (1961).

Gu 1 Guillemin, E. A., *Mathematics of circuit analysis*, Wiley, New York (1949).

Gu 2 *Synthesis of passive networks*, Wiley, New York (1957).

Gu 3 Gunn, J. B., "Instabilities of current in III–V semiconductors," *IBM J. Res. Develop.* **8** (1964), pp. 141–159.

Gu 4 "Instabilities of current and of potential distribution in GaAs and InP," in *Plasma Effects in Solids.* Academic, New York (1965).

Gu 5 Gunther, R. L. and B. I. H. Scott, "Effect of temperature on bioelectric oscillations of bean roots," *Nature* **211** (1966), pp. 967–968.

Gu 5a Gupta, A. K., M. T. Landahl, and E. L. Mollo-Christensen, "Experimental and theoretical investigation of the stability of air flow over a water surface," *J. Fluid. Mech.* **33** (1968), pp. 673–691.

Gu 6 Gutzwiller, M. C. and W. L. Miranker, "Nonlinear wave propagation in a transmission line loaded with thin permalloy films," *IBM J. Res. Develop.* **7** (1963), pp. 278–287.

Ha 1 Hahn, W., *Theory and application of Liapunov's direct method.* Prentice-Hall, New York (1963).

Ha 2 Haken, H. and H. Sauerman, "Nonlinear interaction of laser modes," *Z. Physik* **173** (1963), pp. 261–275.

Ha 3 Haken, H. and M. Pauthier, "Nonlinear theory of multimode action in loss modulated lasers," *IEEE Journal of Quantum Electronics* **QE-4** (1968), pp. 454–459.

Ha 4 Hakki, B. W., "Amplification in two-valley semiconductors," *J. Appl. Phys.* **38** (1967), pp. 808–818.

Ha 5 Hall, L. S. and W. Heckrotte, "Instabilities: convective versus absolute," *Phys. Rev.* **166** (1968), pp. 120–128.

Ha 6 Harmon, L. D. and E. R. Lewis, "Neural modeling," *Physiological Reviews* **46** (1966), pp. 513–591.

Ha 7 Hasselmann, K., "Nonlinear interactions treated by the methods of theoretical physics (with application to the generation of waves by wind)," *Proc. Roy. Soc.* (London) **299A** (1967), pp. 77–100.

Ha 8 Hatfield, W. B. and B. A. Auld, "Electromagnetic shock waves in gyromagnetic media," *J. Appl. Phys.* **34** (1963), pp. 2941–2946.

Ha 9 "Method of characteristic solution for electromagnetic wave propagation in a gyromagnetic medium," *J. Math. & Phys.* **43** (1964), pp. 34–37.

Ha 10 Haus, H. A. and T. K. Gustafson, "Steady-state electromagnetic shock in Kerr liquid," *IEEE Journal of Quantum Electronics* **QE-4** (1968), pp. 519–522.

Ha 11 Havelock, T. H., *The propagation of disturbances in dispersive media,* Cambridge University Press, New York (1914).

Ha 12 Hayasaka, A. and J. Nishizawa, "Pulse characteristics of the distributed Esaki diode," *Electronics and Communications in Japan* **49** (1966), pp. 123–133.

Ha 13 Hayashi, C. *Nonlinear oscillations in physical systems.* McGraw-Hill, New York (1964).

He 1 Heinle, W., "Principles of a phenomenological theory of Gunn-effect domain dynamics," *S.S. Elec.* **11** (1968), pp. 583–598.

He 2 Heisenberg, W., "Zur Quantentheorie nichtrenormierbarer Wellengleichungen," *Z. Naturforsch.* **A9** (1954), pp. 292–303.

He 3 *Introduction to the unified field theory of elementary particles.* Interscience, New York (1967).

Hi 1 Hilsum, C., "Transferred electron amplifiers and oscillators," *Proc. IRE* **50** (1962), pp. 185–189.

Hi 2 Hines, M. E., "High frequency negative-resistance circuit principles for Esaki diode applications," *Bell System Tech. J.* **34** (1960), pp. 477–513.

Hi 3 Hirooka, H. and Saito, N., "Computer studies on the approach to thermal equilibrium in coupled anharmonic oscillators. I. Two dimensional case." *J. Phys. Soc. Japan* **26** (1969), pp. 624–630.

Ho 1 Hobart, R. H., "On the instability of a class of unitary field models," *Proc. Phys. Soc.* (London) **82** (1963), pp. 201–203.

Ho 2 Hodgkin, A. L., A. F. Huxley, and B. Katz, "Measurement of current-voltage relations in the membrane of the giant axon of *Loligo*," *J. Physiol.* (London) **116** (1952), pp. 424–448.

Ho 3 Hodgkin, A. L. and A. F. Huxley, "Currents carried by sodium and potassium ions through the membrane of the giant axon of *Loligo*," *J. Physiol.* (London) **116** (1952), pp. 449–472.

Ho 4 "The components of membrane conductance in the giant axon of *Loligo*," *J. Physiol.* (London) **116** (1952), pp. 473–496.

Ho 5 "A quantitative description of membrane current and its application to conduction and excitation in nerve," *J. Physiol.* (London) **117** (1952), pp. 500–544.

Ho 6 Hohn, F. E., *Elementary matrix algebra*. Macmillan, New York (1958).

Hs 1 Hsuan, H. C. S., R. C. Ajmera, and K. E. Lonngren, "The nonlinear effect of altering the zeroth order density of a plasma," *Appl. Phys. Lett.* **11** (1967), pp. 277–279.

Hu 1 Huggins, W. H., "Multifrequency bunching in reflex klystrons," *Proc. IRE* **36** (1948), pp. 624–630.

Hu 2 Hughes, W. L., *Nonlinear electrical networks*. Ronald, New York (1960).

Hu 3 Hurewicz, W., *Lectures on ordinary differential equations*. Wiley, New York (1958).

Il 1 Il'inova, T. M. and R. V. Khokhlov, "Wave processes in lines with nonlinear shunt resistance," *REEP* **8** (1963), pp. 1864–1972.

Il 2 Il'inova, T. M., "Interaction of waves in a distributed line with nonlinear parallel loss," *REEP* **9** (1964), pp. 1728–1735.

In 1 Inoue, Y., "Solitary waves propagating at an angle to a magnetic field in a collisionless warm plasma," *J. Phys. Soc. Japan* **25** (1968), pp. 881–887.

Iv 1 Ivanchenko, Yu., A. V. Svidzinsky, and V. A. Slyusaryev, "Electrodynamics of the Josephson effect," *Sov. Phys.—JETP* **24** (1967), pp. 131–135.

Iw 1 Iwata, K. and R. Sato, "Pulse transmission line with active element," *Electronics and Communication in Japan* **50** (1967), pp. 44–53.

Ja 1 Jackson, E. A., "Nonlinear coupled oscillators. I. Perturbation theory; ergodic problem," *J. Math. Phys.* **4** (1963), pp. 551–558.

Ja 2 Janus, T., "Moving source model of neuristor triggering," *Proc. IEEE* **51** (1963), pp. 1049–1050.

Je 1 Jeffrey, A. and T. Tanuti, *Nonlinear wave propagation*. Academic, New York (1964).

Je 2 Jeffreys, H., "On the formation of water waves by wind," *Proc. Roy. Soc.* (London) **107A** (1925), pp. 189–206.

Jo 1 Johnson, R. A., "Cascaded active twoports," *Trans. IRE* **CT-9** (1962), pp. 33–37.

Jo 2 Johnson, W. J., "Nonlinear wave propagation on superconducting tunneling junctions," Ph.D. Thesis, University of Wisconsin (1968).

Jo 3 Josephson, B. D., "Supercurrents through barriers," *Advances in Physics* **14** (1965), pp. 419–451.

Ju 1 Jurkus, A. and P. N. Robson, "Saturation effects in a travelling-wave parametric amplifier," *Proc. IEE* **107b** (1960), pp. 119–126.

Ju 2 "Gain saturation in a travelling wave parametric amplifier," *Proc. IRE* **49** (1961), pp. 1433–1434.

Ka 1 Kabaservice, T. P., "The active RC line—a family of negative conductance circuits," *Trans. IEEE* *CT-16* (1969), pp. 13–16.

Ka   1a   Kalashnikov, S. G. and V. L. Bonch-Bruyevich, "The wave velocity of the space charge (electric domains) in semiconductors," *REEP* **11** (1966), pp. 1514–1516.

Ka   2   Katz, B., *Nerve, muscle, and synapse*. McGraw-Hill, New York (1966).

Ke   1   Ketterer, F. D. and J. R. Melcher, "Electromechanical costreaming and counterstreaming instabilities." *Phys. of Fluids* **11** (1968), pp. 2179–2191.

Kh   1   Khokhlov, R. V., "The theory of radio shock waves in nonlinear transmission lines," *REEP* **6** (1961), pp. 817–824.

Kh   2   "On nonlinear wave processes," *Sov. Phys.—Usp.* **8** (1966), pp. 642–645.

Ki   1   Kiel, A. and P. Parzen, "Nonlinear wave propagation in traveling-wave amplifiers," *Trans. IRE* **ED-2** (1955), pp. 26–29.

Ki   2   Kinsman, B., *Wind waves*. Prentice-Hall, New York (1965).

Kn   1   Knight, B. W. and G. A. Peterson, "Theory of the Gunn effect," *Phys. Rev.* **155** (1967), pp. 393–404.

Kn   2   Knopp, K., *Theory of functions*. Part II. Dover, New York (1947).

Ko   1   Kochendorfer, A., A. Seeger, and H. Donth, "Theorie der Versetzungen in eindimensionalen Atomreihen," *Z. Physik* **127** (1950), pp. 533–550; **130** (1951), pp. 321–336; and **134** (1953), pp. 173–193.

Ko   1a   Kolesnikov, P. M., "Integration of nonlinear equations of electrodynamics by separation of variables," *Sov. Phys. Tech—Phys.* **13** (1969), pp. 845–848.

Ko   1b   Kolesnikov, P. M., "Analytic solutions of boundary value problems in nonlinear electrodynamics by means of complete integrals," *Sov. Phys.— Tech. Phys.* **13** (1969), pp. 849–852.

Ko   2   Kolmogoroff, A., I. Petrovsky, and N. Piscounoff, "Study of the equation of diffusion with growth of a quantity of material and its application to a biological problem," *Bulletin of Moscow State University* **1**, Section A (1937), pp. 1–25. (In French)

Ko   3   Korteweg, D. J. and G. deVries, "On the change of form of long waves advancing in a rectangular canal, and on a new type of long stationary wave," *Phil. Mag.* **39** (1895), pp. 422–443.

Kr   1   Krasovitskii, V. B. and A. R. Linetskii, "The excitation of a nonlinear active medium by a beam of oscillators," *Sov. Phys.—Tech. Phys.* **13** (1968), pp. 349–352.

Kr   2   Kravtsov, Yu. A., "Saturation power of certain types of nonlinear-capacitance amplifiers," *REEP* **8** (1963), pp. 1479–1484.

Kr   3   Kroemer, H., "Theory of the Gunn effect," *Proc. IEEE* **52** (1964), p. 1736.

Kr   4   Kruskal, M. D. and N. J. Zabusky, "Stroboscopic-perturbation procedure for treating a class of nonlinear wave equations," *J. Math. Phys.* **5** (1964), pp. 231–244.

Kr   5   Kryloff, N. and N. Bogoliuboff, *Introduction to nonlinear mechanics*. Princeton University Press, Princeton, New Jersey (1947).

Ku   1   Kulik, I. O., "Wave propagation in a Josephson tunnel junction in the presence of vortices and the electrodynamics of weak superconductivity," *Sov. Phys.—JETP* **24** (1967), pp. 1307–1317.

Ku   1a   Kundt, W. and E. T. Newman, "Hyperbolic differential equations in two dimensions," *J. Math. Phys.* **9** (1968), pp. 2193–2210.

Ku 2 Kunov, H., "Controllable piecewise linear lumped neuristor realization," *Elec. Lett.* **1** (1965), p. 134.

Ku 3 *Nonlinear transmission lines simulating nerve axon.* Laboratory of Electronics, Technical University of Denmark, Kgs. Lyngby, Denmark, February 1966.

Ku 4 "On recovery in a certain class of neuristors," *Proc. IEEE* **55** (1967), pp. 428–429.

Ky 1 Kyhl, R. L., "Negative L and C in solid-state masers," *Proc. IRE* **48** (1960), p. 1157.

Ky 2 Kyhl, R. L., R. A. McFarlane, and M. W. P. Strandberg, "Negative L and C in solid-state masers," *Proc. IRE* **50** (1962), pp. 1608–1623.

La 1 La Salle, J. and S. Lefschetz, *Stability by Liapunov's direct method.* Academic, New York (1961).

La 1a Lamb, G. L. Jr., "Propagation of ultrashort optical pulses," *Phys. Letters* **25A** (1967), pp. 181–182.

La 1b "π pulse propagation in a lossless amplifier," *Phys. Letters* **29A** (1969), pp. 507–508.

La 2 Lamb, H., *Hydrodynamics.* Dover, New York (1945).

La 3 Lampert, M. A., "Plasma oscillations at extremely high frequencies," *J. Appl. Phys.* **27** (1956), pp. 5–11.

La 4 Landauer, R., "Shock waves in nonlinear transmission lines and their effect upon parametric amplification," *IBM J. Res. Develop.* **4** (1960), pp. 391–401.

La 5 Langenberg, D. N., D. L. Scalapino, and B. N. Taylor, "Josephson-type superconducting tunnel junctions as generators," *Proc. IEEE* **54** (1966), pp. 550–575.

La 6 Lax, P. D., "Integrals of nonlinear equations of evolution and solitary waves," *Commun. Pure Appl. Math.* **21** (1968), pp. 467–490.

Le 1 Lebwohl, P. and M. J. Stephen, "Properties of vortex lines in super-conducting barriers," *Phys. Rev.* **163** (1967), pp. 376–379.

Le 2 Letokhov, V. S., "Nonlinear amplification of light pulses. II. Velocity of propagation," *Sov. Phys.—Tech. Phys.* **13** (1968), pp. 644–649.

Li 1 Lieb, E. H. and D. C. Mattis, *Mathematical physics in one dimension.* Academic, New York (1966).

Li 1a Lieberstein, H. M., "On the Hodgkin-Huxley partial differential equation," *Math. Biosciences* **1** (1967), pp. 45–69; and "Numerical studies of the steady-state equations for a Hodgkin-Huxley model," *Math. Biosciences* **1** (1967), pp. 181–211.

Li 2 Lighthill, M. J., "Group velocity," *Journal of the Institute of Mathematical Applications* **1** (1965), pp. 1–28.

Li 3 Lighthill, M. J. and G. B. Whitham, "On kinematic waves. I. Flood movement in long rivers," *Proc. Roy. Soc.* (London) **229A** (1965), pp. 281–316.

Li 4 "On kinematic waves. II. A theory of traffic flow on long crowded roads," *Proc. Roy. Soc.* (London) **229A** (1965), pp. 317–345.

Li 5 Lighthill, M. J., "Some special cases treated by the Whitham theory," *Proc. Roy. Soc.* (London) **299A** (1967), pp. 28–53.

Li 6 Lillie, R. S., "The passive iron wire model of protoplasmic and nervous transmission and its physiological analogues," *Biological Reviews* **11** (1936), pp. 181–209.

Li 7 Lindgren, A. G. and R. J. Buratti, "Stability of waveforms on active nonlinear transmission lines." *Trans. IEEE. CT-16* (1969), pp. 274–279.

Ll 1 Llwellyn, F. B., "Some fundamental properties of transmission systems," *Proc. IRE* **40** (1952), pp. 271–283.

Lo 1 Logunov, L. A., I. V. Polykov, and V. N. Serebryakov, "Distributed tunnel diodes," *REEP* **12** (1967), pp. 149–153.

Lo 2 Loladze, Ts. D. and N. L. Tsintsadze, "Nonlinear vibrations of a two component plasma in a magnetic field," *Sov. Phys.—Tech. Phys.* **6** (1962), pp. 944–946.

Lo 3 Longuet-Higgins, M. S. and A. E. Gill, "Resonant interactions between planetary waves," *Proc. Roy. Soc.* (London) **299A** (1967), pp. 120–140.

Lo 4 Louisell, W. H., *Coupled mode and parametric electronics*. Wiley, New York (1960).

Lu 1 Luke, J. C., "A perturbation method for nonlinear dispersive wave problems," *Proc. Roy. Soc.* (London) **292A** (1966), pp. 403–412.

Ma 1 McCall, S. L. and E. L. Hahn, "Self induced transparency by pulsed coherent light," *Phys. Rev. Letters* **18** (1967), pp. 908–911.

Ma 2 Malyshev, V. A., "Quasi-linear negative conductivity of quantum devices," *REEP* **11** (1966), pp. 662–665.

Ma 3 Manley, J. M. and H. E. Rowe, "Some general properties of nonlinear elements," *Proc. IRE* **44** (1956), pp. 904–913.

Ma 4 Matson, R. C. and C. O. Harbourt, "Analysis of distributed amplifier structures," T.R. #34, Lab. for Electronics, University of Texas, May 24, 1967, AD 655 080.

Ma 5 Matson, R. C., C. O. Harbourt, and O. B. Kesler, "Nonreciprocal tunnel diode distributed amplifier," *Trans. IEEE* **ED-14** (1967), pp. 174–175.

Ma 6 Mattson, R. H., "A neuristor realization," *Proc. IEEE* **52** (1964), pp. 618–619.

Me 1 Melcher, J. R., "Complex waves," *IEEE Spectrum* **5**, No. 10 (1968), pp. 86–101.

Me 2 Mendelson, P., "On phase portraits of critical points in n-space," in *Contributions to the theory of nonlinear oscillations, IV*. Princeton University Press, Princeton, New Jersey (1958), Chap. 9.

Me 3 Menne, T. J. and F. J. Rosenbaum, "Effect of spatial dependence in the single-mode laser rate equations," *Trans. IEEE* **QE-2** (1966), pp. 47–49.

Mi 1 Mie, G., "Grundlagen einer Theorie der Materie," *Ann. Physik* **37** (1912), pp. 511–530; **39** (1912), pp. 1–37; and **40** (1913), pp. 1–64.

Mi 2 Mikaelyan, A. L., M. L. Ter-Mikayelyan and Yu. G. Turkov, "Theory of a continuously operating light generator (laser)," *REEP* **9** (1964), pp. 1119–1127.

Mi 3 "On calculating the nonstationary processes in lasers," *REEP* **9** (1964), pp. 1482–1491.

Mi 4 Mikaelyan, A. L., M. L. Ter-Mikayelyan, Yu. G. Turkov and V. V. D'yackenko, "The use of quasi-classical and balance equations for the design of steady state lasers," *REEP* **11** (1966), pp. 1321–1323.

Mi 5 Mikaelyan, A. L. and M. L. Ter-Mikayelyan, "Propagation of a light pulse through a medium with population inversion," *Sov. Phys.—JETP* **24** (1967), pp. 450–451.

Mi 5a Millman, M. H. and J. B. Keller, "Perturbation theory of nonlinear boundary value problems," *J. Math. Phys.* **10** (1969), pp. 342–361.

Mi 6 Minorsky, N., *Nonlinear oscillations*. Van Nostrand, Princeton, New Jersey (1962).

Mi 7 Mirsky, I., "Pulse velocities in initially stressed cylindrical rubber tubes," *Bull. Math. Biophysics* **30** (1968), pp. 299–308.

Mi 8 Mitskevich, N. V., "The scalar field of a stationary nucleon in a non-linear theory," *Sov. Phys.—JETP* **2** (1956), pp. 197–202.

Mi 9 Miura, R. M., "Korteweg—de Vries equation and generalizations. I. A remarkable explicit nonlinear transformation," *J. Math. Phys.* **9** (1968), pp. 1202–1204.

Mi 10 Miura, R. M., C. S. Gardner, and M. D. Kruskal, "Korteweg-de Vries equation and generalizations. II. Existence of conservation laws and constants of motion," *J. Math. Phys.* **9** (1968), pp. 1204–1209.

Mo 1 Moore, J. W., "Electronic control of some active bielectric membranes," *Proc. IRE* **47** (1959), pp. 1869–1880.

Mo 2 Morawetz, C. S., "Time decay for the nonlinear Klein-Gordon equation," *Proc. Roy. Soc.* (London) **A306** (1968), pp. 291–296.

Mo 3 Morse, P. M. and H. Feshbach, *Methods of theoretical physics*. McGraw-Hill, New York (1953).

Mo 4 Moskvitin, L. L. and Yu. Ye. Naumov, "Saturation in paramagnetic maser amplifiers at large input signals," *REEP* **9** (1964), pp. 1749–1755.

Mu 1 Mueller, P. and D. O. Rudin, "Resting and action potentials in experimental bimolecular lipid membranes," *J. Theoret. Biol.* **18** (1968), pp. 222–258.

Mu 2 Munk, W. H., "A critical wind speed for air-sea boundary processes," *Journal of Marine Research* **6** (1947), pp. 203–218.

Mu 3 Murray, J. D., "Singular perturbations of a class of nonlinear hyperbolic and parabolic equations," *J. Math & Phys.* **47** (1968), pp. 111–133.

Mu 4 Musha, T., "Unified consideration of wave amplification in moving media," *J. Appl. Phys.* **35** (1964), pp. 3273–3279.

My 1 Myers, P. S., O. A. Uyehara, and G. L. Borman, "Fundamentals of heat flow in welding," *Welding Research Council Bulletin*, No. 123, July 1967.

Na 1 Nagumo, J., S. Arimoto, and S. Yoshizawa, "An active pulse transmission line simulating nerve axon," *Proc. IRE* **50** (1962), pp. 2061–2070.

Na 2 "Bistable transmission lines," *Trans. IEEE* **CT-12** (1965), pp. 400–412.

Ne 1 Neamtan, S. M., "The Čerenkov effect and the dielectric constant," *Phys. Rev.* **92** (1953), pp. 1362–1367.

Ni 1 Nishizawa, J., A. Hayasaka, and I. Sasaki, "Pulse characteristics of the distributed Esaki diode and its application to S-T conversion and to panel display," TR-12 (1966) Research Institute of Elec. Comm. Tohoku University.

No 1 Noguchi, S., Y. Kumagai, and J. Oizuma, "General considerations on the neuristor circuits," Report of the Research Institute of Elec. Comm., Tohoku University, Sendai B. (Elect. Comm.) Vol. 14, No. 3–4 (1963).

No 2 Nordsieck, A., "Theory of the large signal behavior of traveling wave amplifiers," *Proc. IRE* **41** (1953), pp. 630–637.

Of 1 Offner, F., A. Weinberg, and G. Young, "Nerve conduction theory: some mathematical consequences of Bernstein's model," *Bull. Math. Biophysics* **2** (1940), pp. 89–103.

Oi 1 Oizumi, J., S. Noguchi, Y. Kumagi, and S. Aono, "Fundamental characteristics of the active line," Report of University of Shizuoka Electronics Laboratory, Vol. 1, No. 2 (1966) (In Japanese).

Os 1 Ostrovskii, L. A. and E. I. Yakubovich, "Averaged laser equations and their stationary solutions," *Sov. Phys.—JETP* **19** (1964), pp. 656–660.

Os 2 Ostrovskii, L. A., "Electromagnetic waves in nonlinear media with dispersion," *Sov. Phys.—Tech. Phys.* **8** (1964), pp. 679–681.

Os 3 "Shock envelope waves," *Zhurnal Eksperimental'noi i Teoreticheskoi Fiziki* **54** (1968), pp. 1235–1243.

Ot 1 Otis, D. R., "Solving the melting problem using the electrical analogy to heat conduction," *Trans. ASME* **79** (1957), pp. 759–764.

Pa 1 Padovani, F. A. L., "A study of superconductive neuristors," Technical Report No. 1658-1, Stanford Electronics Laboratories, October 1962.

Pa 2 Parmentier, R. D., "The superconductive tunnel junction neuristor." Ph.D. Thesis, University of Wisconsin (1967).

Pa 3 "Stability analysis of neuristor waveforms," *Proc. IEEE* **55** (1967), pp. 1498–1499.

Pa 4 Parmentier, R. D. and A. C. Scott, "Electronic grey matter," *J. Appl. Phys.* **39** (1968), p. 2587. (abstract).

Pa 5 Parmentier, R. D., "Neuristor waveform stability analysis by Lyapunov's second method," *Proc. IEEE* **56** (1968), pp. 1607–1608.

Pa 6 "Recoverable neuristor propagation on superconductive tunnel junction strip lines." *S.S. Elec.* **12** (1969), pp. 287–297

Pe 1 Pease, M. C., "Analytic proof of operability of a second-order neuristor line," Interim Report No. 3, Stanford Research Institute Project 3286, February 1961 (OTS 159491).

Pe 2 Penfield, P., Jr., *Frequency-power formulas*. Wiley, New York (1960).

Pe 3 Perring, J. K. and T. H. R. Skyrme, "A model unified field equation," *Nucl. Phys.* **31** (1962), pp. 550–555.

Ph 1 Phillips, O. M., "Theoretical and experimental studies of gravity wave interactions," *Proc. Roy. Soc.* (London) **299A** (1967), pp. 104–119.

Pi 1 Pickard, W. F., "On the propagation of the nervous impulse down medullated and unmedullated fibers," *J. Theoret. Biol.* **11** (1966), pp. 30–45.

Pi 2 Pierce, J. R., *Traveling wave tubes*. Van Nostrand, Princeton, New Jersey (1950).

Pi 3 "Waves in electron streams and circuits," *Bell System Tech. J.* **30** (1951), pp. 626–651.

Pi 4 "The wave picture of microwave tubes," *Bell System Tech. J.* **33** (1954), pp. 1343–1372.

Pi   5   "Interaction of moving charges with wave circuits," *J. Appl. Phys.* **26** (1955), pp. 627–638.

Pi   5a   Pilkuhn, "The quantum efficiency of injection lasers," *9th Int. Conf. on Physics of Semiconductors.* I. Nauka, Leningrad (1968), pp. 523–528.

Pi   6   Pinski, G., "Interaction of particlelike solutions in a classical nonlinear model field theory," *J. Math. Phys.* **9** (1968), pp. 1323–1326.

Pi   7   Pipes, L. A., *Operational methods in nonlinear mechanics.* Dover, New York (1965).

Po   1   Pol, B. van der, "An oscillation hysteresis in a triode generator with two degrees of freedom," *Phil. Mag.* **43** (1922), pp. 700–719.

Po   2   "On relaxation oscillations," *Phil. Mag.* ser. 7, **2** (1926), pp. 978–992.

Po   3   "The nonlinear theory of electric oscillations," *Proc. IRE* **22** (1934), pp. 1051–1086.

Po   4   "On a generalization of the non-linear differential equation $d^2u/dt^2 - \varepsilon(1 - u^2) \, du/dt + u = 0$," *Proc. Acad. Sci. Amsterdam* **A60** (1957), pp. 477–480.

Po   5   Polovin, R. V., "Criteria for instability and gain," *Sov. Phys.—Tech. Phys.* **6** (1962), pp. 889–895.

Pr   1   Prasanna, B. N., "Wave propagation on lossless nonlinear transmission lines exhibiting dispersion," Ph.D. Thesis, University of Wisconsin (1965).

Pr   1a   Predonzani, G. and A. Roveri, "Criteri di stabilità per una linea contente bipoli attivi concentrati non lineari," *Note, Recensioni e Notizie* **17** (1968), pp. 1433–1453.

Pr   2   Pribram, K. H., "The neurophysiology of remembering," *Scientific American* **220** (1969), pp. 73–86.

Ra   1   Rabinovich, M. I., "Self oscillations in a transmission line with tunnel diodes," *REEP* **11** (1966), pp. 1271–1278.

Ra   2   Ramo, S. and J. R. Whinnery, *Fields and waves in modern radio.* Wiley, New York (1953).

Re   1   Reimann, O. A. and W. F. Kosonocky, "Progress in optical computer research," *IEEE Spectrum* **2**, No. 3 (1965), pp. 181–195.

Re   2   Reiss, R. F., *Neural theory and modelling*, Ed., Stanford, Stanford, California.

Ri   1   Richer, I., "Pulse propagation along certain lumped nonlinear transmission lines," *Elec. Lett.* **1** (1965), pp. 135–136.

Ri   2   "The switch-line: a simple lumped transmission line that can support unattenuated propagation," *Trans. IEEE* **CT-13** (1966), pp. 388–392.

Ri   3   Rideout, V. C. and D. E. Dick, "Difference-differential equations for fluid flow in distensible tubes," *Trans. IEEE* **BME-14** (1967), pp. 171–177.

Ri   4   Rideout, V. C. and J. B. Sims, "A computer model study of nonlinear effects in arterial flow," Proceedings of the Annual Conference on Engineering in Medicine and Biology, Vol. 10, Houston, Texas, Nov. 18–21, 1968.

Ri   5   "Computer study of the effects of small nonlinearities in the arterial system." *Math. Biosciences* **4** (1969), pp. 411–426.

Ri   6   Ridley, B. K. and T. B. Watkins, "The possibility of negative resistance effects in semiconductors," *Proc. Phys. Soc.* (London) **78** (1961), pp. 293–304.

Ri   7   "Specific negative resistance in solids," *Proc. Phys. Soc.* (London) **82** (1963), pp. 954–966.

Ri   8   Rigrod, W. W., "Gain saturation and output power of optical masers," *J. Appl. Phys.* **34** (1963), pp. 2602–2609.

Ri   9   Riley, R. B., "Analysis of a nonlinear transmission line," International Solid-State Circuits Conference Digest (1961), pp. 10–11; and Ph.D. Thesis, Stanford University, Tech. Rept. No. 1707-1.

Ro   1   Rosen, G., "Particlelike solutions to nonlinear scalar wave theories," *J. Math. Phys.* **6** (1965), pp. 1269–1272.

Ro   2   "Solutions of a certain nonlinear wave equation," *J. Math. & Phys.* **45** (1966), pp. 235–265.

Ro   3   "Equations of motion in classical nonlinear field theories," *J. Math. Phys.* **8** (1967), pp. 573–575.

Ro   4   "Internal dynamics of particlelike solutions to nonlinear field theories," *J. Math. Phys.* **8** (1967), pp. 2400–2406.

Ro   5   "Nonexistence of finite-energy stationary quantum states in nonlinear field theories," *J. Math. Phys.* **9** (1968), pp. 804–805.

Ro   6   "Particlelike solutions to nonlinear complex scalar field theories with positive-definite energy densities," *J. Math. Phys.* **9** (1968), pp. 996–998.

Ro   7   "Charged particlelike solutions to nonlinear complex scalar field theories," *J. Math. Phys.* **9** (1968), pp. 999–1002.

Ro   8   Rosen, N., "A field theory of elementary particles," *Phys. Rev.* **55** (1939), pp. 94–101.

Ro   9   Rosen, N. and H. B. Rosenstock, "The force between particles in a nonlinear field theory," *Phys. Rev.* **85** (1952), pp. 257–259.

Ro   10   Rowe, H. E., "Stability of active transmission lines with arbitrary imperfections," *Bell System Tech. J.* **43** (1964), pp. 293–328.

Ro   11   Rowe, J. E., "Design information on large signal traveling-wave amplifiers," *Proc. IRE* **44** (1956), pp. 200–210.

Ro   12   *Nonlinear electron-wave interaction phenomena.* Academic, New York (1965).

Sa   1   Sagdeev, R. Z., and A. A. Galeev, *Nonlinear plasma theory.* Benjamin, New York (1969).

Sc   1   Schaffner, J., "Simultaneous oscillations in oscillators," *Trans. IRE* **CT-1** (1954), pp. 2–8.

Sc   2   Schiff, H., "A classical theory of bosons," *Proc. Roy. Soc.* (London) **269A** (1962), pp. 277–286.

Sc   3   Scott, A. C., "Analysis of nonlinear distributed systems," *Trans. IRE* **CT-9** (1962), pp. 192–195.

Sc   4   "Saturation power flow on a transmission line loaded with Esaki diodes," *Trans. IRE* **CT-9** (1962), pp. 284–286.

Sc   5   "Distributed effects in large area Esaki diodes," *Trans. IRE* **ED-9** (1962), pp. 417–422.

Sc   6   "The distributed tunnel diode oscillator," *Trans. IEEE* **CT-10** (1963), pp. 53–59.

Sc   7   "Neuristor propagation on a tunnel diode loaded transmission line," *Proc. IEEE* **51** (1963), p. 240.

316   *Bibliography*

Sc   8   "The quarter wave tunnel diode oscillator," *Trans. IEEE* **ED-10** (1963), pp. 291–292.

Sc   9   "Analysis of a myelinated nerve model," *Bull. Math. Biophysics* **26** (1964), pp. 247–254; and **29** (1967), pp. 363–371.

Sc   10   "Distributed device applications of the superconducting tunnel junction," *S.S. Elec.* **7** (1964), pp. 137–146.

Sc   11   "Efficiency of a *p-n* diode laser," *Proc. IEEE* **52** (1964), pp. 325–326.

Sc   12   "Nonlinear theory for laser diodes," *Trans. IEEE* **ED-11** (1964), pp. 41–46.

Sc   13   "Steady propagation on nonlinear transmission lines," *Trans. IEEE* **CT-11** (1964), pp. 146–154.

Sc   14   "Laser efficiency at high pump levels," *S.S. Elec.* **8** (1965), pp. 551–561; and **10** (1967), pp. 1115–1116.

Sc   15   "Single mode differential efficiency for circular and rectangular laser diodes," *Proc. IEEE* **53** (1965), pp. 315–316.

Sc   16   "Steady propagation on long Josephson junctions," *Bull. Am. Phys. Soc.* **12** (1967), pp. 308–309.

Sc   17   "Distributed Multimode oscillators of one and two spatial dimensions," *Trans. IEEE* **CT-17** (in press).

Sc   18   "A nonlinear Klein-Gordon equation," *Am. J. Phys.* **37** (1969), pp. 52–61.

Sc   18a   Scott, A. C. and W. J. Johnson, "Internal flux motion in large Josephson junctions," *Appl. Phys. Letters* **14** (1969), pp. 316–318.

Sc   18b   Scott, A. C., "Waveform stability on a nonlinear Klein-Gordon equation," *Proc. IEEE* **57** (1969), pp. 1338–1339.

Sc   19   Scott, B. I. H., "Electricity in plants," *Scientific American* **211** (1962), pp. 107–114.

Sc   20   "Electric fields in plants," *Annual Review of Plant Physiology* **18** (1967), pp. 409–418.

Sc   21   Scott, B. I. H., H. Gulline, and C. K. Pallaghy, "The electrochemical state of cells of broad bean roots," *Australian Journal of Biological Sciences* **21** (1968), pp. 185–200.

Se   1   Seeber, K. N., "Saturation effects in solid-state laser amplifiers," *Trans. IEEE* **ED-12** (1965), pp. 63–66.

Sh   1   Shikin, G. N., "On the question of particle-like solutions of nonlinear equations of the electromagnetic field," *Vestnik Moskovskovo Universiteta* No. 2 (1967), pp. 3–10. (In Russian)

Sh   2   Shulz-DuBois, E. O., "Pulse sharpening and gain saturation in traveling-wave masers," *Bell System Tech. J.* **43** (1964), pp. 625–658.

Sk   1   Skinner, L. V., "Criteria for stability in circuits containing nonlinear resistance," Ph.D. Thesis, University of Illinois (1948).

Sk   2   Skyrme, T. H. R., "Particle states of a quantized meson field," *Proc. Roy. Soc.* (London) **262A** (1961), pp. 237–245.

Sl   1   Slater, J. C., *Quantum theory of matter*. McGraw-Hill, New York (1951).

Sm   1   Smith, D. R. and C. H. Davidson, "Maintained activity in neural nets," *Journal of the Association for Computing Machinery* **9** (1962), pp. 268–279.

Sn   1   Snyder, M. F., V. C. Rideout, and R. J. Hillestad, "Computer modeling of the human system arterial tree," *Journal of Biomechanics* **I** (1968).

St 1 Stoker, J. J., *Water waves*. Interscience, New York (1957).

St 2 Sturrock, P. A., "Kinematics of growing waves," *Phys. Rev.* **112** (1958), pp. 1488–1503.

St 3 "Amplifying and evanescent wave, convective and nonconvective instabilities," in *Plasma Physics*, J. E. Drummond, Ed., McGraw-Hill, New York (1961).

Su 1 Sudan, R. N., "Classification of instabilities from their dispersion relations," *Phys. Fluids* **8** (1965), pp. 1899–1904.

Su 2 Suezaki, T. and S. Mori, "Theory of quasi-sinusoidal nonlinear networks." To be published in *Trans. IEEE on Circuit Theory*.

Su 3 Suzuki, R., "Mathematical analysis and application of iron-wire neuron model," *Trans. IEEE* **BME-14** (1967), pp. 114–124.

Sw 1 Swihart, J. C., "Field solutions for a thin-film superconducting strip transmission line," *J. Appl. Phys.* **32** (1961), pp. 461–469.

Ta 1 Tang, C. L. and H. Statz, "Maximum-emission principle and phase locking in multimode lasers," *J. Appl. Phys.* **38** (1967), pp. 2963–2968.

Ta 2 Tasaki, I., "Conduction of the nerve impulse," in *Handbook of Physiology: Neurophysiology* Vol I, J. Field, Ed., American Physiological Society, Washington, D.C. (1959), Chap. 3.

Ta 3 Taylor, B. N., "Device applications of superconductive tunneling," *J. Appl. Phys.* **39** (1968), pp. 2490–2502.

Te 1 Teorell, T., "Transport processes and electrical phenomena in ionic membranes," *Progress in Biophysics (and Biophysical Chemistry)* **3** (1953), pp. 305–369.

Te 2 "Electrokinetic considerations of mechanoelectrical transduction," *Annals of the New York Academy of Sciences* **137** (1966), pp. 950–966.

Te 3 Terhune, R. W., P. D. Maker and C. M. Savage, "Optical harmonic generation in calcite," *Phys. Rev. Letters* **8** (1962), pp. 404–406.

Ti 1 Tien, P. K., L. R. Walker, and V. M. Wolontis, "A large signal theory of traveling-wave amplifiers," *Proc. IRE* **43** (1955), pp. 260–277.

To 1 Toda, M., "Mechanics and statistics of nonlinear chains," *J. Phys. Soc. Japan* **26** *Supp. proc. Inst. Conf. Stat. Mech.* (1969), pp. 235–237.

Ur 1 Ursell, F., "Wave generation by wind," in *Surveys in Mechanics*, G. K. Batchelor and R. M. Davies, Eds., Cambridge (1956), pp. 216–249.

Ve 1 Vedenov, A. A., "Quasi-linear plasma theory (theory of a weakly turbulent plasma)," *Plasma Physics (J. Nucl. Energy Part C)* **5** (1963), pp. 169–186.

Vo 1 Volkov, A. F., "Waves in semiconductors having negative differential resistivity," *Sov. Phys.—Solid State* **8** (1967), pp. 2552–2557.

Vo 2 Voloshchenko, Yu. P. and V. A. Malyshev, "Nonlinear theory of negative conductance traveling wave amplifiers," *REEP* **11** (1966), pp. 598–606.

Vo 2a Voloshchenko, Yu. P., "Contribution to the theory of traveling wave amplifiers," *REEP* **12** (1967), pp. 1403–1406.

Vo 3 Vorontsov, Yu. I., "Certain properties of delay lines containing tunnel diodes," *REEP* **9** (1964), pp. 478–483.

Vo 4 "Velocity of propagation of stationary signals in lines having nonlinear resistance," *REEP* **9** (1964), pp. 1414–1416.

Vo 5 "On the interaction between oppositely traveling signals in lines containing a nonlinear resistance," *REEP* **9** (1964), pp. 1812–1815.

Vo 6 Vorontsov, Yu. I. and I. V. Polyakov, "Investigation of undamped signals in lines with a nonlinear resistance," *REEP* **11** (1966), pp. 1449–1456.

Vo 7 Vorontsov, Yu. I., M. I. Kozhevnikova, and I. V. Polyakov, "Wave processes in active RC-lines," *REEP* **12** (1967), pp. 644–648.

Wa 1 Wang, P. K. C., "Theory of stability and control for distributed systems," *International Journal of Control* **7** (1968), pp. 101–116. (A bibliography.)

Wa 2 Waters, J. and J. Ford, "A method of solution for resonant nonlinear coupled oscillator systems," *J. Math. Phys.* **7** (1966), pp. 399–403.

We 1 Wei, L. Y., "A new theory of nerve conduction," *IEEE Spectrum* **3**, No. 9, (1966), pp. 123–127.

We 2 Weiss, M. T., "Quantum derivation of energy relations analogous to those for nonlinear reactances," *Proc. IRE* **45** (1957), pp. 1012–1013.

Wh 1 White, J. A., "Stability of traveling waves in lasers," *Phys. Rev.* **137** (1965), pp. A1651–A1654.

Wh 2 Whitham, G. B., "A general approach to linear and nonlinear dispersive waves using a Lagrangian," *J. Fluid Mech.* **22** (1965), pp. 273–283.

Wh 3 "Nonlinear dispersive waves," *Proc. Roy. Soc.* (London) **283A** (1965), pp. 238–261.

Wh 4 "Nonlinear dispersion of water waves," *J. Fluid Mech.* **27** (1967), pp. 399–412.

Wh 5 "Variational methods and applications to water waves," *Proc. Roy. Soc.* (London) **299A** (1967), pp. 6–25.

Wi 1 Wittke, J. P. and P. J. Warter, "Pulse propagation in a laser amplifier," *J. Appl. Phys.* **35** (1964), pp. 1668–1672.

Wo 1 Wood, W. W. and Z. W. Salsburg, "Analysis of steady-state supported one-dimensional detonations and shocks," *Phys. Fluids* **3** (1960), pp. 549–566.

Wu 1 Wu, J., "Laboratory studies of wind-wave interactions," *J. Fluid Mech.* **34** (1968), pp. 91–111.

Ya 1 Yariv, A., "On the coupling coefficients in the 'coupled mode' theory," *Proc. IRE* **46** (1958), p. 1956.

Yu 1 Yuan, H. T. and A. C. Scott, "Distributed superconductive oscillator and neuristor," *S.S. Elec.* **9** (1966), pp. 1149–1150.

Za 1 Zabusky, N. J. and M. D. Kruskal, "Interaction of 'solitons' in a collisionless plasma and the recurrence of initial states," *Phys. Rev. Letters* **15** (1965), pp. 240–243.

Za 2 Zabusky, N. J., "Nonlinear lattice dynamics and energy sharing," *J. Phys. Soc. Japan* **26** *Supp. Proc. Int. Conf. Stat. Mech.* (1969), pp. 196–202.

Ze 1 Zelby, L. W., "The theory of Čerenkov effect based on Lorentz transformations," *J. Appl. Phys.* **33** (1962), pp. 2995–2998.

Zu 1 Zubov, V. I., *Methods of A. M. Lyapunov and their applications.* Noordhoff, the Netherlands (1964).

Cross-reference Listing

1 Mathematics
By 1, Ga 2, Gu 1, Ho 6, Hu 3, Kn 2, La 1, Me 2, Mi 6, Mo 3, Pi 7, Po 2, Po 3.

2 Linear circuit theory
Bo 1, Ga 2, Gh 1, Gr 4, Gu 1, Gu 2, Ll 1, Ka 1.

3 Linear wave theory
Ad 1, Br 7, Br 8, Gh 1, Gr 4, Li 1, Ma 4, Ma 5, Mu 4, Ra 2, Ro 10, Sc 5, Sw 1.

4 Nonlinear circuit theory
An 1, Ch 3, Di 4, Ed 1, Fo 1, Ha 13, Hu 2, Kr 5, La 1, Pi 7, Po 1, Po 2, Po 3, Sc 1, Sk 1.

5 Nonlinear wave theory
Am 3, Am 4, Am 5, Bi 2, Co 12, Co 13, Je 1, Kh 2, Kr 4, Li 1, Po 4, St 1.

6 Classical mechanics and quantum theory
Go 2, Li 1, Mo 3, Sl 1.

7 Dispersion equations
Br 3, Br 4, Ca 5, Ca 6, Me 1, Po 5, St 2, St 3, Su 1.

8 Group velocity
Br 8, Ha 11, Li 2.

9 Moving media
Am 5, Br 4, Cr 3, Fe 4, Ga 3, Ge 1, Ge 2, Gu 5a, Ke 1, Me 1, Mu 4, Pi 5.

10 Linear wave stability
Be 7, Br 3, Ca 6, Ch 1, Cr 3, El 1, Fe 1, Fr 1, Ge 2, Gu 5a, Ha 5, Jo 1, Ke 1, Ll 1, Me 1, Po 5, Ro 10, St 2, St 3, Su 1.

11 Quasiharmonic theory
Be 11, Bo 3, Ma 2, Mi 2, Mi 3, Mi 4, Mi 5a, Os 1, Ra 1, Sc 4, Sc 6, Sc 10, Sc 11, Sc 12, Sc 14, Sc 15, Sc 17, Su 2, Ve 1, Vo 2, Vo 2a.

12 Waves of permanent profile
In 1, Ja 2, Ko 3, Ku 3, La 6, Li 7, Ma 1, Mi 9, Mi 10, Na 1, Na 2, Ni 1, No 1, Oi 1, Pa 2, Pa 6, Pe 1, Po 4, Sc 3, Sc 10, Sc 13, Sc 16, Sc 18, Vo 4, Vo 6, Vo 7, Za 1.

13 Nonlinear active propagation
El 2, Ha 12, Il 1, Il 2, Jo 2, Ku 3, Li 7, Na 1, Na 2, Ni 1, No 1, Of 1, Oi 1, Pa 2, Pi 1, Po 4, Ri 1, Ri 2, Sc 3, Sc 4, Sc 9, Sc 10, Sc 13, Vo 2, Vo 3, Vo 4, Vo 6, Vo 7, Vo 2a.

14 Nonlinear wave stability
Br 2, Bu 1, Ec 2, El 2, Er 1, Er 2, Er 3, Fe 3, Fi 1, Ha 1, Kn 1, Li 5, Li 7, Lu 1, Pa 2, Pa 3, Pa 5, Pe 1, Pr 1a, Sc 13, Sc 18, Sc 18b, Wa 1, Wh 1, Wh 2, Wh 3, Wh 4, Wh 5, Zu 1.

15 Pulse interaction
Ba 3, Il 2, Ku 1a, La 6, Mi 9, Mi 10, Sc 18, Vo 5, Za 1.

16 Nonlinear lossless transmission lines
Ak 1, Ak 2, Au 1, Be 2, Be 5, Be 6, Bi 1, Br 9, Fa 1, Ga 3, Gu 6, Ha 8, Ha 9, Iv 1, Ju 1, Ju 2, Kh 1, Ko 1a, Ko 1b, La 4, Li 5, Lu 1, Mi 9, Mi 10, Mu 3, Os 2, Pr 1, Ri 9, Sc 18, Wh 2, Wh 3, Wh 4, Wh 5, Za 1.

17 Kinematic waves
Mu 3, Li 3, Li 4.

18 Manley-Rowe relations
Br 13, Ma 3, Pe 2, We 2.

19 Shock waves
Br 1, Co 12, Fa 1, Ha 10, Kh 1, La 4, Wo 1.

20 Neurons and nerve axons
Bu 2, Co 1, Co 2, Co 3, Co 5, Co 6, Fi 5, Fi 6, Fr 2, Go 1, Ho 2, Ho 3, Ho 4, Ho 5, Mo 1, Of 1, Pi 1, Re 2, Ta 2, We 1, Li 1a, Li 1b.

21 Nerve models and the neuristor
Am 2, Be 10, Co 8, Co 9, Co 11, Cr 1, Cr 2, Fe 4, Fr 2, Ha 6, Ha 12, Ja 2, Jo 2, Ka 2, Ku 2, Ku 3, Ku 4, Li 6, Lo 1, Ma 6, Mu 1, Na 1, No 1, Pa 1, Pa 2, Pa 6, Pe 1, Re 1, Re 2, Ri 1, Ri 2, Sc 3, Sc 7, Sc 9, Su 3, Te 1, Te 2, Yu 1.

22 Semiconductor tunnel diodes
Ch 2, Co 9, Co 11, Ha 12, Hi 2, Lo 1, Ma 4, Ma 5, Na 1, Ni 1, Oi 1, Sc 3, Sc 4, Sc 5, Sc 6, Sc 7, Sc 8, Vo 2a, Vo 3.

23 Superconductor tunnel diodes
Pa 2, Pa 4, Pa 6, Ra 1, Sc 10, Ta 3, Yu 1.

24 Josephson tunnel diodes
Dm 1, Ec 1, Iv 1, Jo 2, Jo 3, Ku 1, La 5, Le 1, Pa 2, Sc 16, Sc 18, Sw 1, Ta 3.

25 Masers
Ky 1, Ky 2, Ma 2, Sh 2.

26 Lasers
Am 1, Be 1, Fr 4, Ha 2, Ha 3, Le 2, Ma 2, Me 3, Mi 2, Mi 3, Mi 4, Mi 5, Os 1, Os 3, Pi 5a, Ri 8, Sc 11, Sc 12, Sc 14, Sc 15, Se 1, Ta 1, Wh 1, Wi 1.

27 Plasma waves
Al 1, Be 7, Be 11, Bo 2, Bo 3, Bo 4, Br 3, De 1, Dr 1, Ge 4, Go 4, Hs 1, In 1, Kr 1, La 3, Lo 2, Ve 1, Za 1, Sa 1.

28 Electron beam devices
Ba 1, Br 3, Br 5, Br 6, Ge 4, Go 3, Hu 1, Ki 1, Kr 1, No 2, Pi 2, Pi 3, Pi 4, Pi 5, Ro 11, Ro 12, Ti 1.

29 Nonlinear optics
Ak 3, Am 1, Ar 1, Be 1, Bl 2, Bl 3, Bl 4, Br 9, Fr 3, Fr 4, Ha 8, Ha 9, Ha 10, Le 2, Ma 1, Mi 5, Os 2, Pr 1, Re 1, Te 3.

30 Bulk negative conductance devices (Gunn effect)
Co 7, Gu 3, Gu 4, Ha 4, He 1, Hi 1, Ka 1a, Kn 1, Kr 3, Ri 6, Ri 7, Vo 1.

31 Propagation of dislocations in solids
Fr 5, Ko 1.

32 Domain wall motion
Be 0, Do 1, En 2, Fe 3a.

33 Parametric amplifiers
Bl 1, Ch 2, Co 4, Cu 1, Ju 1, Ju 2, Kr 2, Lo 4, Mo 4.

34 Hydrodynamics and water waves
Be 3, Be 4, Bi 2, Ch 1, Co 12, Fe 3, Fr 1, Ge 2, Gu 5a, Ha 7, Je 2, Ki 2, Ko 3, La 2, Li 3, Lo 3, Mu 2, Ph 1, St 1, Ur 1, Wh 4, Wh 5, Wu 1.

35 Magnetohydrodynamics
Ch 1, Ge 1, Je 1, Ke 1

36 Waves in blood vessels
Be 8, Be 9, Co 1, Di 1, Ge 3, Mi 7, Ri 3, Ri 4, Ri 5, Sn 1.

37 Detonation waves
    Er 1, Er 2, Er 3, Wo 1.

38 Artificial nerve membranes
    Mu 1.

39 Electrical waves in plants
    Gu 5, Sc 19, Sc 20, Sc 21.

40 The Fermi-Pasta-Ulam problem
    Fo 2, Fo 3, Hi 3, Ja 1, To 1, Wa 2, Za 2.

41 Field theories for elementary particles
    Ba 2, Ba 3, Bo 5, Br 10, Br 11, Br 12, De 2, Di 3, En 1, Fe 2, Fi 2, Fi 3, Gl 1,
    He 2, He 3, Ho 1, Mi 1, Mi 8, Mo 2, Pe 3, Pi 6, Ro 1, Ro 2, Ro 3, Ro 4, Ro 5,
    Ro 6, Ro 7, Ro 8, Ro 9, Sc 2, Sh 1, Sk 2.

42 Brain waves
    Be 12, Be 13, Be 14, Be 15, Ca 1, Ca 2, Ca 3, Ca 4, Co 10, Di 2, Ga 1, Gr 1,
    Gr 2, Gr 3, Pa 4, Pr 2, Sin 1.

43 Traffic waves
    Ga 4, Li 4.

44 Nonlinear heat flow
    My 1, Ot 1.

45 Coupled mode theory
    Go 3, Lo 4, Ya 1.

46 Multimode oscillation
    Di 4, Ed 1, Fo 1, Ha 2, Ha 3, Hi 3, Hu 1, Po 1, Sc 1, Sc 17, Sk 1, Ta 1.

47 Genetic diffusion
    Fi 4, Ko 2.

48 Čerenkov effect
    Ne 1, Ze 1.

Films

Complex Waves I: Evanescence and Instability (26 min) and *Complex Waves II: Instability, Convection and Amplification* (23 min) J. R. Melcher, 1968. The various types of wave instability are graphically demonstrated on ingenious electromechanical and magnetomechanical systems. Educational Development Center, 39 Chapel Street, Newton, Mass. 02160. (See [Me 1])

Flow Instabilities (28 min) E. L. Mollo-Christensen for the National Committee for Fluid Mechanics and Educational Services. An excellent introduction to shear instabilities at the surface between standing fluids. The photography is superb. Encyclopedia Britannica Educational Corporation, 4424 Oakton Street, Skokie, Illinois 60076. color.

Formation of Shock Waves (4 min) Educational Services, 1964. A pulsed air jet is used to produce a periodic circular water wave. As the source is moved faster than the water wave velocity, shock waves develop. Ealing Corporation, 2225 Massachusetts Avenue, Cambridge, Mass. 02140.

Formation, Propagation and Interaction of Solitons (35 min) N. J. Zabusky, G. S. Deem and M. D. Kruskal, 1968. Numerical solutions of differential equations describing wave motion in nonlinear dispersive media. Part I: Numerical solution of the Korteweg-deVries equation with periodic boundary conditions, Part II: Interaction of a compressive and rarefractive soliton, Part III: Numerical solutions for an anharmonic lattice initially excited by an intense localized pulse. Available on free loan from Bell Telephone Laboratories, IAC. Film Library, Murray Hill, New Jersey 07971.

Gruppen und Phasengeschwindigkeit (10 min) E. David and G. Bekow, 1952. The concepts of group and phase velocity are introduced using animated diagrams and laboratory experiments with water waves. Physikalisches Staats-Institut, Hamburg, and American Institute of Physics, 335 East 45th Street, New York, N.Y. 10017. (See E. David and G. Bekow, "Gruppen- und Phasengeschwindigkeit" Institut für den Wissenschaftlichen Film, Gottingen, 1959.)

Magnetohydrodynamics (27 min) The National Committee for Fluid Mechanics and Educational Services. A simple experimental introduction to wave propagation in incompressible conducting fluids. Includes a demonstration of Alfven waves in liquid sodium-potassium alloy. Encyclopaedia Britannica Educational Corporation, 4424 Oakton Street, Skokie, Illinois 60076.

Nerve Impulse (2 parts: 2 min, 59 sec and 3 min, 18 sec) Ealing Corporation, 1967. The sciatic nerve of a frog is removed along with its corresponding muscle. Transmission of nerve impulses are observed as an oscilloscope display. Ealing Corporation, 2225 Massachusetts Avenue, Cambridge, Mass. 02140. color.

Nonrecurrent Wavefronts (4 min) F. Miller, 1963. Shock wave phenomena is briefly presented in a variety of physical situations, including tidal waves, people waves, shock waves from a nuclear explosion and shock waves in interstellar space. Ealing Corporation, 2225 Massachusetts Avenue, Cambridge, Mass. 02140.

Tacoma Narrows Bridge Collapse (4 min, 40 sec) F. Miller, 1963. The dramatic quasiharmonic oscillation of the Tacoma Narrows Bridge during its last hour is shown. Ealing Corporation, 2225 Massachusetts Avenue, Cambridge, Mass. 02140. color.

Waves in Fluids (33 min) The National Committee for Fluid Mechanics and Educational Services, 1964. An excellent qualitative introduction to shock waves in fluids and gases. Includes many interesting physical examples. Encyclopaedia Britannica Educational Corporation, 4424 Oakton Street, Skokie, Illinois 60076.

For further information on films, see W. R. Riley, "Resource letter BSPE-1. A Bibliography of selected physics films," *American Journal of Physics* **36**, No. 6 (1968), pp. 1–15. (Available as a reprint from the American Institute of Physics, 335 East 45 Street, New York, N.Y. 10017.)

Abbreviations

The journal abbreviations used in the bibliography are those suggested by the *Style Manual of the American Institute of Physics* (2nd. ed., rev., 1967). Titles not included in its listing have been abbreviated in the following manner:

Applied Physics Letters	*Appl. Phys. Lett.*
Bulletin of Mathematical Biophysics	*Bull. Math. Biophysics*
Electronics Letters	*Elec. Lett.*
Journal of Theoretical Biology	*J. Theoret. Biol.*
Proceedings of the Institution of Electrical Engineers (London)	*Proc. IEE*
Radio Engineering and Electronic Physics	*REEP*
Solid State Electronics	*S.S. Elec.*

INDEX